TOILETS

&♿WC Unisex toilets designed or adapted for disabled people or public toilets within 50 yards. Radar key required in some

WC Ordinary toilets with level access

WC No toilets on site but public ones nearby

👪 Baby changing/parents room available

GENERAL

✕ Restaurant/tea room/cafe/ not accessible due to steps/narrow doorway/first floor with no lift

❙❙ Restaurant/tea room/cafe/vending accessible by ramp or level or lift with 30″ doors

✕ Shop not accessible due to stairs but may be accessible with help

Shop/sales area accessible by ramp or level and 30″ doorway

Picnic area only, or nearby

Wheelchair users are advised to come accompanied

Taped guides available/or person

Facilities for visually handicapped/braille or by request

People available to help (telephone beforehand if you require help)

Telephone accessible for wheelchair users

This site is suitable for elderly people but unsuitable for wheelchair users

Wheelchairs/batricars for loan or hire – telephone for advance booking

NT The National Trust

EH English Heritage

NTS National Trust for Scotland

RSPB Royal Society For the Protection of Birds

FC Forestry Commission

⇌ British Rail

🚌 Bus

☎ Telephone

⊖ Underground

Copyright: 1991 Michael Yarrow

Typesetter: Tradespools Ltd., Frome

Edition: 1

Published: 27.11.91

Publisher: Mediair Marketing Services, Poole

Printed & Bound: In Great Britain by Cox & Wyman Ltd, Reading, Berks.

ISBN No: 0 9518358 0 7

If you would like further information or additional copies, please write to:
Michael B Yarrow
Mediair Marketing Services
72 High St
Poole
Dorset, BH15 1DA

Cartoons: David Hollingsworth of Remploy, Leicester

Front Cover: Of Stowe Landscape Gardens by Sir Hugh Casson, by kind permission of The National Trust.

PLACES THAT CARE

The Access Guide to Places of
Interest
Suitable for Elderly and
Disabled People

Compiled by

Michael B Yarrow
Mediair Marketing Services

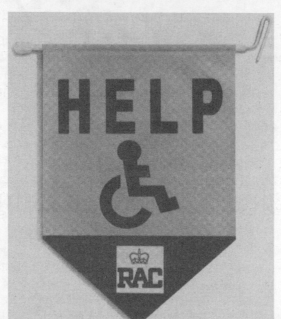

simply flag down the RAC

Response is a different kind of service from the RAC designed to meet the very special needs of motorists with a disability.

The attention-getting flag is only one of the extras you get. There are many others including a pad which you can use to report the details of your breakdown if you cannot contact us yourself. There is also a free copy of 'On the Move', the RAC guide for disabled travellers.

Our first priority is always to get you going again. When your car cannot be repaired or you have special needs, you will be put in touch with a Personal Incident Manager, who will provide a solution tailored to your individual circumstances. Your Personal Incident Manager will also pass on messages to worried relatives or friends.

So, while your car is being recovered to the destination of your choice you will be able to agree with your Personal Incident Manager the most suitable means of onward transport to meet your specific requirements.

Alternatively, if it is not convenient for you to

continue your journey, we can arrange overnight accommodation in a hotel with suitable facilities.

Because Response automatically includes RAC Rescue, Recovery and 'At Home', you can be sure that whatever your motoring problem the RAC will provide a solution to meet your individual needs.

Membership of Response is available to anyone holding a local authority issued parking badge. Parents or Guardians may apply on behalf of anyone under 18 years of age. To join, or for more information, call the free linkline number below.

Or write to RAC Response, RAC Motoring Services Ltd, PO Box 700, Spectrum, Bond Street, Bristol BS99 1RB.

THE NEW KNIGHTS OF THE ROAD

2

PLACES THAT CARE

As Chairman of the Yarrow Fund for Children, a Trustee of the Pelham Charity Trust and a Newsagent for twenty years, I have a desire to improve people's knowledge of venues suitable for their needs together with an urge to raise substantial funds for charity, I felt that a Guide Book of this nature could help fulfil my ambitions.

I should like to convey my thanks to all those who have made this Guide possible, especially the Chief of Executives of Councils and Borough Councils, Tourist Offices, Tourist Boards throughout the British Isles, and the many places who cared enough to contribute information to enable this publication.

My greatest thanks goes to those who have encouraged me to publish this Guide, especially Harry Greaves who was involved in it's conception and Roger Belson, now in a wheelchair resulting from an accident, for whom I was best man in 1974. Both Harry and Roger have been great supporters.

All those involved in compiling this Guide have the same common interests. They wish to enable people of all ages, abilities and disabilities, to visit places of interest about which they may have a "Lack of Knowledge".

The following Charities in supporting and promoting this Guide Book will benefit from the sale of each copy: Radar, Phab, SOS, The Spastic Society, Mencap, Age Concern, The National Trust and the RSPB.

Let us hope we can help all those whose lives may have been limited due to lack of knowledge about places they could enjoy.

MICHAEL B YARROW

BEHIND EVERY DISABLED PERSON SHOULD BE AN ABLE BODY.

One that can only be realised with your support.

We want to be able to provide the level of care that will give disabled people this choice: either to live in the familiar surroundings of their own homes. Or, if they prefer, to move into the comfort of one of ours.

So please help us in any way you can. It is only through legacies, covenants and the generosity of our friends that our work can continue.

THE LEONARD CHESHIRE FOUNDATION

26-29 Maunsel Street, London SW1P 2QN.

Eaton Hall · Chester

FOREWORD
by
THE DUKE OF WESTMINSTER

Welcome to the first edition of "Places That Care".

My association with the compiler, Michael Yarrow, started in 1966 when we were both at Harrow together. Since then, both he and I have had a great deal to do with charities and I am delighted to be in a position to write the foreword for this most worthwhile publication.

The contents of this guide will enable everybody to have a better knowledge of places that they may have otherwise thought impossible to visit. It is with the elderly, disabled and their carers in mind, that this unique guide has been produced, and I am sure that it will bring many happy days to everyone who uses it.

In today's world, many properties are being designed with facilities for disabled people, but this book has included many National Trust, English Heritage, RSPB reserves, museums, stately homes, zoos, railways, gardens, rare breed farms and many other exciting places, where the owners, occupiers or managers have felt that the facilities they have to offer can also be enjoyed by those who experience difficulties travelling and getting out and about.

I am delighted to be associated with this excellent guide and commend it to you. I have no doubt that the charities supporting it will benefit from its production.

6

CONTENTS PAGE

ARE YOU RETIRED?
OR APPROACHING RETIREMENT?

Then you may enjoy reading Retirement World.
A monthly national newspaper packed with interest
and information that addresses the issues
concerning our senior age group.

Send for your **FREE**
complimentary copy
today!

TRY ALSO . . .

RETIREMENT WORLD

GOOD NEIGHBOURS NEWS

Issue No 91

34 Years of Caring 1957 - 1991

published and distributed every 4 weeks

Published every
four weeks, it offers
cash prizes of £20,000 in every
issue, a chance to win a car and a
host of other competitions.

There's a children's corner and lots of news about the
Good Neighbours work for UK charities such as the
Spastics Society.

For a **FREE** sample of either or both publications write to:
Circulation Department, Community Publishing (Avon) Ltd,
Unit 1, City Business Park, Easton Road, Bristol BS5 0SP.

Alas you cannot win any of the competitions with a free paper, to do
that you have to buy it.

HOW TO USE THIS GUIDE BOOK:

This Guide has been divided into counties and regions to enable you to locate the venues you wish to visit.

Name

Address

Telephone number

Details of locations

Details of BR/Bus

Brief details about each venue

Opening times: Most places in this Guide are closed on Christmas Day, Boxing Day and New Years Day, but please check with the venue concerned for further information.

Symbols: Whilst as much information as possible has been symbolized, all the information supplied for this book has been supplied by the venues direct. This book is produced solely as a Guide and unfortunately, we are unable to accept any responsibility or liability for any incorrect details. Every effort has been made to ensure that the information in this guide is believed to be accurate at the time of going to press but no warranty is given and readers should check with venues before making the visit.

Should you feel that any information is inaccurate, or there are places which are suitable for wheelchair users, please advise us so we can improve the contents of this guide to enable everybody to have improved knowledge.

Please write to:

Places that Care
72 High St
Poole
Dorset, BH15 1DA

THE ROYAL ASSOCIATION FOR DISABILITY AND REHABILITATION

RADAR
25 MORTIMER STREET
LONDON
W1N 8AB
Tel No: 071 637 5400

RADAR AND ITS POLICY

RADAR is a national campaigning and advisory organisation working with and for physically disabled people. The Association's policy is to remove architectural, economic and attitudinal barriers which impose restrictions on disabled people. RADAR is particularly involved in the areas of education, employment, mobility, health, social services, housing, access, and social security.

RADAR believes that disabled people should be fully consulted concerning their needs and wishes, and that provision of services should be geared to the needs of the consumer. The Association's research, campaigning and information work is aimed at furthering this objective.

PARLIAMENTARY WORK

The RADAR monitors all proposed legislation, and, where necessary, promotes amendments to Bills. The Association keeps Government Departments and members of both houses of Parliament informed of the issues which affect disabled people, and campaigns to ensure that legislation which promotes the rights and interests of disabled people is passed and fully implemented. RADAR also works to ensure that legislation which would adversely affect disabled people is resisted.

LOCAL SUPPORT AND CONSULTATION

RADAR's effectiveness depends upon being aware of the needs and wishes of disabled people throughout the country. To achieve this, RADAR consults regularly with its affiliated network of some 500 self–governing organisations. With its network of Regional Services Officers, RADAR is able to provide support and information at a local level, receiving in return the views and concerns of disabled people which will enable its policies and work–programmes to be formulated. The regional staff monitor local provision of services for disabled people, encouraging the extension and improvement of them as necessary.

INFORMATION PROVISION

Through its Information Department, specialist Policy Officers, and Regional Services team, RADAR deals with an estimated 100,000 queries per year by telephone, letter and personal contact. RADAR produces a monthly newsletter, Bulletin, which contains information on proposed legislation, social security matters, new pieces of equipment on the market, items of interest in the fields of education and employment, and details of courses and conferences, amongst other areas. A quarterly magazine (Contact) is also produced, which contains more detailed articles on areas of interest from contributors outside as well as inside RADAR.

The Association produces a number of other publications, including holiday guides, a motoring and mobility guide, access guides to sports centres and arts facilities, and booklets for prospective employees and for newly disabled people. A wide range of fact sheets, briefing notes and reports are produced.

Information is also provided via RADAR's varied conference and exhibition programme. This has included training seminars on contracting services to local authorities, a series of conferences on independence training for disabled children, and conferences on employment, mobility and housing.

SPECIFIC AREAS OF WORK

In its employment work, RADAR encourages employers to recognise the skills and abilities of disabled people. The Association organises projects (such as a pilot initiative to bring six local authorities up to the legal minimum quota of 3% disabled employees) and promotes good practice (through publications such as the "Employer's Guide to Disabilities", for example). Another area of work is education, which has included the running of an education and training bureau, research into self–care and independence for disabled children, and the production of publications such as the "Educational Implications of Disability".

As one of the major barriers to independence and equality for disabled people is the lack of physical access to buildings and the outdoor environment, RADAR's access work involves campaigning for legislative change to overcome these barriers. RADAR is also particularly involved in the areas of housing (an example of its work being the research into whether the housing needs of disabled people are being met, and if not, what can be done to improve the situation), social security (working on the implementation of a comprehensive disability income scheme that would provide an adequate weekly income for all disabled people), mobility (with work focused on the need to make public transport accessible to all members of the public including the 10% of the population who are disabled), and social services provision (working on the full implementation of the 1986 Disabled Persons Act, amongst other areas of work). Further work is taken on as the circumstances require, such as work on the effects of the community charge on disabled people, and research into the system of disabled facilities grants for adaptation work.

Bert Massie
RADAR
25 Mortimer St
London, W1N 8AB
Tel No: 071 637 5400

"Making more of Life together"

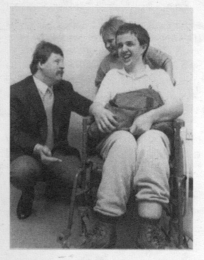

Rolf Harris OBE

Hi, I'm Rolf Harris, President of PHAB. I wish to tell you about an exceptional charity.

Did you know there are six million disabled people in Britain today? That's a staggering 11% of the population. So the need for PHAB is as great as ever.

But what on earth is PHAB?

It started back in 1957. A disabled young man, infuriated by being excluded from everyday activities, told his able bodied friends: "I want opportunity, not pity" – a chance for real integration within the community around him. **Bringing together the Physically Disabled and the Able Bodied.**

"I like coming because it's happy it's fun"

Within a year, the first PHAB events had been organised. People with and without disabilities coming together, on equal terms, to enjoy sports, arts, drama, outings, dances – in short, all the usual things that any group of children and young people would wish to share.

Barriers of fear, ignorance, embarrassment and prejudice simply crumbled. Physically disabled people gained new confidence in themselves, and a realisation that integration with society was indeed possible. As for the able bodied, there was the pleasure of making friends – a sense of new responsibility and awareness.

Just as important, everyone – physically disabled and able bodied alike – had lots of fun. The philosophy of PHAB had well and truly been born.

Enter the PHAB Club

Soon the concept of the PHAB Club was in full swing – 'half way' houses with PHs and ABs organising activities and enjoying themselves together in a unique microcosm of an ideal world.

Playing such an important role, it's hardly surprising that PHAB has become hugely successful. Today, there are over 500 Clubs throughout Britain (there's bound to be one near you), as well as strong links with Europe, America, Asia and Australasia.

But I have to tell you: there's still a long, long way to go . . . Will you help, like so many of my personality friends do!!

BUT THEN THERE'S NEVER BEEN A
CHARITY LIKE Phab

12

S.O.S.

The SOS, Stars Organisation for Spastics, are delighted to be associated with this guide which provides useful access information so enabling people with disabilities to enjoy fully the many places of interest listed.

The SOS is a unique charity founded in 1955 by a group of celebrities who wanted to fund raise for the then newly founded Spastics Society. Today, SOS have over 450 celebrity members who are totally committed to supporting the work of the charity.

The SOS, whilst running its own service projects, continues to work closely with The Spastics Society improving the quality of life for children and adults disabled with cerebral palsy.

The SOS are currently working with The Spastics Society to establish conductive education in the UK. At the moment parents make enormous sacrifices to send their children to Hungary for this vital treatment which gives disabled children the opportunity to achieve and work towards maximum independence despite their handicaps.

Cerebral palsy – cp – is a disability for life. It is injury of the brain which affects control of movement. It is not a single disorder, but a variety of conditions with many causes. Cerebral palsy causes movement problems in varying degrees from barely noticeable to extremely severe. No two people with cp are the same. It's as individual as people themselves.

It affects one in four hundred babies but with help particularly during the pre school years these "little ones" can realise their full potential and learn to lead independent lives in adulthood. Here SOS continues to provide support through the "Independent Living Fund" which finances homes in the community backed by a full care programme enabling adults with cerebral palsy to lead their own lives.

"The Access Guide to Places of Interest Suitable for Elderly and Disabled People" is providing valuable funds so we can continue our work. If you would like to help SOS take the dis out of disability telephone 071 637 9681 at 12, Park Crescent, London, W1N 4EQ.

WHEELCHAIR ACCESSIBLE?

Rolac provides answers to access problems.

- **HANDY** — lightweight ramps.
- **PLATFORM** — Light duty permanent or semi-permanent ramps.
- **PLYFORM** — Plywood topped quick assembly ramps for internal use.
- **TOUGHFORM** — Concrete topped permanent ramps.

Tell them about Rolac if access is difficult. We can smooth the way.

Rolac Ltd, Unit 16, Enterprise Centre Two, Chester Street, Stockport SK3 0BR Tel: 061 - 429 - 8477

Is this a closed book?

Our handbook, "Access to the Underground", has been completely revised to include all new developments on the Underground and also the Docklands Light Railway. Using good clear print, it comprehensively details what to expect at every Underground and Docklands Light Railway station. How many steps, escalators or lifts, location of entrances and opening times. It also shows where and when accompanied passengers in wheelchairs can travel and gives many other useful tips.

"Access to the Underground" is on sale, price 70p, at the London Transport Travel Information Centres at King's Cross, Euston, Oxford Circus, Piccadilly Circus, Victoria and Heathrow Central, or by post (price £1) from:

> The Unit for Disabled Passengers,
> London Regional Transport,
> 55 Broadway,
> London SW1H 0BD.

Hopefully you'll find the system is less of a closed book than you think!

AGE CONCERN

Age Concern England (the National Council on Ageing) is a confederation of over a thousand national and local organisations concerned with promoting the well–being, fulfilment and happiness of older people. Age Concern is the largest charity in this country providing direct services to older people.

Age Concern local groups run a wide and varying range of services appropriate to the needs of elderly people in their area including day centres, lunch clubs, transport schemes, home visiting, practical advice and the provision of intensive care for mentally and physically frail elderly people.

Age Concern England provides assistance and advice to local groups through a network of field officers and advisers based around the country. It also provides direct financial help in the form of grants to groups, including new and innovative schemes run by older people themselves.

Nationally, Age Concern England campaigns with and for older people; briefs MP's and key decision makers on issues affecting them; and provides a wide range of publications and information materials. Age Concern England works closely with Age Concern in Scotland, Wales and N.Ireland to achieve better conditions for older people.

Age Concern England aims to promote good practice in service provision through a range of training courses for professional and voluntary sector workers as well as trainees involved in government employment training schemes. It also promotes academic teaching and research into the needs of older people and quality of service provision through the Age Concern Institute of Gerontology at King's College, London.

At a European level, Age Concern England seeks to influence policy and practice through its work with Eurolink Age, and is an active member of the International Federation on Ageing.

CHRISTMAS WALKS FOR PEOPLE WITH DISABILITIES

BUCKINGHAMSHIRE

Tuesday 31 December 1991
Stowe Landscape Gardens
Contact: Rosemary Jury
Tel No: 0280 822850

CAMBRIDGESHIRE

Saturday 28 December 1991
Wicken Fen
Contact: Tim Bennett
Tel No: 0353 720274

CHESHIRE

Friday 27 December 1991
Alderley Edge
Contact: Richard Littleton
Tel No: 0625 584412

CORNWALL

Wednesday 1 January 1992
Lanhydrock
Contact: Brian Muelaner
Tel No: 0208 74281

DEVON

Sunday 29 December 1991
Killerton
Contact: Bill Lambshead
Tel No: 0392 881418

Tuesday 31 December 1991
Saltram
Contact: Andy Bell
Tel No: 0752 338347

GLOUCESTERSHIRE

Monday 30 December 1991
Sherbourne Park Estate
Contact: Andy Mayled
Tel No: 045 14257

NORTHUMBERLAND

Friday 27 December 1991
Housesteads, Bardon Mill
Contact: Andrew Poad
Tel No: 0434 344314

NOTTINGHAMSHIRE

Thursday 26 December 1991
Clumber Park, Worksop
Contact: Jackie Scott
Tel No: 0909 476592

SUFFOLK

Saturday 28 December 1991
Dunwich Heath
Contact: Heather Moss
Tel No: 072 873 505

SURREY

Saturday 4 January 1992
Box Hill, Nr Dorking
Contact: Peter Creasey
Tel No: 0306 885502

YORKSHIRE

Monday 30 December 1991
Fountains Abbey, Nr Ripon
Contact: Robert Metcalfe
Tel No: 0765 620333

NORTH WALES: CLWYD

Friday 27 December 1991
Erddig Park Estate, Wrexham
Contact: Frank Harvey
Tel No: 0978 355314

SOUTH WALES: DYFED

Monday 30 December 1991
Stackpole Estate, Nr Pembroke
Contact: Angus Oglethorpe
Tel No: 0646 661359

ACCESS FOR EVERYONE WITH THE NATIONAL TRUST

The National Trust is a charity and the country's most active conservation body. Some 11 million known annual visitors are welcomed each year to its numerous historic buildings and gardens – and countless millions more enjoy the 600,000 acres of superb countryside and coast under its protection. The Trust makes every effort to ease access for some 20% of these visitors who have disabilities or infirmities.

Powered self–drive, or volunteer driven vehicles, manual wheelchairs, ramps, and lifts are among the many facilities provided at a variety of National Trust properties. Visually impaired and hearing impaired people may bring their guide dogs and hearing dogs; there are increasing numbers of Braille guides, and the Sympathetic Hearing Scheme is in operation at many properties.

The wide variety of accessible properties includes historic buildings, gardens and landscape parks, countryside and coast, nature walks, bird hides, fishing facilities, restaurants, shops – even an adventure area where disabled and able–bodied people of all ages can take part in outdoor activities such as abseiling (in or out of a wheelchair!) rockclimbing or archery.

Thick handled cutlery is provided in restaurants and tearooms, and the Trust has adapted several holiday cottages for disabled guests in beautiful countryside and on the coast. The necessary companion of a disabled visitor is given free admission on request.

Events such as theatrical performances, concerts and fetes are often accessible; and the Trust is involving children with disabilities in its educational activities.

The National Trust's adviser on access for disabled visitors will gladly advise enquirers, and send them full details of access if required; please write to Valarie Wenham, Adviser, Facilities for Disabled Visitors, The National Trust, 36 Queen Anne's Gate, London, SW1H 9AS.

MENCAP

MENCAP (The Royal Society for Mentally Handicapped Children & Adults) aims to make sure that the needs and aspirations of people with learning disabilities and their families are met.

MENCAP employs more than 3,000 staff working for 50,000 parent members through 500 local societies, who support 150,000 friends with learning disabilities. More than a million volunteers regularly help us throughout England, Wales and Northern Ireland.

MENCAP is the largest voluntary organisation in the UK working exclusively for people with a learning disability and their families through a variety of services.

THE PATHWAY EMPLOYMENT SERVICE

The Pathway Employment Service has helped over 2,000 people with a learning disability to obtain "real jobs for real money" and acts as a liaison between their clients and employers, giving support and advice wherever necessary.

EDUCATION AND TRAINING

Three residential colleges for young adults offer practical training in rural activities and life skills to the students and advice to their advocates and carers, as well as helping education authorities to develop policy and practice in the area of special needs.

GATEWAY

The National Federation of Gateway Clubs celebrates its Silver Jubilee this year with many exciting events, demonstrating the abilities and achievements of people with learning disabilities. Every week more than 740 Gateway clubs provide sporting and leisure opportunities to 150,000 members.

MENCAP

Over the last ten years MENCAP Homes Foundation Project has helped people who have profound and multiple disabilities through training workshops for their families and carers, providing training and support for a wide range of needs from communication and feeding, dental care and diet to legal matters and leisure pursuits.

DISTRICT OFFICERS

MENCAP's District Officers campaign for better services and work closely with local MENCAP societies, individuals, families and other professionals.

COUNTRYSIDE CODE

1. Enjoy the countryside and respect its life and work

2. Guard against all risks of fire

3. Fasten all gates

4. Keep your dogs under close control

5. Keep to public paths across farmland

6. Use gates and stiles to cross fences, hedges and walls

7. Leave livestock, crops and machinery alone

8. Take your litter home

9. Help to keep all water clean

10. Protect wildlife, plants and trees

11. Take special care on country roads

12. Make no unnecessary noise

Please ensure that you keep your dog on a lead when walking through farmland and on the open moorland to avoid disturbance to grazing stock and ground nesting birds.

Please go properly equipped when walking on the high moors.

Winged Fellowship
Holidays for Disabled People

* Five holiday centres for severely disabled people

* Full care provided and 24 hour nursing

* Special interest weeks including No-smoking, Garden Visits

* Swimming pools at three centres

* Holidays arranged overseas

* Centres open from February to December

* Special weeks for Alzheimers sufferers and carers

ALL ENQUIRIES TO: Winged Fellowship, Angel House, 20-32 Pentonville Road, London N1 4XD

ENGLAND

SYMBOL DESCRIPTIONS

£   Admission charge

F   No admission charge but donation in some places

©   Special concession charge for disabled people, elderly people, carers and children

    Groups must book in advance – special rates may apply

    Guide dogs accepted except in certain areas

    Sympathetic Hearing Scheme participated in or Loop System

    Special information available for disabled people

PARKING

P   Designated disabled parking space

P   Own car park with a dropping off point within 50 yards

P   Public car park nearby and/or street parking within 200 yards

P   Dropping off point or disabled parking place by telephone appointment

MAIN ENTRANCE

    Entrance level or ramped and over 30" wide

    Steps into building 1–5 or bumpy

    Steps into building 6 or more

    More suitable entrance freely available, telephone for details or help. Temporary ramps to be made available.

    Steps within the buildings that cannot be overcome by ramps

    More than one floor level and no lift

    More than one floor level and suitable lift/stairclimber/stairlift for wheelchair users

OUTSIDE

    Routes around the site are free of steps or steps can be avoided

    Seats available around the site

    Routes indicated for wheelchair users

    Routes indicated for visually handicapped people

    Transport around the site suitable for disabled people and wheelchair users – telephone in advance

    Transport around the site not suitable for disabled people or elderly people

    There are limited areas that cannot be reached due to steps or doorways less than 30"

TOILETS

&wc Unisex toilets designed or adapted for disabled people or public toilets within 50 yards. Radar key required in some

WC Ordinary toilets with level access

WC No toilets on site but public ones nearby

⚼ Baby changing/parents room available

GENERAL

⚔ Restaurant/tea room/cafe/ not accessible due to steps/narrow doorway/first floor with no lift

¶¶ Restaurant/tea room/cafe/vending accessible by ramp or level or lift with 30″ doors

⚒ Shop not accessible due to stairs but may be accessible with help

⚒ Shop/sales area accessible by ramp or level and 30″ doorway

⚖ Picnic area only, or nearby

♿ Wheelchair users are advised to come accompanied

🎧 Taped guides available/or person

◆ Facilities for visually handicapped/braille or by request

✋ People available to help (telephone beforehand if you require help)

© Telephone accessible for wheelchair users

⚖ This site is suitable for elderly people but unsuitable for wheelchair users

♿L Wheelchairs/batricars for loan or hire – telephone for advance booking

NT The National Trust

EH English Heritage

NTS National Trust for Scotland

RSPB Royal Society For the Protection of Birds

FC Forestry Commission

⇌ British Rail

🚌 Bus

☎ Telephone

⊖ Underground

23

NOTES

ENGLAND

AVON

Avon Valley Railway

Bitton Station
Willsbridge
Bristol, Avon, BS15 6ED
☎ 0272 240990
A431 Bristol/Bath
≉ Bristol or Bath 🚌 to Willsbridge

Two mile return trip on wonderful steam trains. Tarmac and gravel paths.

£🚌✳️🅿️⬆️♿🚻🍴 🛒🏕️
🧑‍🦽♿️🐟

City of Bristol Museum and Art Gallery

Queen's Rd
Clifton
Bristol, Avon, BS8 1RI
☎ 0272 223571
Bristol
≉ Temple Meads 🚌 Bristol Omnibus

Worldwide collections including dinosaurs, Egyptology, ethnography, Bristol ceramics, silver, oriental ceramics and glass.

Jan–Dec Mon–Sun 10am–5pm
Closed: May and Spring BH

F🚌✳️🅿️🅿️♿🏕️🏛️⬆️→
⊣➕♿🚻🍴🛒🧑‍🦽🐟

Clifton Observatory Camera Obscura and Cave

By Suspension Bridge
Bristol, Avon, BS8 3TY
☎ 0275 393798
Clifton, Bristol.
≉ 🚌 Bristol, Temple Meads.

The only camera obscura open to the public in England. A cave with viewing platform giving view of Avon Gorge and Suspension Bridge. Tarmac paths.

Winter Mon–Sun 11am–4pm
Summer Mon–Sun 11am–6pm

£🚌✳️🅿️♿🏕️🏛️→⊣⇒
➕🚻🛒🏕️🧑‍🦽🐟

The Royal Photographic Society

Milsom St
Bath, Avon, BA1 1DN
☎ 0225 462841
Bath – A4 London Rd
≉ Bath

Oldest photographic society in the world with galleries and museum

Jan–Dec Mon–Sun 9.30am–5.00pm

£©🚌🅿️🗝️♿🏕️🛒🚻♿🏕️🍴
🧑‍🦽🐟

American Museum

Claverton Manor
Bath, Avon, BA2 7BD
☎ 0225 460503
A36
≉ Bath – 2½ miles

18 period furnished rooms from 17th to 19th centuries. American Arboretum. Many exhibits in beautiful gardens. Teas with American cookies. Gravel and paved paths

Jan–Dec Tues–Sun 2pm–5pm

£©🚌✳️🅿️🅿️♿🏛️→⊣➕♿
🚻🍴🛒🏕️🧑‍🦽

Bath Postal Museum

8 Broad St
Bath, Avon, BA1 5LJ
☎ 0225 460333
Bath
≉ 🚌 Bath

Story of development of postal service from time of Henry VIII to present day. Various changing exhibitions. Air Mail room.

Jan–Dec Mon–Sat 11am–5pm
Apr–Oct Sun 2pm–5pm

£©🚌✳️🅿️♿🏛️🚻✖️🛒♿
🧑‍🦽

At George Bayntun's

Manvres St
Bath, Avon, BA1 1JW
☎ 0225 466000
Bath
≉ 🚌 Bath

History and examples of the bookbinding craft. Museum situated in George Bayntun's antiquarian bookshop.

Jan–Dec Mon–Fri 9am–1pm & 2pm–5.30pm
Sat am by appt.

AVON

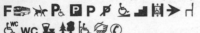

Bristol Industrial Museum

Princes Wharf
City Docks
Bristol, Avon, BS1 4RN
☎ 0272 251470

Bristol

≥ 🚌 Temple Meads

Dockside museum of Bristol's industrial history, including road, rail and water transport. Maximum of 2 wheelchairs upstairs at any one time. 20 acres with paved paths.

Jan–Dec Sat–Wed 10am–1pm & 2pm–5pm

F🚌☀️Ⓟ₰ⓟ₰♿♿📶🏃➜🚻
⚹ᵂᶜwc🍴🚻🚶♿

Clifton Cathedral

Clifton Park
Bristol, Avon, BS8 3BX
☎ 0272 738411

M4, M5, M32

≥ 🚌 Temple Meads

Modern cathedral. Hexagonal shape. Excellent organ. Magnificent stained glass windows. Opened 1973 and built for present day liturgy. Paved paths.

Jan–Dec: Mon–Sun 7am–9pm

F🚌☀️♫Ⓟ♿🏃➜🚻⇒⚹ᵂᶜwc
⚿🚶♿🍴

Dauphines Victorian Streets & Costume Museum

☎ 0272 551700 or 551997

End of M32 – Nr Evening Post Building, Broad Mead Shopping Centre

≥ 🚌 Temple Meads

Victorian streets with shops and school room. Theatrical and historical costumes. Uniforms and wedding dresses through the ages. Face painting and dressing up facilities available. Paved paths.

Jan–Dec Mon–Sat 9am–5.30pm
Evening bookings for groups available

£©🚌☀️🚗Ⓟ₰Ⓟ₰♿🔧🔌🔌
📶🏃⚹ᵂᶜwc⚿🍴🚶♿🎧🔌
🍴🍴

The Museum of Costume

Assembly Rooms
Bennett St
Bath, Avon, BA1 2QH
☎ 0225 461111 x 2789

Bath city centre. M4 junction 18

≥ 🚌 Bath Spa

One of the most extensive and prestigious collections of fashionable dress for men, women and children from the late C16th to the present day. One acre of hilly ground, level areas with paved paths.

Mar–Oct: Mon–Sat: 9.30am–6pm
Sun: 10am–6pm
Nov–Feb: Mon–Sat: 10am–5pm
Sun: 11am–5pm

International Helicopter Museum

Weston Airport
Locking Moor Rd
Weston–super–Mare, Avon, BS22 8PP
☎ 0934 635227

Weston–super–Mare: A371 3 miles from Junction 21 of M5

≥ Milton Halt

The only helicopter museum in the UK, with more than 50 rotocraft in the collection, displayed indoors and outdoors. 2 acres of level ground with paved and grass paths.

Apr–Oct: Mon–Sun: 10am–6pm
Nov–Mar: Thu–Sun: 10.30am–4pm

£🚌☀️♿Ⓟ♿➜⚹ᵂᶜwc🍴🚶🍴
🍴

Bristol Cathedral

College Green
Bristol, Avon, BS1 5TJ
☎ 0272 264879

Centre of city

≥ Bristol Temple Meads

The Augustinian Abbey, now a cathedral, dates from 1140. Fine Norman chapter house, unique hall–church, east end & choir.

Jan–Dec: Mon–Sun 8am–6pm

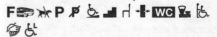

Woodspring Museum

Burlington St
Weston–super–Mare, Avon, BS23 1PR
☎ 0934 621028

Weston–super–Mare A370 – M5

≥ 🚌 Weston–super–Mare

Environmental Gallery, Royal Potteries, The Victorian Seaside Holiday, local history and temporary exhibitions.

Jan–Dec: Mon–Sat 10am–5pm

F🚐🐕🎿P🅿️ ♿🏛️♿wc 🍴 🍽️
🦽

BEDFORDSHIRE

Leighton Buzzard Railway

Page's Park Station
Billington Rd
Leighton Buzzard, Beds., LU7 8TN
☎ 0525 373888

Leighton Buzzard, off A4146
⇌ 🚌 Leighton Buzzard

Narrow gauge railway operations, rare steam and diesel engines on passenger trains through uniquely varied scenery around this historic market town. 2 stations in total with tarmaced paths.

5 Apr–4 Oct: Sun & BH Mon
5 Aug–10 Sep: Wed & Thur

£©🚐🎿🎿 🅿️P♿➔ ⌐♿wc 🍴
🍽️🌳🌳

Harrold–Odell Country Park

Carlton Rd
Harrold, Beds., MK43 7AP
☎ 0234 720016

Bedford on A428, turn right at Turvey Park then signposted

🚌 Bedford services 51,108 and 133

144 acres of former gravel quarry with gravel paths. Half the site is water. Visitor centre with Natural History exhibits, etc.

Park: Jan–Dec.
Centre: Summer: Tue–Fri 1pm–4.30pm
Sat–Sun 1pm–6pm
Winter: Sat–Sun 1pm–4.30pm

F🎿P♿ 🅿️ ♿➔ ⌐♿wc 🍽️🌳🌳

Stockwood Craft Museum

Farley Hill
Luton, Beds.,
☎ 0582 38714

Luton A6
⇌ Luton

Craft demonstrations most weekends. Lovely gardens. Gravel and paved paths. Restaurant weekends only
Jan–Dec Wed–Sat: 10am–5pm

Sun: 10am–6pm

F🚐🎿 🅿️♿☞➔ ⌐♿wc 🍽️
🦽🌳

Luton Museum and Art Gallery

Wardown Park
Luton, Beds., LU2 7HA
☎ 0582 36941

Off A6 north of Luton
⇌ 🚌 Luton

The museum for South Bedfordshire including archaeology, local history, costume lace, hat making and military history.

Jan–Dec Mon–Fri: 10am–5pm
Sun: 1pm–5pm

F🚐🎿 🅿️🔑☞ 🔲wc🔲 🍽️🔦🦽
🌳🎓

Cecil Biggins Art Gallery & Museum

Castle Close
Beds., MK40 3NY
☎ 0234 211222

A428
⇌ 🚌 Bedford

Award winning re–created Victorian Mansion set in pleasant grounds by the river embankment. Adjoining gallery housing outstanding collections of watercolours. Refreshments provided by prior notice. Level area with paved paths.

Jan–Dec: Tues–Fri & BH Mon
12.30pm–5pm
Sat: 11am–5pm
Sun: 2pm–5pm.

F🚐🎿 🅿️P♿🔲🏺➔ ⌐♿wc
🍽️🔦🌳🎓

Woburn Abbey

Woburn, Beds., MK43 0TP
☎ 0525 290666

Milton Keynes A5
⇌ Bletchley and Flitwick (both 5 miles away)

Woburn Abbey houses a most impressive and important private collection of paintings, furniture, porcelain and silver. 3000 acre deer park. Extensive picnic areas. Antiques centre and pottery. Guide dogs accepted by prior arrangement. 40 acres with asphalt paths.

Jan–Mar: Sat/Sun/BH

BEDFORDSHIRE

Apr–Nov: Mon–Sun

£©🚌 🅿 ♿ ▪ 🏢 → ⌐ ♿ WC 🍴
🏊 🚶 ♿ 🙌 ©

Whipsnade Wild Animal Park

Dunstable, Beds., LU6 2LF
☎ 0582 872171

Sign–posted from Junction 9 and 12 on M1

≷ Luton 🚌 Seasonal from Hemel
Hempstead

The Park is 600 acres of beautiful parkland,
home of 3000 animals. Wallabies,
peacocks, mara and chinese waterdeer
roam free among the woods. No dogs
allowed (including guide dogs).

Jan–Dec: Mon–Sun 10am–dusk

£©🚌 🅿 🅿 🔔 ☞ → ⌐ 🏍 🐎 ♿
WC 🚻 🍴 🏊 🚶 🙌 ©

Woodside Farm & Wildfowl Park

Mancroft Rd
Slip End
Luton, Beds., LU1 4DG
☎ 0582 841044

Luton off A5 or A6 on M1, junction 9

Hop n Stopped service

Country park with rare breeds, poultry
centre and blacksmith craft centre. Ideal for
all ages. 6½ acres with paved paths.

Jan–Dec: Mon–Sat 8am–5.30pm

£©🚌 🔨 🅿 🅿 ♿ → ⌐ ♿ WC 🚻
🍴 🏊 🚶 ♿ ©

Wrest Park House and Gardens EH

Silsoe, Beds., MK45 4HS
☎ 0525 60000/60152

10 miles from Luton and Beds off the A6

Leisure link bus to the house

Once home of the De Gray family inspired
by 18th century French Chateaux with
wonderful gardens, fascinating buildings
and statues. 90 acres with gravel paths.

Apr–Sept: Sat/Sun/BH's: 10am–6pm

£©🚌 🔨 🅿 🅿 ♿ 🔔 ☞ → ⊹ WC
🍴 🏊 🚶 ♿ 🙌 ©

Stagsden Bird Gardens

Stagsden, Beds., MK43 8SL
☎ 02302 2745

Bedford. Take A428 then A422

🚌 Stagsden village

A bird garden and breeding centre in a
country setting, specialising in cranes, rare
pheasants, waterfowl and owls. Rose
collections. 8½ acres with paved and grass
paths.

Jan–Dec: Mon–Sun 11am–6pm

£©🚌 🅿 ♿ → ⌐ WC 🏊 🚶 ♿

Bedford Museum

Castle Lane
Bedford, MK40 3XD
☎ 0234 353323

Bedford

≷ 🚌 Bedford

Housed in converted 19th century brewery,
close to Castle mound.

Jan–Dec: Tue–Sat 11am–5pm
Sun & BH Mon 2pm–5pm

F🚌 🔨 🅿 🅿 🅿 ♿ → ⌐ ♿ WC 🏊
🚶 ©

The Lodge RSPB

Sandy
Beds., SG19 2DL
☎ 0767 80551

Entered from the B1042 road to Cambridge,
one mile east of Sandy.

Formal gardens and woodland
surroundings all of which are accessible to
wheelchair users.

Mon–Sun: 9am–9pm

🅿 → ⌐ ⇒ ♿ 🏊 🚶 ♿

BERKSHIRE

Courage Shire Horse Centre

Cherry Garden Lane
Maidenhead
Thicket
Maidenhead, Berks., SL6 3QD
☎ 0628 824848

M4 Junction 8/9 on A4 between
Maidenhead and Reading

≷ Maidenhead

Home of up to 16 shire horses. See their
home surroundings, stables and harness
room. Audio visual, dray rides, Shetland
ponies and small animal area. 6 acres with
gravel and paved paths. Day rides for
disabled persons. Wheelchairs can be put
onto dray.

1 Mar–31 Oct: 10.30am–5pm (6pm weekends and BH's)

£ © 🚌 ✕ 🅿 🅿 ♿ ➤ ⊢ 🚻 🚻 ⅱ 🏛 🏕 ♿ 🎧 ✋ ©

The Herb Farm

Peppard Rd
Sonning Common
Reading, Berks., RG4 9NJ
☎ 0734 724220

Nearest town is Reading

🚌 Reading

Herb nursery growing 200+ varieties of herbs. 2 acres with paved and gravel paths. Herb garden and extensive range of herbal products (from toothpaste to tablemats). Newly opened Saxon Maze, large symbolic hedge maze, wildlife areas.

Jan–Dec Tue–Sun: 10am–5pm

£ 🚌 ✕ 🅿 ♿ ➤ ⊢ -¦- 🚻 ⅱ 🏛 🏕 ♿

Beale Bird Park (Part of the ChildBeale Wildlife Trust)

Church Farm
Lower Basildon
Nr Reading, Berks., RG8 9NH
☎ 0734 845171/2 or 0491 671325

Pangbourne A329

🚌 No5 Reading/Oxford. 🚆 Pangbourne

A charitable trust housing vast collections of birds, deer, pets corner, rare breeds + shops, pools, play areas, train. 30 acres with tarmac and Breedon gravel paths.

1 Mar–23 Dec 1992 10am – 6pm (last admissions 5pm)

£ © 🚌 ✕ 🅿 ♿ ➤ ⊢ 🚻 🚻 🏛 🏕 ©

The Look Out Exhibition

Nine Mile Ride
Bracknell, Berks., RG12 4QW
☎ 0344 868222

Bracknell A322

🚆 Bracknell

Facilities include a coffee shop, shop and schoolroom. The exhibition examines the history, natural history, business and industry of the borough. 2600 acres of woodland.

Summer: Tue–Fri: 10am–6pm
Sat–Sun: 10am–8pm
Winter: Wed–Sun: 10am–5pm

F © 🚌 ✕ 🅿 🅿 🅿 ♿ 🏛 🏛 ➤ -¦- 🚻 🚻 🏛 ⅱ 🏛 🏕 ♿ ✋ ©

Windsor Castle

Windsor, Berks., SL4 1NJ
☎ 0753 831118

Windsor Castle

🚆 London Waterloo Station every 30 minutes. Mon–Sat and every hour on Sunday. Tel No 071 928 5100 for details.

🚌 Victoria Coach Station every 30 minutes. Tel No 081 668 7261 for details.

For over 9 centuries this Royal Palace and Fortress, still under direct control of the Sovereign, has provided an awesome background to the great Ceremonies of State and today gives an unrivalled insight into the life in England through the centuries. 13 acres with hilly and level areas. Paths are all tarmac. Busiest times are weekends, July and August. Car park 400 yards away from main building.

Open 10.30am – 7pm
Opening times for 1992: Ring for details.

Disabled access:
Precincts: All areas accessible
State Apartments: Long flight of steps at entrance and exit.
Wheelchairs by arrangement (not Sundays).
Telephone: 0753 868286 ext 2235
Dolls' House: No access
Exhibits: Majority Accessible

Toilets for the Disabled:

Engine Court, Exhibition of The Queen's Presents and Royal Carriages.

£ © 🚌 ✕ 🅿 🏛 ✋ 🏛 🏛 ➤ ⊢ -¦- ♿ 🚻 🏛 🏛 ♿ 🎧 © ✋

Windsor Safari Park

Winkfield Rd
Windsor, Berks., SL4 4AY
☎ 0753 869841

Windsor

🚆 Windsor Riverside Bus

The Park offers an 'African Adventure' with the Egyptian Entrance and Moroccan Village, wild animal reserves, a host of shows including the famous Seaworld show, and many other attractions such as the African Queen Riverboat Ride. No dogs/ guide dogs.

Jan–Dec: Mon–Sun 10am–dusk

BERKSHIRE

£©🚐🅿️🅿️♿➤⊣⇒🚂♿WC
⛺🍴🎒🚶♿🤝

Maidenhead & Cookham Commons NT

☎ 0628 21501

Large areas of commonland; mostly accessible via level paths, with good car park. Winter Hill provides a delightful viewpoint.

BUCKINGHAMSHIRE

The Stables Music Theatre

Stockwell Lane
Wavendon, Bucks., MK17 8LT
☎ 0908 583928

Nearest town is Milton Keynes

The Wavendon Allmusic Plan was established in 1969 at The Stables Theatre and promotes all different styles of music throughout the year.

July–Sept: Fri–Sun evenings

£©🚐🐾🅿️♿➤⊣♿WC♿🤝

Emberton Country Park

Emberton
Nr Olney, Bucks., MK46 5JH
☎ 0234 713325

South of Olney on A509

🚌 Milton Keynes and Bedford. ≈ Central Milton Keynes

Country park with car entrance to most areas. Fishing and boating on 40 acres of lakes bordered by River Ouse to north of park. Vehicle access to all building entrances. 176 acres of grass with grassed paths.

Jan–Dec: Mon–Sun

£©🐾🅿️♿➤⊣♿WC🍴🎒🚶

Bekonscot Model Village

Warwick Rd
Beaconsfield, Bucks., HP09 2PL
☎ 0494 672919

Beaconsfield Junction 2 M40

≈ Beaconsfield–Marylebone Line

Oldest model village in the world, depicting rural England in the 30's. All in minature. A paradise for photographers, an admiration for gardeners. 1½ acres with paved paths. Morning term times with school children are very busy.

Mar–Oct: Mon–Sun: 10am–5pm

£©🚐🐾🅿️🅿️♿➤⊣🚶♿WC
⛺🍴🎒🚶

Claydon House

Middle Claydon
Bucks., MK18 2EY
☎ 0296 730349

Aylesbury A413

🚌 Aylesbury

17th Century house. Fine carved wood decoration and home of Verheys since 1620. 4 acres with gravel and paved paths.

Sat–Wed: 1pm–5pm

£🚐🐾🐎🔭🅿️🏚️➤⊣🚶♿
⛺🍴🎒🚶♿☺♿

Buckinghamshire Railway Centre

Quinton Road Station
Quinton
Nr Aylesbury, Bucks., HP22 4BY
☎ 029675 450/029675 720

A41 from Aylesbury 5 miles

≈ Aylesbury 🚌 to centre weekdays only

Large collection of operating steam railway locomotives, steaming when open. Large static collection of historical railway relics and equipment. 30 acres of mainly level ground with gravel and surfaced paths.

Easter–31 Oct: Sun only
Jun/Jul/Aug: Wed only

£©🚐🐾🅿️🅿️🅿️➤⊣🚶♿WC🍴
🎒🚶♿🐟🤝☺

Boarstall Duck Decoy

Boarstall
Nr Aylesbury, Bucks.,
☎ 0844 237488

2m W of Brill

An C18th duck decoy in working order. 13 acres of natural woodland, nature trail and adapted bird hide

Good Fri–26 Aug: Wed 2pm–5pm
Sat,Sun & BH Mon 10am–5pm

♿♿

Coombe Hill NT

Nr Wendover
Bucks.,

This lovely Chiltern viewpoint is flat grassland which is accessible to wheelchair users and ambulant disabled visitors. A key for the gate is obtainable from the cottage nearby.

Stowe Landscape Gardens NT

Buckingham, Bucks., MK18 5EH
☎ 0280 822850

Buckingham, A442

A Georgian landscape gardens of Vistas and Temples by Vanbrugh, Kent, Gibbs and Capability Brown. Britain's largest work of art. The terrain is rolling, with some steep sharp inclines. The paths are made up of wood chips, which are fine for the Batricars but hard on both wheelchair users and pushers. The house is Stowe Public School and not part of the NT. Most of the Temples that have access also have steps but are visually part of the landscape and need not be entered to be enjoyed. National Trust volunteers who are on hand to help with the Batricars but no one with skills able to lift the very disabled.

1–5 Jan: 10am–5pm
28 Mar–20 Apr: 10am–5pm
28 Jun–6 Sep: 10am–5pm
24 Oct–1 Nov: 10am–5pm

CAMBRIDGESHIRE

Downfield Windmill

Fordham Rd
Soham, Cambs., CB7 5BS
☎ 0353 720333

Between Ely and Newmarket on A142
⇌ Ely and Newmarket. 🚌 to Mill

This is a wind powered flour mill dating from 1726. ½ acre with gravel and grass paths. The full milling process can be seen (wind allowing). Flour for sale.

Sunday 11am – 5pm + BH Mon

University of Archaeology and Anthropology

Downing St
Cambs., CB2 3DZ
☎ 0223 333516

Cambridge
⇌ Cambridge

Up–to–date exhibits of world anthropology. World prehistory and local archaeology. Also special exhibitions.

Mon–Fri: 2pm–4pm
Sat: 10am–12.30pm
Closed: Easter.

The Wildfowl & Wetlands Trust

Peakirk
Peterborough, Cambs., PE6 7NP
☎ 0733 252271

North of Peterborough off the A15 Lincoln Road

🚌 weekdays only

The centre holds 700 waterfowl of 108 species including Flamingos. Landscaped ponds and garden areas. No dogs or guide dogs

Summer: 9.30am–6.30pm
Winter: 9.30am–dusk

Linton Zoological Gardens

Hadstock Rd
Linton, Cambs., CB1 6NT
☎ 0223 891308

10 miles SE of Cambs along B1052 off A604, J9 M11 from London
⇌ 🚌 Cambridge

Wonderful combination of beautiful gardens and wildlife from all over the world. From snakes and tarantula spiders up to big cats. No dogs or guide dogs in zoo area.

Summer: 10am–6pm
Winter: 10am–dusk

Sacrewell Farm & Country Centre

Sacrewell
Thornhaugh
Peterborough, Cambs., PE8 6HJ
☎ 0780 782222

On North side of A47 8 miles West of Peterborough

🚌 Limited services from Peterborough and Stamford

Working arable farm, with considerable

CAMBRIDGESHIRE

historic interest and much natural history and general interest. Working water mill and huge bygones collection. 15 acres with paved paths, surrounded by 500 acres of farmland.

Jan–Dec: Mon–Sun

£©🚌🅿️ 🅿 ⛲ ♿ 🏛 ➤ 🚂 🐴 ♿WC
WC ⚔ ♿ 🌳 ♿

Fitzwilliam Museum

Trumpington St
Cambs., CB2 1RB
☎ 0223 332900

Nr central Cambridge

🚌 ⇌ Cambridge

University museum founded 1816, opened 1848. Extensive and important collections: European paintings, ceramics, antiques, clocks, furniture, etc.

Tues–Sat: 10am–5pm
Sun: 2.15pm–5pm
+ Easter Monday, Spring and Summer Holidays.
Closed Good Friday, May Day, 24 Dec–1 Jan inc.

F🚌 ♿ 🅿️ P ♿ ♿ ➤ ♿WC
WC ⚔ ♿ ♿ 🐟 🎁©

Cambridge & County Folk Museum

2/3 Castle St
Cambs., CB3 0AQ
☎ 0223 355159

Cambridge

⇌ 🚌 Cambridge

The 10 rooms of this fine 16th century building contain objects illustrating life in Cambridgeshire from 1650 to the present day.

1 Apr–30 Sept: Mon–Sat 10.30am – 5pm
Sun 2pm – 5pm
1 Oct–31 Mar: Tue–Sat 10.30am – 5pm
Sun 2pm – 5pm

£©🚌♿P ♿ ♿ 🏛 ➤ WC ♿
♿ 🎧 🐟 ♿

St John's College

Cambs., CB2 1TP
☎ 0223 338600

⇌ 🚌 Cambridge: M11, A1, A604, A45
Cambridge

The hospital of St.John was in existence by the early C13th which later became

St.John's college. Set in 88 acres. Paths are mostly paved with a few cobbled. Lunchtimes and weekends are very busy.

1 Jul–1 May: 10.30am–5.30pm
May–Jun: Closed for exam period

F🚌 ♿ P ♿ ♿ ➤ WC ♿ ♿

Kettles Yard Art Gallery

Castle St
Cambs., CB3 0AQ
☎ 0223 352124

Cambridge

🚌 ⇌ Cambridge

Kettles Yard House created in 1957, was home of the founder, Jim Ede. Art in a domestic setting. Not a museum, but a home now opened to the public. 20th Century paintings, sculpture, gallery, changing exhibitions of contemporary art. Gallery to be improved in 1992/3 for disabled people to include ramps and toilets.

House: Tues–Sun 2pm–4pm
Gallery: Mon–Sat 12.30pm–5.30pm
Sun 2pm–5.30pm

F🚌 ♿ P ♿ ♿ ♿ 🏛 ♿ WC ♿ 🐟
🎁 ♿

Grafham Water

Huntingdon
Cambs., PE18 0BX
☎ 0480 810531

A1 between Bedford and Huntington

⇌ 🚌 Huntington

25 year old reservoir recently improved to provide leisure facilities including exhibition centre and catering, cycle hire, bird hides, boating fishing for trout, car parks and nature reserve. Sailing every day. Fishing April to December. 2000 acres, with paved paths and the occasional rolled stone path.

Jan–Dec: Mon–Sun

£©🚌♿ 🐴 ♿ 🅿 ♿ ➤ ♿ ♿ ♿WC WC
⚔ ♿ 🌳 🎁©

Imperial War Museum Duxford

Duxford Airfield
Cambs., CB2 4QR
☎ 0223 833963 or 0223 835000
(information line)

Duxford is next to Juntion 10 of the M11

⇌ 🚌 Cambridge

Duxford is a former Battle of Britain fighter station and part of the Imperial War

32

Museum. 250 acres with paved paths.
Mid March–31 Oct: 10am – 6pm
1 Nov–Mid March: 10am – 4pm

£©🚌🚫🛏️ P ♿ 🚼 🚻 ⛓️ WC
⛲ 🍴 📷 🎣 ♿ 🎧 🐟 🖼️ⓘ 📶

Wicken Fen Nature Reserve NT

Warden's House
Lode Lane
Wicken
Ely, Cambs., CB7 5XP
☎ 0353 720274

Wicken on A7123 between Stretham and
Soham

≈ Ely

This is the only readily accessible remnant
of the once extensive fens of East Anglia's
Great Level. It is also one of the oldest
nature reserves in Britain, parts of it having
been owned and managed by the National
Trust since 1899. There is a great variety of
plant life, hawking dragonflies and dykes
teeming with wildlife. 605 acres with
boarded circuit and close mown vegetation.

Jan–Dec: Mon–Sun

£🚌🚫 P♿ P ♿ → ⛓️ ⇒ 🚻 WC 📷
📶 🖼️ⓘ ♿

Wildfowl and Wetlands Trust

100 Bank
Welney
Wisbech, Cambs., PE14 9TN
☎ 0353 860711

Ely or Downham Market: A10

≈ 🚌 Littleport – 7 miles

A nature reserve featuring spectacular
numbers of ducks and swans in the
Autumn/Winter period. Guide dogs only
allowed in winter and to main hide.

Jan–Dec: Mon–Sun 10am–5pm

£©🚌🚫 P ♿ → ⛓️ 🚻 WC 🍴 📷
📶 🖼️ⓘ 📶

Nene Valley Railway Ltd

Wansford Station
Stibbington
Peterborough, Cambs., PE8 6LR
☎ 0780 780782

Adjacent to A1 – 8 miles west of
Peterborough

≈ Peterborough ½ mile

This railway has over 30 steam and diesel
locomotives and many items of carriage and

wagon stock from European countries, and
provides the ideal outing for those who love
steam and the younger members of the
family who have never experienced a steam
locomotive in action.

Mar–Oct: Weekends & public hols
29 May–Aug: Wed services
Special events throughout the year

£©🚌🚫 P ♿ → ⛓️ 🚂 🚻 WC
🍴 📷 📶 🖼️

Hamerton Wildlife Centre

Hamerton
Huntingdon, Cambs., PE17 5RE
☎ 08323 362

Peterborough, Huntingdon A1 – A1–M1 Link
(A604)

A unique collection of 120 rare and
endangered species of birds and mammals.
Guide dogs by prior arrangement

Summer: Mon–Sun: 10.30am–6pm
Winter: Mon–Sun: 10.30am–4pm

£©🚌🚫 P ♿ → ⛓️ WC 🍴 📷 📶
♿

Peterborough Cathedral

Minister Precincts
Peterborough, Cambs., PE1 1XS
☎ 0733 897337 or 62125 or 343342

Centre of Peterborough

≈ 🚌 Peterborough

Norman cathedral with Gothic west front.
Burial place of Katharine of Aragon and
formerly of Mary Queen of Scots. Fan
vaulting. 4 acres with gravel and paved
paths.

Winter: 7am–6.30pm
Summer: 7am–8pm

F🚌🚫🐾🛏️P♿P 🍴 ♿ → ⛓️ ⇒
WC 🍴 📷 📶 🎧 🐟 🖼️ⓘ 📶

Fowlmere Nature Reserve RSPB

Nr Royston, Cambs., SG8 7SU
☎ 0767 80551

Off A10 from Cambridge to Royston, turning
by Shepreth.

A 150 yard boardwalk for wheelchairs leads
from car park to accessible hide, with views
of fen and scrub. Further improvements for
disabled persons access in hand.

Jan–Dec: Mon–Sun

WC

CAMBRIDGESHIRE

Norris Museum

The Broadway
St Ives
Huntingdon, Cambs., PE17 4BX
☎ 0480 65101

Cambridge or Huntingdon A604

≋ 🚌 Cambridge or Huntingdon

The museum details Huntingdon from the earliest times to the present day.

May–Sep: Mon–Fri & BH: 10am–1pm & 2pm–5pm
Sat: 10am–12noon & 2pm–5pm
Sun: 2pm–5pm
Oct–Apr: Tue–Fri: 10am–1pm & 2pm–4pm
Sat: 10am–12noon
Sun/BH: closed

F🚌✳P♿➤ ⊣ WC ▓ ⊘♿

Scott Polar Research Centre

Lewsfield Rd
Cambridge, Cambs., CB2 1ER
☎ 0223 336540

Town centre of Cambridge

≋ 🚌 Cambridge

Institute founded in 1920 as memorial to Captain Scott. Museum houses artifacts and collections from both Polar regions. Special displays advertised separately. World's largest Polar library and archive.

Museum: Jan–Dec: Mon–Sat 2pm–4pm
Library and archive: by appointment

F🚌✳P♿P📖 ▄🏛WC▓🖐⊘

Community of Christ the Sower

Little Gidding
Huntingdon, Cambs., PE17 5RY
☎ 0480 890333

5m W of A1 between Huntingdon & Peterborough

≋ Huntingdon

Site of a C17th Christian Community, of which the chapel remains. The present community is housed around a farm courtyard nearby.

Jan–Dec: Mon–Sat 11am–5pm
Sun 2pm–5pm

F🚌✳P♿📖➤⊣👁🍴WC🍴
▓🚶♿🖐⊘

University Botanic Garden

Cory Lodge
Bateman St
Cambridge, Cambs., CB2 1JF
☎ 0223 336265

S Cambridge, on E side of A10

(Trumpington Rd)
≋ Cambridge

Owned by University of Cambridge. Opened on this site 1864. Large collection of plants, fine specimen trees and shrubs. Attractive glasshouses which are unsuitable for wheelchair users.

Winter: Mon–Sat 8am–4pm
Sun 10am–4pm
Summer: Mon–Sat 8am–6pm
Sun 10am–6pm

F🚌✳P🖐▄🖐🗄⊣🍴♿WC
🚶⊘⊘🚶♿

Wood Green Animal Shelters

London Rd
Godmanchester, Cambs., PE18 8LJ
☎ 0480 830014

A1198 Royston to Huntingdon

≋ 🚌 Huntingdon

Many types of animals are kept in idyllic surroundings until where possible new homes are found.

Jan–Dec: Mon–Sun 9am–3pm

F🚌✳P♿P♿➤⊣♿WC🍴▓
🚶🖐🖌⊘

Flag Fen Excavation

Fenland Archaeological Trust
Fourth Drive, Fengate
Peterborough, Cambs., PE1 5UR
☎ 0733 313414

Peterborough

An on–going excavation of a Bronze Age Platform, with re–created Bronze Age Landscape and exhibition of finds from the site.

Jan–Dec: Mon–Sun 11am–4pm

£©🚌✳P♿➤⊣♿WC🍴▓
🚶🖌

CHESHIRE

Machine Knitting Centre

Metropolitan
The Pinfold
Poole
Nantwich, Cheshire, CW5 6AL
☎ 0270 628414

The Nantwich A51

≋ Crewe

This purpose built centre where knitting machines and a large range of yarns, books and accessories are all displayed.

Mon–Sat: 10am–4pm

F🚂🐾 🅿 ♿➔ ⌐ ♿ wc ¶ ꕔ🌳 🎿ℂ

Catalyst Museum of the Chemical Industry

Mersey Rd
Widnes, Cheshire, WA8 0DF
☎ 051 420 1121

Widnes

≋ 🚌 Runcorn

Unusual and entertaining experience. Explore the chemical industry and it's impact on our lives. Interactive exhibits.

Jan–Dec: Tues–Sun 10am – 5pm + BH Mon
Closed: Good Fri.

£©🚌🐾 🅿♿ 🅿 ♿➔ ⌐ ♿ wc ⚙
¶ ꕔ🌳♿🎿ℂ

Dunham Massey Hall NT

Altrincham, Cheshire, WA14 4SJ
☎ 061 941 1025

3 miles SW of Altrincham off A56

🚌 No38 Altrincham ≋ Altrincham/Warrington

Georgian house with Edwardian interiors. Fine furniture, silver & portraits. Extensive garden with moat and woodland, deer park & working water mill. 250 acres with gravel paths.

Hall: 1 Apr–1 Nov Sat–Thurs 1pm–5pm
Gardens: 1 Apr–1 Nov Mon–Sun 12 noon–5.30pm

£©🚌🐾✏🍃 🅿🔦🏭🏰➔ ⌐
♿ wc 🍴 ꕔ🌳♿ 🎧 ✈🎿ℂ

Tatton Park NT

Knutsford, Cheshire, WA16 6DN
☎ 0565 654822

Knutsford: A556 off M6, Junction 19

Most visited heritage attraction in the North West. National Trust's most popular property. Magnificent mansion. Glorious gardens rank amongst Britain's top ten. Working farm. Medieval old hall. Set in 1000 acres.

Apr–Sept: Mon–Sun 11am–7pm

£©🚌🐾🍃🅿 🅿♿ ꕔ🏭🏰➔ ⌐
▪♿ wc ⚙ ¶ ꕔ🌳♿ℂ♿

Jodrell Bank Science Centre

Macclesfield, Cheshire, SK11 9DL
☎ 0477 71339

Macclesfield A537

World famous Lovell Radio Telescope. Science Centre has interactive exhibits, astronomical displays, planitarium. 35 acres of arboretum with lovely scenery. Gravel paths.

Easter–31 Oct: Mon–Sun 10.30am–5.30pm
Nov–Easter: w/ends & Xmas hols only 12 noon–5pm

£©🚌🐾 🅿♿ 🅿 ♿➔♿ wc ¶ ꕔ
🌳ℂ

Stapeley Water Gardens

London Rd
Stapeley
Nantwich, Cheshire, CW5 7LH
☎ 0270 628628 / 0270 623868

Nantwich A51

≋ 🚌 Nantwich

World's largest water garden centre on 53 acre site.

Jan–Dec: Mon–Fri 10am–6pm
Sat–Sun 10am–7pm
Last entries 45 minutes prior to closing

£F©🚌🐾🍃🅿♿ 🅿 ♿➔ ⌐ ▪
♿ wc ¶ ꕔ✈ℂ♿

Paradise Mill Museum

Park Lane
Macclesfield, Cheshire, SK11 6TJ
☎ 0625 618228

Macclesfield

≋ 🚌 Macclesfield

Working mill up to 1981. 26 Jacquard handlooms, fully restored & used by contemporary designer weavers. Guides available, many of whom have worked in the industry.

Jan–Dec: Tues–Sun 1pm–5pm + BH Mon

£©🚌🐾 🅿🔦🏭🏛➔ ⌐ wc ꕔ
🌳♿✈

CHESHIRE

Adlington Hall

Macclesfield, Cheshire, SK10 4LF
☎ 0625 829206

5 miles north of Macclesfield (A523)
� Adlington

Tudor/Elizabethan/Georgian Manor House. 'Father' Smith Organ 1670, played on by Handel. Home of the Legh family since 1315. 80 acres including Capability Brown garden with gravel and grass paths.

Good Fri–4th Oct: Mon–Sun 2pm–5.30pm

£ ✶ P♿ P ♿ ➤ ⊣ ⊥ wc ❚❚ ⌷ ⚘ ♿ ⊛ ©

Arley Hall & Gardens

Northwich, Cheshire, CW9 6NA
☎ 0565 8777353

Signposted from M6 (exits 19 & 20) and M56 (exits 9 & 10)

An historic house, still a residence, set in 12 acres of one of the finest gardens in England. Garden of the Year award in 1988.

Easter–Sept: Tues–Sun 2pm–6pm

£➽ ✶ P♿ P ♿ ⊒ 🏠 ⊣ ⊥ ♿ wc ⌷ ⚘ ⊛ ©

The Boat Museum

Dockyard Rd
Ellesmere Port
South Wirral, Cheshire, L65 4EF
☎ 051 355 5017

Junction 9 off M56. 5 miles from Chester
≈ Ellesmere Port

World's largest collection of inland waterways craft. 7½ acres of restored docklands, with paved paths. 7 indoor exhibitions. Period cottages, blacksmith, steam engines, stables. All buildings are different; some are ramped; one has a lift and one is inaccessible.

Winter: Sat–Thurs 11am–4pm
Summer: Mon–Sun 10am–5pm

£➽ ✶ ◡ P♿ P ♿ 🏠 ⊣ ⇒ ⊥ ♿

WC ⚒ ❚❚ ⌷ ⚘ ♿ 🎧 ◀ ⊛ ©

West Park Museum

Prestbury Rd
Macclesfield, Cheshire, SK10 3BJ
☎ 0625 613210

Macclesfield
≈ 🚌 Macclesfield

This museum houses a small but significant exhibition of Egyptian antiquities, fine arts,

and the early works of the well–known bird artist, Charles Tunnicliffe.

Jan–Dec: Tues–Sun 2pm–5pm

£ © ➽ ✶ P ♿ ⊒ 🏠 ♿ wc ❚❚ ⌷ ⚘ ♿ ♿ ⊛

The Silk Museum

The Heritage Centre
Roe St
Macclesfield, Cheshire, SK11 6UT
☎ 0625 613210

Macclesfield
≈ 🚌 Macclesfield

The story of silk (with audio visual programme), exhibitions, textiles, garments, models and room settings situated in the old Sunday School room.

Jan–Dec: Tues–Sat 11am–5pm
Sun & BH 1pm–5pm

F ➽ ✶ P ♿ WC ⌷ ⚘ ♿

Whitegate Way

Clay Lane
Marton, Nr Winsford
Cheshire
☎ 0606 77741

Winsford A54, Northwich A556
≈ Winsford or Cuddington

This old railway line was originally used to carry salt from Winsford Mines. Now open as a 7 mile country park. Cinder ash compacted paths.

Jan–Dec: Mon–Sun

F ➽ ✶ P ♿ ➤ ⊣ ⇒ ♿ wc ⚘

Alderley Edge NT

Nr Macclesfield
Cheshire
☎ 0625 584412

Splendid views of Cheshire Plain. Signed route for wheelchairs from car park to the main points of interest along the Edge. A strong escort is essential. Puddles cover this route in wet weather, so it is best to visit on dry days.

P♿ ♿

Styal Country Park NT

Nr Wilmslow
Cheshire
☎ 0625 523012

Due to the steeply sloping nature of the site most of the Country Park is unsuitable for wheelchairs. However, the picnic area adjacent to the main car park is accessible and a signed path for wheelchairs follows a circular route through the southern woods but is only accessible from Twinnies Bridge car park.

P& ⇒ WC ♦♿

Chester Zoo
Upton–by–Chester
Cheshire, CH2 1LH
☎ 0244 380280
Chester A41
🚍 Chester
UK's largest zoo, set in 110 acres of landscaped gardens. Paved paths.
Jan–Dec: Mon–Sun 10am

CLEVELAND

Stewart Park
The Grove
Morton
Middlesborough, Cleveland
☎ 0642 300202
Middlesborough – A172
🚍 Middlesborough
Stewart Park consists of 120 acres, Captain Cook Museum, Conservatory, animal enclosures, lakes & mature woodland.
Jan–Dec Mon–Sun
Museum & conservatory restricted opening times; tel. for details.

Newham Grange Leisure Farm
Wyecombe Way
Off Newham Way
Croolby
Newham, Cleveland
☎ 0642 300202/300261
Middlesborough – off B3165
🚍 Middlesborough
A 20 acre working farm suitable for families. Several museums, play area, pond, & many breeds of animals. Various special events and demonstrations arranged during the spring and summer.

Winter: Sun only 9am–5pm
Summer: Tues–Sun & BH 9am–5pm

Gray Art Gallery & Museum
Clarence Rd
Hartlepool, Cleveland, TS24 8BT
☎ 0429 266522 x 2610
Hartlepool Town Centre
🚍 Hartlepool
Local history museum, art gallery & oriental collection. Situated in attractive gardens with recreated historic buildings. Paved & tarmac paths.
Jan–Dec: Mon–Sat 10am–5.30pm
Sun 2pm–5pm

Cleveland Crafts Centre
57 Gilkes Street
Middlesborough, Cleveland, TS1 5EL
☎ 0642 226351
Centre of Middlesborough
🚍 Middlesborough
Craft Council listed exhibition centre with important collections of studio pottery and jewellery.
Jan–Dec: Tues–Sat 10am–5pm
Closed: Bank Holidays, Xmas to New Year inc.

Middlesborough Art Gallery
320 Linthorpe Rd
Middlesborough, Cleveland, TS1 4AW
☎ 0642 247445
Middlesborough
🚍 Middlesborough
Municipal art gallery with collections of British 20th century art. Temporary exhibitions including lecture series and practical workshops.
Jan–Dec: Tues–Sat: 10am–1pm, 2pm–6pm
Closed: Between exhibitions

CLEVELAND

Kirkleatham Old Hall Museum

Kirkleatham
Redcar, Cleveland, TS10 3RG
☎ 0642 479500

Redcar, A174

≽ 🚌 Redcar

Collections are used to illustrate this area's rich and varied past and present. Displays include natural history, working and domestic life objects, maritime collections, transport, etc. 5 acres with gravel and paved paths.

Jan–Dec Mon–Sun 9am–5pm

Gisborough Priory

Church St
Guisborough, Cleveland, TS14 6HL
☎ 0287 638301

Guisborough on A171

🚌 Guisborough

Priory founded in first half of C12th. Remains include C12th Gatehouse and decorated Gothic east end of C14th church. Gravel paths and extensive grassed area.

1 Apr–30 Sept: Tue–Sun 10am–6pm
1 Oct–31 Mar: Tue–Sun 10am–4pm

CORNWALL

Monkey Sanctuary

Nr Looe
Cornwall, PL13 1NZ
☎ 0503 262532

Plymouth A38 – 20 miles from Looe, 4 miles from Liskeard

First breeding colony of woolly monkeys outside Amazon. All monkeys present born at the 9 acre sanctuary. Visitors can see monkeys at close quarters. Guide dogs welcome by appointment.

Easter: Sun before to Sun after, but closed Sats.
1 May–30 Sept: Sun–Thurs 10.30am–5pm

Dairyland Farm

Tresillian Barton
Summercourt
Newquay, Cornwall, TR8 5AA
☎ 0872 510246

4 miles from Newquay on A3058

≽ Quintrell Downs

First farm diversification of its kind in the UK, with merry–go–round milking, countrylife museum, farm nature trail, farm park and playground. 4 acres with paved paths except nature trail which is gravelled. For the visually handicapped, the animals can be handled and exhibits touched.

Apr & Oct: 12 noon–5pm
Easter, May & Sept: 10.30am–5.30pm
Calf feeding 1.30pm Milking 3.30pm

Tehidy Country Park

Tehidy
Camborne
Cornwall, TR14 0HA
☎ 0209 714494

Signed from the A30

Hoppa bus from Camborne

Wooded estate once belonging to Basset family, now owned by Cornwall County Council. 250 acres with level gravel paths around lake.

Jan–Dec Mon–Sun

Cornish Seal Sanctuary

Gweek
Nr Helston, Cornwall, TR12 6UG
☎ 0326 22 361

Helston

🚌 Falmouth

Marine animal rescue centre to care for sick and injured animals until their return to sea. Gravel, paved and tarmaced paths. 🚌 service with wheelchair accommodation.

Easter–Nov: 9.30am–6pm
Dec–Mar: 9.30am–4.30pm

Trerice NT

Kestle Mill
Newquay, Cornwall, TR8 4PG
☎ 0637 875404

3 miles SE of Newquay signposed off A3058 at Kestle Mill

Kestle Mill ⇌ Quintrell Down

Elizabethan manor house built in 1571. Contains fine furniture, summer garden & lawnmower museum. 7 acres of hilly ground with level areas & gravel paths.

1 Apr–31 Oct: Wed–Mon 11am–5pm

Trelissick Gardens NT

Fepock
Truro, Cornwall, TR3 6QL
☎ 0872 862090 or 0872 865808
(information line)

Truro – A39 to Falmouth

twice daily. (Cornwall coaches)

A plantsman's garden with a wide range of hydrangeas, rhododendrons, camellias, maples and other exotic plants and shrubs. Beautiful views over Falmouth harbour and estuary.
House not open but art and craft gallery by Home Farm Courtyard. Woodland walk open Nov–Mar.

1 Mar–31 Mar/1 Oct–31 Oct: Mon–Sat 11am–5pm
Sun 1pm–5pm
1 Apr–30 Sept: Mon–Sat 11am–6pm
Sun 1pm–6pm

Cornish Shire Horse Trust & Carriage Museum

Lower Gryllis
Treskillard
Redruth, Cornwall, TR16 6LA
☎ 0209 713606

Redruth

⇌ Redruth

Enjoy a day seeing the horses and foals, wheelwright's and blacksmith's shops. Display of private carriages & commercial wagons. Farm walks; all displays under cover.

Jan–Dec: Sun–Fri 10am–6pm
Jul–Aug: Sun–Sat 10am–6pm

Trethorne Leisure Farm

Kennards House
Launceston, Cornwall, PL15 8QE
☎ 0566 86324

Launceston A30

Visit a family owned 140 acre working dairy farm with opportunities of feeding friendly animals with many leisure attractions including golf driving range.

Jan–Dec: Mon–Sat – 10am–6pm

Tamar Valley Donkey Park

St Anns Chapel
Gunnislake, Cornwall, PL18 9HW
☎ 0822 834072

A390 Tavistock to Callington

⇌ Gunnislake

Parkland setting designed as a donkey and animal paradise, where the animals have freedom to join the people and be extremely friendly. Set in 14 acres with hard grit surface paths. Donkey cart adapted for wheelchair users.

Easter–31 Oct: Mon–Sun 10am–5.30pm
Winter: Sat–Sun 10am–5.30pm
Closed: Throughout January

Trewithen Gardens

Grampound Road
Nr Truro, Cornwall, TR2 4DD
☎ 0726 882763/882764

Truro/St Austell A390

⇌ Truro or St Austell

Woodland garden with magnolias, camelias, ornamental trees and shrubs – best seen in spring. House not suitable for wheelchair users. 30 acres with gravel paths

Gardens: 1 Mar–30 Sept Mon–Sat 10am–4.30pm
House: Apr–July Mon & Tues inc BH 2pm–4.30pm

CORNWALL

Boscastle Pottery,

The Old Bakery,
Boscastle,
Cornwall, PL35 0HE
☎ 0840 250291

Between Bude, Camelford
≋ Bodmin Parkway

Family run studio pottery making
Mochaware, a form of pottery decorated
with a herb which creates trees as if by
magic.

Jan–Dec Mon–Sun: 9am–Dusk

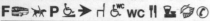

Flambards Theme Park

Culdrose Manor
Helston, Cornwall, TR13 0GA
☎ 0326 574549

Helston: A39 from Truro
🚐 Western National to Park

Three major award winning undercover
attractions. Flambards Victorian village,
Britain in the Blitz, the aeropark collection,
many family rides & amusements. 35 acres
with paved and tarmaced paths.

Easter–31 Oct: Mon–Sun 10am–5.30pm

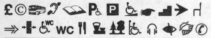

St Agnes Leisure Park

St Agnes, Cornwall, TR5 0SH
☎ 0872 552793

A390 from Truro, A30 from Penzance

Cornwall in miniature displayed in beautiful
gardens. World of dinosaurs and Magical
fairyland.

29 Mar–6 Jul: Mon–Sun 10am–6pm
6 Jul–10 Sep: Mon–Sun 10am–10pm

Royal Cornwall Museum

River St
Truro, Cornwall, TR1 2SJ
☎ 0872 72205

Truro A390
≋ 🚐 Truro

Large and lively museum of art,
archaeology, local history and minerals.
Founded in 1818.

Jan–Dec: Mon–Sat: 9am–5pm
Closed: BH's

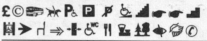

Mount Edgcumbe House & Country Park

Cremyll
Torpoint, Cornwall, PL10 1HZ
☎ 0752 822236

A38 to Plymouth or A374 to Torpoint
≋ 🚐 Plymouth

Historic house & furniture recently restored
to reflect C18th. Grade I historic garden with
formal gardens, landscaped parkland,
coastal views, National Camellia collection.

House & Earls Garden:
1 Apr or Easter–31 Oct: Wed–Sun & BH
11am–5.30pm

Parkland & Formal Gardens:
Jan–Dec: Mon–Sun

Cadsonbury NT

Nr Callington
Cornwall

2m from Callington on Liskeard Rd

Level hard paths through woodland beside
west bank of River Lynher, with viewing
platforms, car park.

Carn Galver NT

West Penwith
Cornwall

Small car park next to engine house gives
coast and moorland views. The coastal road
between St Ives and Pendeen gives
exceptional views over spectacular scenery
much of which the Trust protects.

Godrevy NT

Nr Portreach
Cornwall

A series of coastal car parks with sea views.
At Reskajeage a viewing enclosure with low
wall gives wide views along the coast.

Kynance NT

The Lizard
Cornwall

Parking area with views to Lizard Head.
Wheelchair path to cliff view.

Nare Head NT

Nr Veryan Bay

Cornwall

Ramped viewing point for disabled visitors in the visitors car park above Kiberick Cove.

Respryn NT

Lanhydrock
Cornwall

Hard path along the bank of the River Fowey, with fishing platforms.

Tintagel NT

Glebe Cliff
Cornwall

Parking by the church; wheelchair access to the clifftop by rough track; good views over Port Isaac Bay.

Wheal Coates NT

Nr St Agnes
Cornwall

Ramp from car park by road allows wheelchair access to cliff top remains of this striking tin mine. Stunning views of North Cornwall coast.

Trengwainton Gardens NT

Penzance, Cornwall, TR20 8RZ
☎ 0736 63148

2m NW of Penzance, on Heamoor Rd, B3312

⇌ 🚌 Penzance

A woodland garden with rhododendrons, magnolias and azaleas along main drive. Stream garden, views from top lawns to Mount's Bay. Series of unique walled gardens containing wide range of tender plants. Best April and May.

1 Mar–31 Oct: Wed–Sat & BH
10.30am–5.30pm

© 🚌 ⚡ 🅿 ♿ ➤ ⌐ ⇒ ♿ WC ❚❚ 🛍
🚪 🅼 ⓒ ♿

Dobwalls Family Adventure Park

Dobwalls
Liskeard, Cornwall, PL14 6HD
☎ 0579 20578/20325

Liskeard

⇌ 🚌 Liskeard

The biggest and best of its kind in Britain. The most extensive miniature railway in Europe. 25 acres with gravel and cobble paths.

Easter–Nov: Mon–Sun 10am–6pm
Nov–Easter: Sat–Sun & School Hols

£ © 🚌 ⚡ 2 🖐 🅿 🅿 ♿ ➤ ⌐ ⇒
🔌 ♿ WC 🛍 🐵 ❚❚ 🛍 🚪 🎧 ✦ 🎁 ⓒ
♿

Newquay Zoo

Trenance Park
Newquay, Cornwall, TR7 2LZ
☎ 0637 873342

Newquay

⇌ 🚌 Newquay

Landscaped gardens covering 8 acres with over 700 animals including new lion house, tropical house, maze, capybaras, deer, wallabies and children's zoo.

Easter–Oct: Mon–Sun 10am

£ © 🚌 ⚡ 🅿 🅿 ♿ ➤ ⌐ 🔌 ♿ WC
❚❚ 🛍 🚪 ⓒ ♿

Windermere Iron Steamboat Co.

Lakeside
Ulverston, Cumbria, LA12 8AS
☎ 05395 31188

Ulverston A590, Bowness A591, and Ambleside A591

🚌 to Bowness or Ambleside Piers

Large ships sailing between Lakeside, Bowness and Ambleside. Open and covered accommodation on 2 decks. Luxurious saloons, coffee shops and licenced bars. Car parks at Lakeside, Ambleside, and Bowness.

Mar–Nov: Mon–Sun
All other times by arrangement

£ F © 🚌 ⚡ 🅿 🅿 ♿ ➤ ⌐ ♿ WC 🐵
❚❚ 🛍 🚪 🍽 🎁

Pennine Tweeds

Farfield Mill
Sedbergh, Cumbria, LA10 5LW
☎ 05396 20558

A684 from Sedbergh to Hawes

⇌ Garsdale 5 miles, Oxenholme 10 miles

Experience weaving on 1930's looms in a Victorian mill. All wool tweeds, ties, hats and rugs on sale in shop.

Apr–Nov: Mon–Sun 9.30am–5.30pm
Nov–Apr: Mon–Sat 9.30am–5.30pm

CUMBRIA

National Park Visitor Centre

Brockhole
Windermere, Cumbria, LA23 1LJ
☎ 09662 6601

Windermere A591 to Ambleside

≈ Windermere

The major visitor centre for the Lake District National Park, covering 32 acres with paved paths. Superb gardens overlooking lake.

Apr–Nov: Mon–Sun 10am–5pm
Jul–Aug: Mon–Sun 10am–10pm

Lowther Leisure Park

Hackthorpe
Penrith, Cumbria, CA10 2HG
☎ 09312 523

Penrith A6

Lowther park has a great deal to offer all its visitors. A combination of great natural beauty, large red deer herd and an outstanding range of family attractions suitable for all age groups. 150 acres with gravel paths

Easter Weeks
May–Sept: Mon–Sun 10am–6pm

Dove Cottage & The Wordsworth Museum

Grasmere, Cumbria, LA22 9SH
☎ 09665 544 or 547

On A591 Kendal/Keswick Road, near Ambleside

≈ Windermere

Dove Cottage, home of William Wordsworth, 1799–1808. Visitors are offered guided tours of house. Award winning Wordsworth Museum houses permanent and seasonal exhibits.

Mid Feb–Mid Jan: Mon–Sun 9.30am–5.30pm

Whinlatter Visitor Centre FC

Braithwaite
Keswick, Cumbria, CA12 5TW
☎ 07687 78469

Keswick 5 miles NW A66 off at Braithwaite onto B5292

Earliest National Forest, interpreting forestry with displays, computers, working models, audio–visuals. Many acres of gravel and paved paths. Nature trails cannot be reached by wheelchair users. Restaurant opening in 1992.

Feb–Dec: Mon–Sun 10am–5.30pm

Dalemain Historic House & Gdns

Nr Penrith, Cumbria, CA11 0HB
☎ 07684 86450

Penrith A592

≈ Penrith

Enjoy the Westmorland and Cumberland Yeomanry museums, Countryside museum containing collections of stuffed birds. Glorious gardens, and many small attractions suitable for adults and children. 4 acres with a cobbled yard. The Wild Garden is only accessible by steps and an entrance less than 30″.

Easter Sun–4 Oct: Sun–Thurs 11.15am–5pm

Windermere Steamboat Museum

Rayrigg Rd
Windermere, Cumbria, LA23 1BN
☎ 09662 5565

Windermere A592

Houses the finest collection of steamboats in the world, all in working order, afloat and undercover. Classic motorboats and others.

Easter–Oct Mon–Sun

Carthel Priory

Carthel
Grange–over–Sands, Cumbria, LA11 6PU
☎ 05395 36261

From A590 – signposted tourist signs

≈ Grange–over–Sands 3 miles

12th century priory church with much

historic interest remaining an active place of worship. 2 acres with paved paths.
Summer: Mon–Sun 9.30am–5.30pm
Winter: Mon–Sun 9.30am–3.30pm
Open– services permitting

F 🚌 ⚹ P 🏍 ♿ ➤ ᚺ WC 🛍 🏞 🤝

Talkin Tarn Country Park

Brampton, Cumbria, CA8 1HN
☎ 06977 3129

Brampton B6413
≽ 🚌 Milton Junction

200 acre recreational Country Park with beautiful 65 acre lake and surrounding path (not suitable for wheelchairs at present). Boats for hire and campsite with nature trail.
Jan–Dec Mon–Sun

F 🚌 ⚹ P ♿ ᚺ ⫶ wc ⫶⫶ 🛍 🏕 🐟 🐚 🅒

Holker House & Gardens

Cark in Cartmel
Grange–over–Sands, Cumbria, LA11 7PL
☎ 05395 58328/0839 222011 (24hr information line)

Nr Grange–over–Sands A590
≽ Cark and Cartmel

Home of Lord and Lady Cavendish. Magnificent 25 acre formal and woodland gardens with water features. Exhibitions and deer park. Paved and gravel paths.
1 Apr–31 Oct: Sun–Fri 10.30am–6pm
(Last admissions 4.30pm)

£ © 🚌 ⚹ P♿ 🍴 🏰 ➤ ᚺ ⫶⫶ ♿ᵂᶜ wc
🏪 ⫶⫶ 🛍 🏕 🐚

Border Regiment & Kings Own Royal Border Regiment Museum

Queen Mary's Tower
The Castle
Carlisle, Cumbria, CA3 8UR
☎ 0228 32774

North end of Carlisle City Centre
≽ 🚌 Carlisle

300 year history of Cumbria's county Regiment told by displays, dioramas & videos.
Mar–Oct: Mon–Sun 9.30am–6.30pm
Oct–Mar: Mon–Sun 9.30am–4pm

£ © 🚌 ⚹ P♿ P P♿ ᚺ ⫶⫶ WC 🛍
♿ 🅒

Carlisle Cathedral

Castle St
Carlisle, Cumbria, CA3 8TZ
☎ 0228 35169 or 0228 48151

Carlisle
≽ 🚌 Carlisle

The cathedral, founded in 1122, has fine examples of carving, stained glass and painted panelling. Treasury exhibition.
7.30am–6.30pm Mon–Sun (apart from service times)

F 🚌 ⚹ P♿ P ♿ 🍴 ⫯ 🏰 ➤ ᚺ ⫶⫶
WC ⫶⫶ 🛍 🏕 ♿ 🐚 🅒

Whitehaven Museum & Art Gallery

Civic Hall
Lowther St
Whitehaven, Cumbria, CA28 7SH
☎ 0946 693111 x 307

Whitehaven
≽ 🚌 Whitehaven

Local history – maritime, coal and iron mining, archaeology, local pottery, etc. Programmes of lectures and exhibitions. Local history publications sold. Meals can be served in museum gallery by arrangement.
Jan–Dec Mon–Sat: 10am–4.30pm (not BH Mon)

F 🚌 ⚹ P 🏰 🍴 ♿ᵂᶜ wc 🍴 🛍 ♿ 🐚

The Ravenglass and Eskdale Railway

Ravenglass, Cumbria, CA18 1SW
☎ 0229 717171

Between Barrow and Whitehaven off A595
≽ 🚌 Ravenglass

England's oldest narrow gauge railway runs through 7 miles of glorious mountain scenery. Railway museum. Ramps to Ratty Arms for bar meals. 2 acres with paved paths.
31 Mar–31 Oct: Mon–Sun
Limited service at other times

£ © 🚌 ⚹ P 🍴 🏰 ➤ ᚺ 🚂 ⫯ ♿ᵂᶜ
WC ⫶⫶ 🛍 🏕 ♿ 🐚 🅒

Fibrecrafts

Barnhowe
Elterwater
Ambleside, Cumbria, LA22 9HW
☎ 09667 346

Ambleside, just off B5343 at entrance to

CUMBRIA

Elterwater village
🚌 Ambleside

Leading northern specialist centre for handspinners, weavers dyers & other textile workers

Easter–30 Nov: Mon–Sat 10am–5pm
Sunday 2pm–5pm
Winter months: Open as required, pls tel.

F 🚌 ✕ P ♿ ⫟ WC 🎒 👫 👨‍🦽 ℂ

Ullswater Navigation and Transit Co Ltd

13 Maude St
Kendal, Cumbria, LA9 4QD
☎ 0539 721626 or 07684 82229
Penrith

Two 19th century vessels offering one and two hour cruises on Ullswater, or try our combined cruise and lunch. Wheelchair users telephone in advance.
Apr–Oct inc.

£ © 🚌 ✕ P 🐎 ♿ WC

Yorkshire Dales National Park Information Centre

72 Main St
Sedbergh, Cumbria, LA16 5AD
☎ 05396 20125
Sedbergh

Information Centre and local Bed booking service.

Easter–31 Oct: Mon–Sun 10am–4.30pm

F 🚌 P ♿ ⫟ WC 🎒 👫 ℂ

The Langdale Craft Shop

Chapel Stile
Great Langdale
Ambleside, Cumbria, LA22 9JJ
☎ 09667 296
Ambleside B5343 to Langdale
≋ 🚌 Windermere

Interesting and original selection of craft products created by local people. Beautiful area to visit. Tarmac car park and entrance.

Jan–Dec: Tue–Sat – 10.30am–6pm
Sundays – 2pm–5pm
Winter: Tel. first

F 🚌 P ♿ ➤ WC 🍴 🎒 ℂ

Appleby Castle Animal Conservation Centre

Appleby Castle
Appleby, Cumbria, CA16 6XH
☎ 07683 51402
Appleby–in–Westmorland A66 12 miles SE of Penrith
≋ 🚌 Appleby–on–Settle

Beautiful riverside grounds supporting a display of birds and rare breeds of farm animals. Eleventh century Keep and Great Hall. 27 acres which is not all accessible to wheelchairs users, with gravel, grass and tarmac paths.

Easter–30 Sep: Mon–Sun 10am–5pm

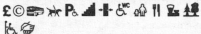 £ © 🚌 ✕ 🐎 ▦ ⫟ WC 🎣 🍴 🎒 👫

♿ 🤝

Penrith Town Museum

Robinsons School
Middlegate
Penrith, Cumbria, CA11 7PT
☎ 0768 64671 x 228
Penrith A6 + M6 Junction 40
≋ 🚌 Penrith

Formerly a school for the poor, the museum now offers displays to provide an introduction to the local history, archaeology and geology of the area.

1 Oct–29 May: Mon–Sat 10am–5pm
1 Jun–30 Sep: Mon–Sat 10am–7pm
Sundays 1pm–6pm

F 🚌 ✕ ⤳ P ♿ 🤝 🏛

Lanercort Priory

Brampton, Cumbria, CA8 2HQ
☎ 06977 2478
Brampton A69
≋ 🚌 Brampton

Founded in 1169; an Augustine Priory, which fell into ruin. Restored as a parish church in 1740.

Jan–Dec: Mon–Sun 9am–dusk

F 🚌 ✕ P 🪑 ▱ ➤ ⌐ WC 🎒 👫

♿ 🤝 ♿

St Bees Head RSPB

Nr Whitehaven
Cumbria

Only cars with disabled visitors are permitted to drive along private road from Sandwith to lighthouse. A wheelchair with a strong companion – or the warden by prior arrangement, through Sandwith Post Office

– can descend steep, concrete track to platform overlooking the cliffs with flocks of seabirds offshore.

Gelt Woods RSPB

Nr Brampton
Carlisle, Cumbria, CA4 9NF
☎ 069 77 46717

West off B6413, three miles south of Brampton.

Parking next to the viaduct from where a 400 yard surfaced path, suitable for wheelchair users, follows the wooded River Gelt. Benches are provided beside path.

Wordsworth House NT

Main St
Cockermouth, Cumbria, CA13 9RX
☎ 0900 824805

Cockermouth

⇌ Penrith/Carlisle 🚌 Keswick

Birthplace of Poet Laureate William Wordsworth and sister Dorothy. Georgian house (1745) with walled garden and terrace walk along River Derwent.

1 Apr–1 Nov: Mon–Wed/Fri–Sat: 11am–5pm
Sundays: 2pm–5pm

£©🚌🕊P🏰⛰⛰🏛➤✝wc🍴
🦽♿

Grizedale Forest Park FC

Grizedale
Hawkshead
Nr Ambleside, Cumbria, LA22 0LQ
☎ 0229 860873

3m S of Hawkshead

Visitor centre and forestry walks. 6000 acres with gravel and paved paths.

Visitor Centre & Shop:
Easter–31 Oct: Mon–Sun 10am–5pm
Forest: Dec–Jan: Mon–Sun

F🚌🕊♿P♿➤✝⇨✝♿wc
🍴🦽⛱

Rexel Cumberland Pencil Museum

Exhibition Centre
Southey Works
Greta Bridge
Keswick, Cumbria, CA12 5NG
☎ 07687 73626

Keswick

🚌 Keswick

History of pencils from cottage industry to modern writing instruments, through words, pictures, videos and carefully restored equipment and machinery.

Jan–Dec: Mon–Sun 9.30am–4pm

£©🚌🕊P♿➤✝⇨✝wc
🦽👐

Borrowdale NT

Crow Park
Cumbria

Access from Lake Rd to Derwentwater shore over grass.

Castlerigg Stone Circle NT

Ambleside side of Keswick
Cumbria

Access through gate up gradual grass slope to the prehistoric circle.

Fell Foot Park NT

Newby Bridge
Cumbria
☎ 05395 31273

18 acre park with lake shore access and magnificent views.

🕊♿P♿wc🍴♿

Friars Cragg Walk NT

Keswick–on–Derwentwater
☎ 05394 33883

A circular walk of about 1½m; accessible to wheelchair users, includes spectacular views from Friar's Cragg, lakeshore and woodland. Illustrated guides available from NT information centre at the start of the walk.

🦽♿wc

Lanthwaite Woods NT

Buttermere
Cumbria

Adapted gate next to car park leads to short route on firm gravel path to Crummock Water.

Sandscale Haws NT

Duddon Valley
Cumbria

Boardwalks run from the car park to the beach, and to a viewing platform.

CUMBRIA

Steam Yacht Gondola NT

Coniston Water
Cumbria
☎ 05394 41288

The yacht provides a steam–powered passenger service on Coniston. Access is not easy but crew will help, please telephone ahead. Suitable for accompanied visually handicapped visitors. Guide dogs admitted to saloons.

Tarn Hows NT

Monk Coniston
Cumbria
☎ 05394 33883

Special car parking and short route on firm gravel path from car park to a good viewpoint over the tarns.

White Moss Common NT

Nr Ambleside
Cumbria

Between Ambleside and Grasmere.

Access to adapted WC's and to the River Rothay from the lower car park, on the left of the road toward Grasmere.

Stott Park Bobbin Mill Museum

Newby Bridge
Nr Ulverston, Cumbria, LA22 0LQ
☎ 053 95 31087

Ulverston, A590

Typical C19th bobbin mill; part working mill. 3 acres with gravel paths.

1 Apr–31 Oct: Mon–Sun 10am–6pm

£©🚌🐾 P ⌂ ċ WC 🎗️🛬 ⅃ 🌳

Brougham Castle

Nr Penrith, Cumbria, CA10 2AA
☎ 0768 62488

Penrith, A66 (1½m)

≥ 🚌 Penrith

Impressive Norman Keep and later buildings on the banks of River Eamont. Cobbled paths.

1 Apr–30 Sep: Mon–Sun 10am–6pm
1 Oct–31 Mar: Tue–Sun 10am–4pm

£©🚌🐾 P 🏃 ⌂ ▄ 🏛️ ⅃ ┼ WC
🛬 ċ ⅄

Carlisle Castle

Carlisle, Cumbria, CA3 8UR
☎ 0228 31777

Carlisle, Cumbria
≥ 🚌 Carlisle

Impressive Norman Stronghold; many sieges, battles, three Parliaments under Edward I. Aristocratic Governors. Mary Queen of Scots detained here in 1568. Jacobite occupation in 1745. 4 acres with paved paths.

Winter: Mon–Sun 9.30–4.00
Summer: Mon–Sun 9.30–6.30

£©🚌🐾 P ⌂ ▄ 🏛️ ┼ WC 🎗️
🛬 ċ ⅄

Furness Abbey EH

Barrow–in–Furness
Cumbria

Barrow–in–Furness, A590

≥ 🚌 Barrow–in–Furness

Furness Abbey was the second richest Cistercian Abbey in England. The Abbey was built in local red sandstone and their are extensive remains.

1 Apr–30 Sep: Tue–Sun 10am–6pm
1 Oct–31 Mar: Tue–Sun 10am–4pm

£©🚌🐾 Pċ P ċ ➤ ċ WC 🎗️ ċ
🎧 ◆

Lanercost Priory EH

Nr Brampton, Cumbria, CA8 2HQ
☎ 069 77 3030

Brampton, off Minor Rd, 2m NE of town

The priory was founded in around 1166 by William de Vaux, for Augustinian Canons. The nave of the church has survived and is still used, and makes a strange contrast with the ruined priory buildings around.

1 Apr–30 Sep: Mon–Sun 10am–6pm

£©🚌🐾 P 🏃 ⌂ ▄ 🏛️ ⅃ WC🛬
ċ 🌀

Muncaster Castle

Ravenglass, Cumbria, CA18 1RQ
☎ 0229 717614/717203

West coast of Cumbria, 1m E of Ravenglass on A595

≥ Ravenglass

Historic castle and superb gardens commanding fantastic views of the lakeland fells. Owl centre with daily flying displays (weather permitting). 77 acres with various paths.

Gardens & Owl Centre: Jan–Dec: Mon–Sun
Castle: 29 Mar–1 Nov: Tue–Sun

£ © 🚌 ✈ P♿ P ♿ 🐕 🏛 ➤ ⊣ ⊣⊢
♿WC WC 🍴 🏋 👥♿ ♿ 🎧 🤝 ♿

DERBYSHIRE

The Cathedral of All Saints

Derby Cathedral Office
St Michaels House
Queen St
Derby, DE1 3DT
☎ 0332 41201

Derby

≋ 🚌 Derby

Early 16th century tower, 18th century nave designed by James Gibbs, 20th century windows and retrochoir wrought iron screen by Robert Bakewell. Level with paved paths.

Jan–Dec Mon–Sun

F 🚌 ✈ 🐕 P ♿ 🏛 ⊣ ⊣⊢ WC 🍴 🤝
🤝 © ♿

Shipley Country Park

Slack Lane
Heanor, Derbys, DE7 7GX
☎ 0773 719961

Heanor/Ilkeston

600 acres of woodland, lakes and parkland, with gravel paths in hilly and level areas. 1000 years of history – historic buildings, gardens and features.

Park: Jan–Dec Mon–Sun
Visitor Centre: Easter–Sep Mon–Fri
11am–4.30pm
Sat–Sun 10am–6pm
Oct–Easter Mon–Fri 12noon–4.30
Sat–Sun 10am–4.30

£ © 🚌 🐕 P♿ P ♿ ⊣ 🚂 ⊣⊢ ♿WC
🍴 🏋 👥 🤝 © ♿

Midland Railway Centre

Butterley Station
Ripley, Derbys, DE5 3TL
☎ 0773 570140

1 mile north of Ripley on B6179 (signposted from A38)

Trent buses 148/242/243 pass the centre.
≋ Alfreyon & Mansfield 5 miles

3½ mile preserved railway with 57 acre musuem site and 35 acre country park, with gravel and paved paths. Large collection of steam and diesel locomotives together with coaches and wagons. New museum open.

Narrow gauge and miniature lines operate summer Sundays.

Apr–Oct and Dec: Sat & Sun
Daily during Easter and Spring BH's
Mid Jul–1st wk in Sep: Tue–Sun

£ © 🚌 ✈ P ♿ ⊣ 🚂 ⊣⊢ ♿WC WC 🍴
🏋 👥♿ 🤝

Cromford Mill

Mill Lane
Cromford, Derbys, DE4 3RQ
☎ 0629 824297

Matlock A6

≋ Cromford

Arkwrights Cromford Mill was built in 1771, the site was completed in 1791. Its contribution to the Industrial Revolution is the 'Factory System'. Gravel and paved paths.

Jan–Dec Mon–Sun 10am–4.30pm

£ © 🚌 ✈ P P♿ 🏛 ➤ ⊣ ⊣⊢
♿WC WC 🍴 🏋 👥♿ 🤝

The Donington Collection

Donington Park
Castle Donington
Nr Derby, DE7 2RP
☎ 0332 812919

A6 – Derby

≋ 🚌 Derby

Pre–war and post–war motor racing circuit, museum & racing drivers' school. Paved paths.

Jan–Dec Mon–Fri: 10am–5pm
Sat–Sun: 10am–6pm

£ © 🚌 ✈ P ♿ 🐕 ➤ WC 🍴 🏋 👥

New Mills Heritage & Information Ctr

Rock Mill Lane
New Mills
Stockport, Derbys, SK12 3BN
☎ 0663 746904

A6 from Buxton or Stockport, then A6015

≋ 🚌 Stockport

Centre giving information on the area. Viewing platform over the Torrs Gorge below.

Jan–Dec Tue–Fri: 11am–4pm
Sat–Sun: 10.30am–4.30pm
BH Mon : 11am–4pm

DERBYSHIRE

F🚌✳P♿➜⊣⇒♿ᵂᶜwc🍴♿
♿🌳🤟

🅿🚌✳♂🅿🅿♿⬛🏛➜⊣♿ᵂᶜ
wc✗♿♿♿

Pickford's House Museum

41 Friargate
Derby, DE1 1BS
☎ 0332 255363

Derby (A52 – Ashbourne Rd)
⇌ 🚌 Derby

Georgian House built in 1771 with period
rooms. Dining room, morning room, kitchen,
bedroom, dressing room. Georgian style
garden with gravel paths.

Jan–Dec Mon: 11am–5pm
Tue–Sat: 10am–5pm
Sun & BH: 2pm–5pm

£©🚌✳ 🅿 ♿🏛➜ ⊣ 🔌wc♿
🌳♿🤟🕐

Chatsworth Historic House & Gardens

Bakewell, Derby, DE4 1PP
☎ 0246 582204

Bakewell A619
⇌ Chesterfield

The garden covers over 100 acres providing
many delights and surprises. A cascade of
spectacular fountains and rocks.
Herbaceous borders and forest trees. Hilly
and level areas with gravel paths. House is
not suitable for wheelchair users.

Easter–31 Oct: Mon–Sun 11am–4.30pm

£©🚌✳ 🛶 🅿 ⬛👆⬛🏛 ⊣ ♿ᵂᶜ
wc♿🍴♿♿🎧🕐⊘♿♿

Hardwick Hall NT

Doe Lea
Nr Chesterfield, Derby, S44 5Q5
☎ 0246 850430

Mansfield A617

20 acres of level ground with gravel paths
and grassland. An Elizabethan house built
for Bess of Hardwick. Spectacular
architecture. Tapestries and needlework,
outstanding furniture. Walled courtyards
enclose fine gardens, orchards and herb
garden.

Hall: End Mar–End Oct: Wed– Sun
12.30–4.30
Garden: End Mar–End Oct: Mon–Sun
12.00–5.00

The American Adventure Theme Park

Pit Lane
Ilkeston, Derbys, DE7 5SX
☎ 0773 769931

A6007 between Ilkeston and Heanor
🚌 Nottingham/Derby ⇌ Langley Mill

A great value themed family day out. Over
100 rides, attractions, shoot–outs and
shows.

Easter–Nov: Mon–Sun 10am–5/6/7pm –
tel.for details

£©🚌✳ 🅿 🅿♿➜ ⊣ 🚂🔌♿ᵂᶜ
wc🍴♿🌳♿🤟🕐♿♿

Derby Industrial Museum

The Silk Mill
Off Full St
Derby, DE7 2HJ
☎ 0332 255308

⇌ 🚌 Derby

Displays form an introduction to the
industrial history of Derby and Derbyshire. A
major collection of Rolls–Royce aero
engines.

Jan–Dec Tue–Sat: 10am–5pm
Mon: 11am–5pm
Sun & BH: 2pm–5pm

£©🚌✳ 🅿 🅿♿⬛🏠ᵂᶜwc♿
🤟🕐

Elvaston Castle Country Park

Nr Derby, DE7 3EP
☎ 0332 571342

Derby – on B5010 5 miles SE of Derby.
Signposted from A6 and A52

200 acre country park with historic gardens
and grounds with accessible paths. Walled
old English garden. Working estate
museum.

Jan–Dec Mon–Sun

£©🚌✳ 🅿 🅿🏴♿🏛⬛🏛➜
⊣🔌♿ᵂᶜwc♿🍴♿🌳♿🤟

Blue John Museum (The Ollerenshaw Collection)

Cross St
Castleton
Nr Sheffield. Derby, S30 2WH
☎ 0433 20642
Sheffield A625
⇌ 🚌 Sheffield

Privately owned museum of Derbyshire treasures, including one of the finest collections of Blue John stone in the world. Greatly enhanced by the superb method of display, illumination & written presentation.
Jan–Dec Mon–Sun 9.45am–5.30pm

£ © 🚌 ⚥ 👓 P ♿ ➔ ⊣ WC ▯
🌳 🕐

Peak District Mining Museum

The Pavilion
Matlock Bath, Derbys, DE4 3PS
☎ 0629 583834
On A6 at Southern end of Matlock Bath
⇌ Matlock Bath

Describes 2000 years of lead mining in the Peak District. Hands–on museum, with artefacts to feel and handle.
Jan–Dec Mon–Sun 11am–4pm

£ © 🚌 ⚥ P♿ P ♿ 🏠 ♿ʷᶜ WC ▯
🌳 🤚

Calke Abbey NT

Ticknall
Derby,
Derbyshire, DE7 1LE
☎ 0332 863822/864444
Derby, A514
⇌ 🚌 Derby

An C18th family home which has remained largely unchanged for most of this century. Rare mixture of fine showrooms, dilapidated corridors and rooms where innumerable items from oil lamps to children's toys were stored away in heaps.

House: Apr–Oct: Sat–Wed 1pm–5pm
Gardens: Apr–Oct: Sat–Wed 11am–5pm
Park: Jan–Dec: Mon–Sun

£ © 🚌 ⚥ 🐕 👓 P♿ P ♿ 🦽 🏠 ♿ʷᶜ
WC 🏕 🍴 ▯ 🚶 🔌 🎨 🕐 ♿ᴸ

Matlock Bath Model Railway Museum

Temple Rd
Matlock Bath, Derbys. DE4 3PG
☎ 0629 580797
Off A6 at south end of Matlock Bath
⇌ 🚌 Matlock Bath

Standard model of Millers Dale Station, circa 1906, model shop, new and secondhand railway books.
Apr–Aug: Tue–Sat: 11am–6pm
Sep–Mar: Tue,Wed,Thu,Sat: 11am–4pm

F 🚐 ⚥ P ♿ WC ▯

Denby Pottery Visitors Centre

Derby Road,
Derbys. DE5 8NX
☎ 0773 743644
Ripley, B6179
⇌ 🚌 Derby

Denby pottery was founded in 1809 on the site of a fine bed of stoneware clay, reputedly the best in Europe.
Jan–Dec: Mon–Sun 9.30am–5pm Last tour 3.30pm

£ © 🚌 ⚥ P♿ P ♿ 🏠 ♿ʷᶜ WC 🍴 ▯
🌳 🦽 🔌 🕐

Dovedale NT

Derbys.

Good surfaced path for disabled and visually handicapped visitors. One or two steps with wheelchair access as far as Stepping Stones.

DEVON

Coldharbour Mill & Working Wool Museum

Coldharbour
Offculme, Devon, EX15 3EE
☎ 0884 840960
Tiverton B3181 or Cullompton
🚌 Tiverton, Exeter or Cullompton.⇌ Tiveton Parkway

Former 18th Century textile mill, now a working wool museum. Visitors can see knitting yarn made, and cloth woven on turn–of–the–century machinery. Guided tours only

Easter–Oct: Mon–Sun 11am–5pm Last tour 4pm
Nov–Mar: Mon–Fri –times vary

DEVON

£©🚌✳️🐦📑⚓🐕⚓🏛️🚪🛗
♿WC 🏠🍴🎫👥♿🐟💐🎦

Plymouth City Museum & Art Gallery
Drake Circus
Plymouth, Devon, PL4 8AJ
☎ 0752 264878
Plymouth
≋ 🚌 Plymouth

Wide range of natural history, fine and decorative arts, contemporary art shows changing every 6 weeks. Free lunchtime talks and tours in winter.

Jan–Dec: Tue–Sat 10am–5.30pm
Sun 2pm–5pm

F🚌✳️🐿️P♿♿⚓🐕⚓🏛️WC
🍴🎫♿🐟💐🎦

Toynes Castle EH
Castle St
Totnes, Devon, TQ9 5NU
☎ 0803 864406
At the top of the town
≋ 🚌 Totnes

A superb motte and bailey castle, a fine example of a Norman fortification that never saw the heat of battle to disturb it's surroundings. 80 steps to top of castle keep. Grounds accessible to wheelchair users.

Gd Fri/1 Apr–30 Sep: 10am–1pm & 2pm–6pm
1 Oct–Maundy Thu/31 Mar: 10am–1pm & 2pm–4pm

£©🚌✳️P➤🚪🛗🍴👥♿
💐🦮

Devon County Show
Westpoint
Clyst St Mary
Exeter, Devon, EX5 1DJ
☎ 0392 444777
A3052 from Exeter to Sidmouth
≋ 🚌 Exeter

The show is packed with a selection of entertainment and special feature areas, together with traditional livestock and horses. 650 trade stands. Mainly tarmaced with some grass avenues.

Always 3rd week in May, Thu, Fri and Sat

£©🚌✳️🐦♿📑♿➤🚪🛗♿WC🏠
🍴👥🎫👥♿🍴

Exmoor Steam Centre
Cape of Good Hope Farm
Bratton Fleming
Barnstaple, Devon, EX32 7JN
☎ 0598 710711

Barnstaple or South Molton A399
🚌 Barnstaple

Large farm building converted to a Victorian railway station. Always at least one engine in steam. Level concrete floor with good access for wheelchair users.

Nov–Easter: Sundays only
Easter–31 Oct: Mon–Sun

£🚌✳️P♿➤🚪♿WC🍴👥🎫
♿💐

Dartington Cider Press Centre
Shinners Bridge
Dartington, Devon, TQ9 6TQ
☎ 0803 864171
Totnes A385
≋ 🚌 Totnes

Cider making from 1928–52, subsequently tea rooms. Community centre for elderly. Buildings 17th Century. 12 shops. Paved paths.

Mid Jul–Mid Sep: Mon–Sun 9.30am–5.30pm
Mid Sep–Mid Jul: Mon–Sat 9.30am–5.30pm

F🚌✳️🐦P♿📑♿⚓🏛️🛗♿WC🏠
🍴👥🎫

Plymouth Dome
The Hoe
Plymouth, Devon, PL1 2NZ
☎ 0752 600608
Plymouth seafront
≋ 🚌 Plymouth

£3.5 million centre opened 1989 which has won a series of national awards, telling the story of Plymouth's past and present, including its extraordinary maritime history

Jan–Dec: Mon–Sun from 9am

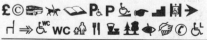
£©🚌✳️🐦P♿P♿⚓🐕⚓🏛️➤
🚪➡️♿WC🏠🍴👥🎫👥♿🐟💐🎦♿

Ilfracombe Museum

Wilder Rd
Ilfracombe, Devon, EX4 8AF
☎ 0271 863541
Barnstaple
⇌ 🚌 Ilfracombe

The Museum consists of seven rooms and has a valuable collection of exhibits – medals and decorations, fossils, working scale model of a steam engine, Columbian printing press, brass rubbing centre, costumes, a tunnel which houses the cobblers and carpenters workshop and many other items of interest.

Easter–Oct: Mon–Sun 10am–5.30pm
Oct–Easter: Mon–Fri 10.30am–12.30pm

£©🚌⚡⚔️🌳P🅿️♿➤⊣ WC 🎟️
🏯🤝

Once Upon A Time – Childrens Theme Park

The Old Station
Station Road
Woolacombe, Devon, EX34 7HH
☎ 0271 867474
B3343
🚌 Woolacombe

A haven of fantasy and fun in safe soft play areas. Train rides, animations and puppet show. 1½ acres with gravel, paved and tarmaced paths.

Jan–Dec : times vary, tel. to clarify

£©🚌⚡🍴P🅿️♿➤⊣🔌♿WC
WC 🍴🎟️🏯♿🤝🎫

Watermouth Castle Theme Park

Nr Ilfracombe, Devon, EX34 9SL
☎ 0271 867474

A399 coast road between Ilfracombe and Combe Martin
🚌 Ilfracombe

Edwardian castle with dungeon labyrinth. Courtyard houses famous water show. Merrygoland rides and games. Tubeslide and gnomeland. 3 acres with tarmaced paths.

Jan–Dec: times vary – please telephone to clarify

£©🚌⚡🍴P🅿️♿➤⊣⇒🔌
♿WC🏯🍴🎟️🏯♿🎫

Crealy Country Visitor Attraction

Sidmouth Rd
Clyst St Mary
Exeter, Devon, EX5 1DR
☎ 0395 33200

Minutes from Exeter on A3052, near M5, junction 30
⇌ 🚌 Exeter

Fantastic adventure playgrounds, animal farm with baby & miniature animals. Crealy Dairy, discovery trails, dragonfly lake, picnic meadows and much more. 250 acres with tarmac and gravel paths.

Apr–Nov: 10am–6pm

£©🚌⚡🍴P🅿️♿➤⊣🔌♿WC
🏯🍴🎟️🏯🤝🎫

Exmoor Bird Gardens

Bratton Fleming
Barnstaple, Devon, EX31 4SG
☎ 05983 352
Barnstaple A39
⇌ 🚌 Barnstaple

Largest collection of tropical birds in North Devon. Over 500 birds and animals. Penguins at liberty within gardens.

Apr–Oct: 10am–6pm
Nov–Mar: 10am–4pm

£©🚌⚡🅿️♿➤⊣🔌WC🍴🎟️
♿🎫♿

The Big Sheep

Abbotsham
Bideford, Devon, EX39 5AP
☎ 0237 472366

Bideford A39 North Devon Link Road
⇌ Barnstaple

'Shear Entertainment'! Sheep milking, woolcrafts centre, sheep racing, duck trialling, sheepdog trials, home cooked food and sheepy shop. All undercover.

Mar–Xmas: Mon–Sun 10am–6pm

£🚌⚡P🅿️♿🛶🏛️➤⊣⇒👁️
🔌WC🏯🍴🎟️🏯🎧🤝🎫

St Marys Steps Parish Church

West St
Exeter, Devon, EX1 1BA
☎ 0392 77685

Turning off the inner by–pass, near the twin bridges over the River Exe

12th century church, neighbouring Medieval and Tudor houses, Medieval street and

DEVON

bridge and city wall.
Church open for services

F🚐✕P♿🔥

National Shire Horse Centre

Yealmpton
Plymouth, Devon, PL8 2EL
☎ 0752 880268

Plymouth A379

🚉 🚌 Plymouth

Get close to the Gentle Giants. Watch the unique Parade of the Shires. See thrilling birds of prey flying displays. Adventure playground. 100 acres with tarmaced roads.

Jan–Dec Mon–Sun: 10am–5pm

£©🚐✕♿🅿♿➤⌐♿wc🐿
🍴🍽🎪🏕🎡⌐♿

Trago Mills Shopping & Leisure Centre

Stover
Newton Abbot, Devon, TQ12 6JD
☎ 0626 821111

A38 – A382

Shopping and leisure centre in countryside surroundings to make the perfect day out for all the family. 80 acres with paved paths.

Jan–Dec: Mon–Sun 9am–5.30pm

F🚐✕♿🅿♿🏰➤⌐♿wc
🐿🍴🍽🎪♿

The Combe Martin Motorcycle Museum

Cross St
Combe Martin, Devon, EX34 0DH
☎ 0271 882346

Ilfracombe A399

🚌 Ilfracombe

Over 50 British motorcycles on display, including old petrol pumps, signs and garage memorabilia. Motoring nostalgia in an old world atmosphere.

Easter/31 May–30 Sep: Mon–Sun 10am–6pm

£©🚐✕P♿♿wc🍽♿🏕

Mullacott Miniature Park

Ilfracombe, Devon, EX34 8NA
☎ 0271 866877

Ilfracombe A361

A facinating and unique collection of miniature horses and ponies. Some of the

smallest and rarest breeds from all over the world. Many other miniature animals. Laid out with disabled people in mind. Tarmac and concrete paths.

Mar–Oct: Mon–Sun 10am–6pm

£🚐✕🐎♿🅿♿➤⌐♿wc🐿
🍴🍽🎪🐟🏕

Exmoor Brass Rubbing & Hobby Craft Centre

Watersmeet Rd
Lynmouth, Devon, EX35 6EP
☎ 0598 52529

Lynton and Lynmouth A39

🚌 Lynmouth

Popular family attraction with large selection of brasses, knights, ladies, clergy, skeletons, animals, childrens themes, oriental dancers. Friendly help given to all visitors.

Easter–31 Oct: Mon–Fri: 10.30am–5pm
School Hols: Mon–Sun: 10.30am–5pm

£F🚐✕♿🅿♿♿wc🍽♿
🐟🏕

Burton Art Gallery

Victoria Park
Kingsley Rd
Bideford, Nth Devon, EX39
☎ 0237 476713

Bideford

🚉 🚌 Barnstaple

A small gallery founded in 1951. Collection of 19th & 20th century oils and watercolours. Ceramics, pewtor, silver, and model ships. Full programme of visiting exhibitions

Summer: Mon–Sat 10am–1pm
Sun 2pm–5pm
Winter: Tue–Sat 10am–1pm & 2pm–4pm
Mon 10am–1pm
Sundays: Closed

F🚐✕P♿♿➤⌐⇒wc🍽
🏕🏕

Buckfast Abbey

Buckfastleigh, Devon, TQ11 0EK
☎ 0364 42519

Buckfastleigh

🚉 🚌 Newton Abbot

Benedictine monastery, rebuilt by the Monks on the medieval foundations. Famous today for its beekeeping, stained glass and tonic wine. 2 acres with paved paths.

Church & Grounds: Mon–Sun
5.30am–9.30pm
Shops & Restaurant: Mon–Sun 9am–5pm
(Easter–31 Oct)
10am–4pm (Nov–Easter)

Totnes Motor Museum

Steamer Quay
Totnes, Devon, TQ9 5AL
☎ 0803 862777

A385 Totnes

Totnes

Converted cider warehouse with two floors of exhibits to interest all ages. Showcases of old instruments, books, engines (some cut open to show how they work). Vintage sports and racing cars span 80 years of motoring. Cars kept in running order.

Easter–31 Oct: Mon–Sun 10am–5pm

Woodland Leisure Park

Blackawton
Totnes, Devon, TQ9 7DQ
☎ 080 421 598

Totnes

International waterfowl collection, bee observatory & animal farm complex. 10 adventure zones & pets corner in 60 acres.

Jan–Dec: Mon–Sun 9.30am–dusk

William Cookworthy Museum

The Old Grammar School
108 Fore St
Kingsbridge, Devon, TQ7 1AW
☎ 0548 853235

Kingsbridge

Totnes.

Housed in the Old Kingsbridge Grammar School. Rural life in South Devon, domestic, local and agricultural history. Much of old architecture still in place including panelling.

Easter–Sep: Mon–Sat 10am–5pm
Oct: Mon–Fri 10.30am–4pm

Bicton Park

East Budleigh, Devon, EX9 7DP
☎ 0395 68465

2m N of Budleigh Salterton on A376

Exmouth

60 acres of formal gardens and parkland. Display greenhouses, famous glass Palmhouse, countryside museum & woodland railway. Special carriage for wheelchair users.

Mar–Oct: Mon–Sun 10am–6pm

The Milky Way

Downland Farm
Clovelly, Devon, EX39 5RY
☎ 0237 431255

Bideford

Barnstaple

The 205 acre Milky Way is one of Devon's premier attractions offering everyone the chance to see how a modern dairy farm really works. Also museum, pottery & falconry.

1 Apr–31 Oct: Mon–Sun 10.30am–6pm

Baggy Point NT

N.Devon

North Devon coast, ½m of coastal footpath has been upgraded to take wheelchair users from the Trust's car park. This allows you to see the sweeping sea views and birds for which the Point is famous.

Bolberry Down NT

S.Devon

South Devon coast, between Salcombe and the Bolt Tail. A tarmac path from Bolverry car park to Saltern Pike means wheelchair users can enjoy this breathtaking coast.

Rosemoor Garden (RHS)

Great Torrington
Devon, EX38 8PH
☎ 0805 24067

1m SE of Torrington on B3220 Exeter Rd

Barnstaple

Lady Anne Palmer's internationally famous garden, now being expanded by The Royal Horticultural Society. New garden will include 2000 roses in 200 varieties. 8 acres

DEVON

(to be 40) with gravel paths.
Jan–Dec: Mon–Sun 10am–4/5/6pm

£©🚌🐕 P ♿ 🛈🔭→ 🚻⇒🚾
WC 🏰 🍴 🖼🎪🎦 ♿

DORSET

Wimborne Minster Model Town
16 King St
Wimborne, Dorset, BH21 1DY
☎ 0202 881924
Wimborne
Local buses

Beautiful landscaped gardens surround
one–tenth scale models and miniature
gardens. Waterfall and ponds. Beyond the
grounds are tranquil views over the Stour
Valley.

25 Mar–27 Oct: Fri–Wed 10am–5pm

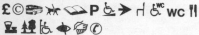

The Blue Pool
Furzebrook
Wareham, Dorset, BH20 5AT
☎ 0929 551408

Signposted at roundabout at southern end
of Wareham Bypass A351

≈ Wareham

Tranquil woods and heathland, designated
an SSSI, surround this old claypit. Museum
and plant centre.

Mar–Nov: Grounds
Easter–Oct: Tea House, shops, museum
and plant centre

£🚌🐕 P 🔆 ♿🛈🚃 🚻 🔌 🚾
WC 🍴 🖼🎪♿🐝🅻

The Dinosaur Museum
Icen Way
Dorchester, Dorset, DT1 1EW
☎ 0305 269880

Centre of Dorchester, near A35

≈🚌 Dorchester

A unique museum combining fossils,
skeletons and life–size reconstructions with
audio–visual and interactive displays
bringing the world of dinosaurs alive.

Jan–Dec: Mon–Sun 9.30am–5.30pm

£©🚌🐕 P 🔆 🛈🚃WC 🖼♿🐝

The Tutankhamun Exhibition
High West St
Dorchester, Dorset, DT1 1UW
☎ 0305 269571

Centre of Dorchester, near A35

≈ Dorchester

Experience the mystery and wonder of the
world's greatest discovery of ancient
treasure. Tutankhamun's tomb and
treasures are superbly recreated.

Jan–Dec: Mon–Sun 9.30am–5.30pm

£©🚌🐕 P ♿🚾 🖼 🐝

Abbotsbury Swannery
New Barn Rd
Abbotsbury
Nr Weymouth, Dorset
☎ 0305 871684

Weymouth follow B3157

🚌 Weymouth

Unique colony of nesting mute swans. 600
yrs old, the only place in the world where
visitors can wander in complete safety
amongst nesting swans. No guide dogs.

Easter–31 Oct Mon–Sun

£©🚌🅿 P ♿→ 🚻🚾WC🎪🐝
🐝♿

Waterfront – Poole Quay
4 High St
Poole, Dorset, BH15 1BW
☎ 0202 683138

Poole, follow A35

≈🚌 Poole

A voyage into Poole's seafaring past, set in
an 18th century warehouse and medieval
Town Cellars. Hear the smuggler's tale,
experience the Victorian atmosphere of
Oakley's Row, learn of the birth of Scouting
on nearby Brownsea Island. Please talk
to us and we will do all we can to help.

Jan–Dec Mon–Sat: 10am–5pm
Sun: 2pm–5pm

£©🚌🐕 🅿P 🔆 ♿🎦🚾WC 🖼
🐝🅲

Red House Museum & Gardens
Quay Rd
Christchurch, Dorset, BH23 1BU
☎ 0202 482860

Christchurch

≈🚌 Christchurch

Georgian building with beautiful gardens.
Displays on local history, natural history,

geology, archaeology, costume and
fishing. Temporary exhibitions.

Jan–Dec Tue–Sat: 10am–5pm
Sun: 2pm–5pm

Smedmore House and Gardens

Smedmore
Kimmeridge
Wareham, Dorset, BH20 5PG
☎ 0929 480719

Wareham: take Wareham bypass towards
Swanage; follow Kimmeridge signposts

≉ 🚌 Wareham

18th century Manor house in marvellous
setting between the Purbeck Hills and the
Dorset coast. Dutch paintings, marquetry
furniture and antique dolls. Walled gardens
with produce for sale.

Mid Jun–Mid Sept: Mon–Sun
2.15pm–5.30pm

Swanage Railway

Station House
Swanage, Dorset, BH19 1HB
☎ 0929 425800

Poole, follow A35

≉ 🚌 Wareham

Steam railway operating between Swanage
and Harman Cross. A round trip of six miles.
Purpose built coach for disabled people.
Tel. to book.

Jan,Feb,Mar,Nov: Sundays only
Apr,May,Oct: Sat–Sun only
Jun: Sat,Sun,Thu only
Jul,Aug,Sep: Mon–Sun

Dorset Rare Breeds Centre

Gillingham, Dorset, SP8 5JG
☎ 0747 822169

B3081 between Gillingham and Shaftesbury

≉ Gillingham

Dorset's largest collection of rare and
endangered farm animals. Many displayed

in large barn, with easy access. Museums
and tea–room

Easter–30 Sep: Mon–Sun 10am–6pm

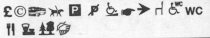

Dorset County Museum

High West St
Dorchester, Dorset, DT1 1XA
☎ 0305 262735

Dorchester, A35

≉ Dorchester

The Dorset County Museum is an award
winning, independant museum, displaying
the history and environment of Dorset &
world famous Thomas Hardy collections.

Jan–Dec Mon–Sat inc BH: 10am–5pm

Natural World

The Quay
Poole, Dorset, BH15 1JH
☎ 0202 686712

Follow either A348, A338, A35 or A350

≉ 🚌 Poole

The most comprehensive indoor exhibition,
housing more species of reptiles than sea–
life

Winter: Mon–Sun 10am–5pm
Summer: Mon–Sun 9.30am–9pm

Merley House Model Museum

Merley Park
Wimborne, Dorset, BH21 3AA
☎ 0202 886533

Wimborne by–pass – A31

≉ 🚌 Poole

Georgian mansion with some of the finest
plaster ceilings in the country. 5000 model
cars of mid–30's to present day, plus
working model 'N' gauge railway layouts

Easter–30 Sep: Mon–Sun 10.30am–5pm

DORSET

Lyme Regis Marine Aquarium
The Cobb
Lyme Regis, Dorset, DT7 3AA
☎ 0297 443678
Lyme Regis
⇌ 🚌 Axminster

Local fish, fishing exhibits and old photographs. Situated in the old warehouses on the end of the quay.

May–Sep: Mon–Sun 10–5pm (dusk Jul & Aug)

£ © 🚌 🎋 P 🅿 🚻 ➤ 🛇 WC 🚻 🐾 🎵

A World Of Toys
Arne House
Arne
Near Wareham, Dorset, BH20 5BJ
☎ 0929 552018
A351 into Wareham
⇌ Wareham

A collection of antique and collectors toys, victorian musical boxes and automaton. The museum was first opened to the public in 1987, based on a private collection.

Apr–Jun: Mon–Sun 2pm–5.30pm
Jul–Aug: Mon–Sun 11am–5.30pm
Sep: Mon–Sun 2pm–5.30pm

£ 🚌 🎋 P 🚻 ➤ 🛇 WC 🚻 🛒 🎋

Chettle House
Chettle
Blandford, Dorset, DT11 8JB
☎ 0258 89209
Follow A354 Blandford to Salisbury
🚌 Salisbury/Blandford

Queen Anne house of baroque style set in attractive gardens.

Easter–Mid Oct

£ 🚌 🎋 🍽 P 🚻 🔺 🏛 ➤ 🛇 WC 🎋 🚻 🚶

Worldwide Butterflies & Lullingstone Silk Farm
Compton House
Nr Sherborne, Dorset, DT9 4QN
☎ 0935 74608
A30 between Sherborne & Yeovil
⇌ 🚌 Sherborne

Elizabethan House, gardens and grounds showing a variety of butterfly displays. World collections, living tropical moths, fat colourful caterpillars and curious insects. Butterflies hatching daily and flying amongst tropical plants.

Apr–30 Oct: Mon–Sun 10am–5pm

£ 🚌 🎋 P 🚻 🔺 🔲 🏛 ➤ 🛇 WC 🚻 🚶

FabLab (Science World Ltd)
Swan Lake
Poole Park
Poole, Dorset, BH15 2DE
☎ 0202 746833
Poole Park
⇌ 🚌 Poole

FabLab is a 'Hands–On' science exhibition which aims to make science fun for all ages.

Summer/Easter/Christmas School Holidays: Daily: 10am–8.30pm
Winter (weekends only): 10am–5.30pm

£ © 🚌 🎋 P 🅿 🚻 ➤ 🛇 WC 🚻 🚶

Compton Acres Gardens
Canford Cliffs Road
Poole, Dorset
☎ 0202 700778
Poole A35
⇌ 🚌 Poole

Nine different and completely separate gardens of the world including Italian, Japanese, Rock and Water Gardens. 9 acres of mainly level ground with tarmac and crazy paving paths. Lower levels of the sub–tropical glen are inaccessible.

1 Mar–31 Oct: Mon–Sun: 10.30am–6.30pm

£ © 🚌 🎋 P 🅿 🚻 ⇒ WC 🐾 🚻 🚶 🎋

Radipole Lake RSPB
Weymouth, Dorset, DT4 0ES
☎ 0305 778313
Access from the Swannery public car park

Reserve and public hide accessible at all times. Visitors centre. Audio & 3D exhibition. Panoramic window. Paths lead to 3 accessible hides which require RSPB membership or permits from reception.

Apr–Oct: Mon–Sun 9am–5pm
Nov–Mar: Mon–Sun 9am–4pm

🐾 🍽 🚻 ➤ 🛇 WC

Lodmoor RSPB
Weymouth, Dorset, DT4 OES
☎ 0305 778313
Access reached from A353 beach road to

Wareham

3 hides overlooking marsh and pools are accessible to wheelchair users. Wheelchair accessible toilets available during holiday season only in nearby Country Park car park

Portland Castle EH

Castletown
Portland, Dorset, DT5 1AZ
☎ 0305 820539

Weymouth A354 on Isle of Portland
≉ 🚌 Weymouth

Henrican Fort, possibly the best preserved. Small displays of cannon, weapons and Elizabethan armour.

Easter–Oct: Mon–Sun 10am–1pm & 2pm–6pm

£ © �;🍴 ☓ P ᴕ Ḻ ┛ 🏰 ┐ ✚ WC
🏊 👫 👨‍🦽 🎧

Cranborne Manor Garden Centre

Cranborne
Nr Wimborne, Dorset, BH21 5PP
☎ 07254 248

A354, B3078 Fordingbridge – Wimborne

Wonderful garden centre set in the grounds of Cranborne Manor. Exquisite gardens, trees, herb garden and daffodils.

Garden Centre: Jan–Dec Tue–Sat 9am–5pm Sun 10am–5pm
Manor Gardens: Mar–Sep Wed 9am–5pm

F © 🚌 ☓ P ᴕ ➔ ┐ WC 🍴 🏊
👫 👨‍🦽

Burton Bradstock NT

Dorset

Easy access from the grassy car park down a gentle slope to the shingle beach.

Stonebarrow Hill NT

Dorset

On the Golden Cap Estate, giving beautiful views over Lyme Bay

Studland Bay & Langdon Hill Wood NT

Nr Swanage, Dorset

One mile level road and a car park giving access to a circular forest route suitable for wheelchair users.

Badbury Rings NT

Wimborne
Dorset

A hill–fort on the estate, groups of disabled adults and children are welcomed; adapted WC available. The restaurant at Kingston Lacy house has thick–handled cutlery available.

Creech Grange Arch NT

Dorset

A folly near Corfe Castle with magnificent views.

Fontmell Down NT

Dorset

Between Shaftesbury & Blandford

From the car park at Fontmell Down, wheelchair users and disabled walkers many enjoy the Down and its superb walks and views.

The Hardy Monument NT

Nr Dorchester
Dorset

Overlooking the Dorset coast 6m SW of Dorchester, gives splendid views from its car park over Dorset and Portland.

Corfe Castle NT

Corfe
Nr Swanage
Dorset

The village is inclined to be hilly, but the NT shop has level access with double doors. The Castle is not accessible. The tea–rooms have thick–handled cutlery available.

Brownsea Island NT

Poole Harbour
☎ 0202 707744

A 500 acre island of heath and woodland. Nature reserve run by the Dorset Trust for Nature Conservation with wide views of Dorset coast. All boats take wheelchairs.

P ᴕ ᵂᶜwc ☓ 🏊 🖐 ᴕᴸ

The Tank Museum

Bovington Camp
Wareham, Dorset, BH20 6JG
☎ 0929 403329/403463

A352
≉ 🚌 Wool

One of the world's largest and most comprehensive collections of armoured fighting vehicles. 3 acres with concrete

DORSET

paths.
Jan–Dec: Mon–Sun 10am–5pm
Closed 10 days over Xmas.

£©📠🐾🪶🎣P♿🛶➜⌐✈
♿ᵂᶜwc🏚🍴🎒👫🎧👁♿ᴸ

Dorset Heavy Horse Centre

Nr Verwood, Dorset, BH21 5RJ
☎ 0202 824040

Off B3081, just over 1m from Verwood
Crossroads.

The Dorset Heavy Horse Centre breeds and
shows 6 different breeds of Heavy Horse
plus miniature Shetland Ponies. 5 acres with
concrete paths.

Gd Fri–31 Oct: Mon–Sun 10am

£©📠🐾P♿🛶➜⌐ᵂᶜwc🍴
🎒👫♿👁👁©�ⁿ

DURHAM

Darlington Art Gallery

Crown St
Darlington, Durham, DL1 1ND
☎ 0325 462034
⇌ 🚌 Darlington

Regular programme of exhibitions by local &
regional artists and items from the gallery's
own collection.

Jan–Dec Mon–Fri: 10am–8pm
Sat: 9am–5.30pm
Closed: Sun, BH and preceeding Sat.

F📠🐾🪶P♿🛶✈wc♿♿

Durham Cathedral

Durham City, Durham, DH1 3EQ
☎ 091 386 2367
⇌ 🚌 Durham

Durham Cathedral is probably the finest
example of Norman church architecture in
England. Tombs of St Cuthbert and
Venerable Bede.

May–Sep: Mon–Sun 7.15am–8pm
Oct–Apr: Mon–Sun 7.15am–6pm

F📠🐾🪶PP♿🛶➜⌐✈ᵂᶜ
wc🏚🍴🎒♿👁©�ⁿ

Lambton Park Garden Centre

Lambton Park
Chester–Le–Street, Durham, DH3 4PZ
☎ 091 385 5154

On A183 Chester–Le–Street/Sunderland
Road 2 miles from A1(M)
🚌 Durham

Large family garden centre with extensive
display gardens. Specialists in water
gardening, clematis, bee–keeping and pet
barn

Winter: Mon–Sun 9am–5pm
Summer: Mon–Sun 9am–6pm

F📠🐾P♿➜⌐♿ᵂᶜwc🍴🎒👫
©�ⁿ♿ᴸ

Durham Light Infantry Museum & Art Gallery

Aykley Heads, Durham, DH1 5TU
☎ 091 384 2214

Durham: on the north side – A690 to
Newcastle
⇌ 🚌 Durham

Museum covers the history of the Durham
Light Infantry 1758–1968. Durham Art
Gallery has a changing programme of
exhibitions, events, concerts and other
activities.

Jan–Dec Tue–Sat & BH: 10am–5pm
Sun: 2pm–5pm

£©📠🛶♿P♿🛶🛶🏛✈ᵂᶜ
wc🍴🎒👫♿

Killhope Leadmining Centre

Upper Weardale, Durham, DL13 1AR
☎ 0388 537505

Midway between Stanhope and Alston on
A689

Summer Sunday bus service

Britain's best preserved leadmining site with
exhibitions on the life of miners and their
families. 10 metre diameter waterwheel

Easter–31 Oct: Mon–Sun 10.30am–5pm
Nov: Sun only 10.30–5pm

£©📠🐾P♿🛶🏛✈ᵂᶜwc🍴
🎒©�ⁿ

Neasham Hill Residential Home & Gdns

Neasham Hill
Darlington, Durham, DL2 1PJ
☎ 0325 721405

A66 to Teeside from Darlington

Darlington

A beautiful village close to Darlington. Home has 18th century garden and a conservatory containing a Victorian type plunge pool. Paved and gravel paths.

Jan–Dec Mon–Sun: 10am–dusk

Barnard Castle Ruins

Castle House
Durham, DL12 9AT
☎ 0833 38212

A67, Barnard Castle

Darlington Barnard Castle

The castle was built by the Normans from 1080. It is split into four sections. There are beautiful views of the Tees and Teesdale. 4 acres with gravel paths.

1 Apr–30 Sep: Mon–Sun 10am–6pm
1 Oct–31 Mar: Tue–Sun 10am–4pm

The Arts Centre

Vane Terrace
Darlington, Durham, DL3 7AX
☎ 0325 483168

Follow A68–A1(M)

Darlington

Extensive and picturesque arts centre with theatre, recital rooms, the prestigious Myles Meehan Gallery, artists' studios and workshops. Offers a full programme of live music, theatre, film and dance

Jan–Dec Mon–Wed: 9am–10.30pm
Thu–Sat: 9am–11pm

ESSEX

Riverside Ice & Leisure

Victoria Rd
Chelmsford, Essex, CM1 1FG
☎ 0245 269417

Chelmsford: A12, A414 or A130 to A1099

Chelmsford

Complex contains ice rink, three pools, flume ride, sports hall, squash courts, health suite, restaurant, fast food area, bars, creche, multi–purpose room and gym. Paved paths.

Mon–Sun: 6am–11pm

Norsey Wood Nature Reserve

Outwood Common Road
Billericay, Essex
☎ 0277 624553

A129 from Brentwood to Billericay

Billericay

Nature reserve, ancient woodland, site of ancient monument: Deerbanks, trenches, burial ground, SSSI, mixed deciduous woodland, coppicing is practiced. Hardcore and woodland paths.

Jan–Dec: 9am–5pm
Closed: 25 Dec–2 Jan

Bradwell Power Station

Bradwell–on–Sea
Southminster, Essex, LM0 7HP
☎ 0621 76331

Bradwell on Sea

Nuclear power station, operating since 1962

Any day or time by arrangement

Colchester Zoo

Maldon Rd
Colchester, Essex, CO3 5SL
☎ 0839 222000

Follow A604, exit off A12

Colchester

East Anglia's largest zoo with 150 different species of animals. Daily presentations includes meeting the elephants, falconry, snake handling, parrots and penguins.No guide dogs.

Mon–Fri: 9.30am–5.30pm

ESSEX

Southend Pier

Western Esplanade
Southend–on–Sea, Essex, SS1 1EE
☎ 0702 355622

Southend–on–Sea, Essex

� Southend

Longest pleasure pier in the world, built 1889. Boat trips from pier head. Trains to pier head

Mon–Sun: 8am–11pm (Summer)
8am–5pm (Winter)

£©🚌🏇P👨‍🦽➔🚻🚻🚻WC🍴🥾🌲

Castle Museum

High St
Colchester, Essex, CO1 17G
☎ 0206 71 2931

Colchester

≥ 🚌 Colchester

Largest Norman Castle Keep ever built. Built when Colchester was capital of Roman Britain. History of Colchester from early man to 1648 Civil War Seige. Paved paths. Lower castle park cannot be reached.

Nov–Mar: Mon–Sat: 10am–5pm
Apr–Oct: Mon–Sat: 10am–5pm
Sun : 2pm–5pm
Closed: Good Fri, 24–27 Dec

£©🚌🏇P🏍👨‍🦽🏭🚻WC🥾
🌲👨‍🦽🤲

Saffron Walden Museum

Museum St
Saffron Walden, Essex, CB10 1JL
☎ 0799 522494

Saffron Walden (M11 – 6m from Stumps Cross)

≥ Audley End Bus

Saffron Waldren Museum is over 150 years old and has fine, varied collections. In addition to the permanent galleries there is a regular programme of special exhibitions and events, including children's activities. The ruins of a C12th castle stand in the grounds.

Apr–Oct: Mon–Sat 11am–5pm
Sun/BH 2.30pm–5.30pm
Nov–Mar: ring to confirm

£©🚌🏇P👨‍🦽🏛➔🚻🚻
WC🥾🌲🤲

Thameside Theatre

Orsett Rd
Grays, Essex, RM17 5DX
☎ 0375 383961

Grays town centre A13

≥ 🚌 Grays

Part of the Thameside complex, a multi–purpose Arts Venue, which includes the Theatre, Thameside Two, Museum and Exhibition area.

Jan–Dec: Mon–Sat 9am–8pm

£©🚌🏇🗡🍽PP👨‍🦽🏛🚻
WC🥾🤲🕐

Chelmsford & Essex Museum & Essex Regiment Museum

Oaklands House
Moulsham St
Chelmsford, Essex, CM2 9AQ
☎ 0245 353066/260614

Chelmsford

≥ 🚌 Chelmsford

Chelmsford & Essex museum housed in Victorian house set in parkland. Purpose built annexe houses Essex Regiment museum which was opened in 1973.

Jan–Dec: Mon–Sat 10am–5pm
Sun 2pm–5pm

F🚌🏇P🏛🤝🏛➔🚻🚻WC🥾
🌲🔽🤲

Mark Hall Cycle Museum

Muskham Rd
Harlow, Essex, CM20 2LF
☎ 0279 439680

Harlow, A414 to the M11

≥ 🚌 Harlow

The facinating display of cycles, accessories and memorabilia have been attractively housed in five galleries within the award–winnng conversion of the C19th stable block. Behind the museum are the manor's three walled gardens. 3 acres.

Jan–Dec: Mon–Sun 10am–1pm & 2pm–5pm

F🚌🏇P👨‍🦽➔🚻🚻WC🥾🌲

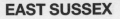

EAST SUSSEX

Booth Museum of Natural History

194 Dyke Road,
Brighton, E. Sussex, BN1 5AA
☎ 0273 552586
Brighton
� 🚌 Brighton

Collection of British birds formed by E T Booth in 19th century. Insects, skeletons, minerals, fossils, environment. Frequent temporary exhibitions. Wheelchair users please give a week's notice.

Mon–Wed: 10am–5pm
Fri–Sat: 10am–5pm
Sun: 2pm–5pm
Closed: Thurs & Gd Fri

F🚌⚡ ⚡ 🦮👈 WC 🍴 ♿ 🐟 👜ⓒ

Preston Manor

Preston Drove
Brighton, E.Sussex
☎ 0273 603005 x 3239
Brighton
≈ 🚌 Preston Park

Impressive Edwardian House set in picturesque grounds. Beautifully furnished rooms. Servants quarters and kitchen to see.

Tue–Sun & BH: 10am–5pm
Closed: Mon & Gd Fri

£ⓒ🚌 ⚡ P ♿ 🏭🏛 🍴 WC ♿ⓒ

Brighton Museum & Art Gallery

Brighton, E. Sussex, BN1 1JE
☎ 0273 603005
A32 London; A27 Worthing/Eastborne
≈ Brighton

Displays of Art Nouveau and Art Deco; fashion; archaeology; history of Brighton; Willet collection of pottery and porcelain, temporary exhibitions.

Mon–Tue: 10am–5.45pm
Thu–Sat: 10am–5.45pm
Sun: 2pm–5pm

F🚌⚡P⚡ ♿➤ WC 🍴 🌲🌳
🐟👜

Bluebell Railway

Sheffield Park Station
Uckfield, E. Sussex, TN22 3QL
☎ 082572 2370 (24hr talking timetable)
Midway between East Grinstead and Lewes on A275
≈ 🚌 Haywards Heath

Britain's first preserved passenger branch line. Travel on Vintage trains for 10 mile round trip. Almost 40 steam locomotives in collection. Museum. Paved paths.

Jun–30 Sep: Mon–Sun
Jan–Feb: Sun only
Weekends throughout rest of year
Tel. for train times

£ⓒ🚌⚡ P P ♿➤🚂 🍴 ♿ WC
🍴 🧺 👥 ♿ 👜ⓒ

Dursillas Park

Alfriston, E. Sussex, BN26 5QS
☎ 0323 870234

Eastbourne A27–A22
🚌 Eastbourne. ≈ Berwick

Set in the beautiful Southdowns. Zoo designed with low level viewing windows for children and wheelchair occupants. Compact site.

Mon–Sun: 10am–dusk

£ⓒ🚌⚡ P P ♿➤ ⊓ 🚂 🍴 ♿
WC 🍴 🧺 👥 👜ⓒ ♿

The Royal Pavilion

The Old Steine
Brighton, E. Sussex, BN1 1UE
☎ 0273 603005
Brighton A23
≈ 🚌 Brighton

Seaside residence of George IV. Exotic eastern style palace with stunning oriental interiors including porcelain, crystal and hand–painted wallpaper

1 Oct–31 May: 10am–5pm
1 Jun–30 Sep: 10am–6pm

£ⓒ🚌⚡ ⚡ P P ♿ 🏭🏛⇒ 🍴 ♿
WC 🏠 🍴 🧺 👥 🐟 👜ⓒ ♿

Hove Museum & Art Gallery

19 New Church Rd
Hove, E. Sussex, BN3 4AB
☎ 0273 779410

Hove: A23/M23 to London
≈ 🚌 Hove
British pictures, furniture, ceramics, etc.

EAST SUSSEX

Display of Hove history including film pioneers, contemporary craft collection.

Tue–Fri: 10am–5pm
Sat: 10am–4.30pm
Sundays 2pm–5pm

De La Warr Pavilion

Marina
Bexhill–on–Sea, E. Sussex, TN40 1DP
☎ 0424 212023

Hastings

≷ 🚌 Bexhill–on–Sea

Built in 1935. Popular venue for disabled people. Entertainment complex. Easy access to promenade.

Mon–Sun: 10am–11pm

F🚌🏇🐾🅿🦽🎪➔⊣⇒♿ WC ‖🍴📷©

The Living World

Seven Sisters Country Park
Exceat
Nr Seaford, E. Sussex, BN25 4AD
☎ 0323 870100

On A259, 5 miles west of Eastbourne, 2 miles east of Seaford

≷ Seaford 🚌 712 between Eastbourne & Brighton

Display of tropical and native wildlife, includes marine life, butterflies, bees, stick insects, spiders and much more. Situated within the Sussex Downs area of outstanding natural beauty.

Mid Mar–1 Nov: Mon–Sun: 10am–5pm
Open weekends, ½ term & school holiday during winter

£©🚌🏇🅿🦽🏛➔♿ WC 🌲🌳🛗📷©

The Palace Pier

Madeira Drive
Brighton, E. Sussex, BN2 1TW
☎ 0273 60361

Brighton – A23

≷ 🚌 Brighton

Grade 2 listed Victorian Pier currently undergoing a massive refurbishment programme. One third mile of wooden slats.

Summer: 9am–2am
Winter: 11am–11pm (weather permitting)

Bayham Abbey Ruins EH

Lamberhurst
Nr Tunbridge Wells, E. Sussex, TN3 8BE
☎ 0892 890381

Tunbridge Wells/Tonbridge A21

🚌 Wadhurst ≷ Frant

Picturesque ruins of a medieval abbey built by White Canons in the 13th century, restored and landscaped to provide a romantic setting for the nearby 18th century Gothic House.

Apr–30 Sep: Mon–Sun: 10am–6pm

£©🚌🏇🅿🛗🏛⊣♿ WC ‖ 🌲🌳📷©

Bentley Wildfowl & Motor Museum

Halland
Nr Lewes, E. Sussex, BN8 5AF
☎ 0825 840573

Lewes A26

≷ 🚌 Lewes

Set in 100 acres amidst green fields and woods. Renowned for its' waterfowl collection and superb collection of veteran cars. Formal gardens.

23 Mar–31 Oct: Mon–Sun 10.30am–4.30pm
Nov–Mar: Sat/Sun 10.30am–4pm

£©🚌🏇🖼🅿🦽➔⊣♿ WC 🛗
‖🌲🌳🛗📷©🛗

Garden Paradise

Avis Rd
Newhaven, E. Sussex, BN9 0DH
☎ 0273 512123

Newhaven A26

≷ 🚌 Newhaven

Planet Earth experience, flowering desert gardens, tropical plant house, fossil museum, landscaped gardens, water features, lakeland miniature railway and garden centre. Gravel paths.

Jan–Dec: Mon–Sun 9am–5pm

£🚌🏇🅿🅿🦽➔⊣🔌♿ WC 🛗
‖🌲🌳📷©🛗

Wilderness Wood

Hadlow Down
Nr Uckfield, E. Sussex, TN22 4HJ
☎ 0825 830509

On A272 between Uckfield and Mayfield

🚂 Buxted

60 acres of varied working woodland, trails, exhibitions in timber barn, guided walks and demonstrations for groups.

Mon–Sun 10am–dusk

Sussex Farm Museum & Craft Workshop

Horam
Heathfield, E. Sussex, TN21 0JB
☎ 04353 3161/2597

A267 Tunbridge Wells/Eastbourne Road

The museum reflects the rural scene during 1900, with both domestic and agricultural. Craft workers use the outer buildings.

Easter–Oct: Mon–Sun 10am–5pm

Bexhill Museum

Edgerton Road
Bexhill, E. Sussex, TN39 3HL

Bexhill

🚂 🚌 Bexhill

Lively displays of local history; wildlife; dinosaurs and geology.

Tue–Fri: 10am–5pm
Sat–Sun: 2pm–5pm
Open BH

Michelham Priory

Hailsham, E. Sussex, BN27 3QS
☎ 0323 844224

Hailsham: off A22 and A27

🚂 🚌 Polegate or Berwick

13–14th century buildings and tudor house, furnished in period. Exhibitions in house, barn, blacksmiths and rope museums, working watermill. 6 acres gravel and paved around house.

25 Mar–31 Oct: Mon–Sun 11am–5.30pm
Nov/Feb/Mar: Sun only 11am–4pm

Towner Art Gallery & Museum

Manor Gardens
High St
Old Town
Eastbourne, E. Sussex, BN20 8BB
☎ 0323 411688

Eastbourne

🚂 🚌 Eastbourne

Lively temporary Art Exhibitions, selection from Towner Collection, local history museum, 19th century manor house, set in delightful public gardens.

Tue–Sat: 10am–5pm
Sun & BH: 2pm–5pm
Closed: Christmas Eve & Good Fri

The Grange Museum

Rottingdean
Brighton, E.Sussex
☎ 0273 301004

A259 to Brighton

🚌 Brighton

The Grange is one of the sites of the Royal Pavilion, Art Gallery and Museums. Remodelled by Sir Edward Lutyens in 1919. First floor exhibition includes an important collection of historic toys, a collection of letters, books and pictures connected to Rudyard Kipling and a display of local illustrations.

Mon–Tue: 10am–5pm
Thu–Sat: 10am–5pm
Sundays: 2pm–5pm

Battle Abbey EH

Battle, E. Sussex, TN33 0AD
☎ 0424 63792

In Battle High Street A2100

🚂 Battle

Site of the Battle of Hastings 1066, where William the Conqueror defeated King Harold. 54 acres of hilly ground with gravel paths.

Good Fri–Sep 30: Mon–Sun 10am–6pm
1 Oct–Maundy Thu: Mon–Sun 10am–4pm

EAST SUSSEX

£©🚐🐕🅿️♿👜🚻⇒▪️🚻 wc 🔋♿🎧👐

Birling Gap NT

Nr Eastbourne
E. Sussex

W of Eastbourne

An adapted lavatory has been provided at this south coast view–point.

GLOUCESTERSHIRE

Cotswold Farm Park

Guiting Power
Cheltenham, Glos., GL54 5UG
☎ 0451 850307

Nr Stow on Wold, between B4068 and B4077

Most comprehensive collection of rare breeds of farm animals in Britain. Displayed in a beautiful farm setting high in the Cotswolds. Gravel paths.

1 Apr–30 Sep: 10.30am–6pm

Cotswold Motor Museum

Bourton on the Water
Glos., GL54 2BY
☎ 0451 21255

Cheltenham 15 miles, Oxford 25 miles

≋ Moreton–in–Marsh

30 beautiful cars and motor cycles with a collection of memorabilia, including the childhood toy collection and Britain's largest display of period advertising signs

Feb–Nov: Mon–Sun 10am–6pm

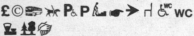

Prinknash Pottery

Prinknash Abbey
Cranham, Glos., GL4 8EU
☎ 0452 812239

Gloucester

≋ 🚐 Gloucester

Pottery with distintive style made by the Benedictine Monks.

Abbey Church Mon–Sun: 5am–8pm
Pottery Mon–Sat: 1030am–4.30pm

Sun: 2pm–4.30pm
Closed: Good Fri.

£🚐🐕🅿️🅿️♿👜🏛️→🚻⇒🚻 wc 🍴🔋🌲♿©♿

Regiments of Gloucestershire Museum

Gloucester Docks
Gloucester, Glos., GL1 2HE
☎ 0452 522682

Gloucester

≋ 🚐 Gloucester

Award winning museum in Gloucester's historic docks. New displays include life–size reconstructions, scale models, sound effects, active photos and film to tell the story of Gloucester's soldiers

Tue–Sun & BH: 10am–5pm

🔋♿👐♿

Cotswold Perfumery

Bourton on the Water
Glos., GL54 2BU
☎ 0451 20698

Cheltenham A429

🚐 Bourton on the Water

The only exhibition of its kind in Europe. Audio visual show, perfume quiz and garden.

Summer: 9.30am–6pm
Winter: 9.30am–5pm

£©🚐🐕🅿️🌿♿⬛→♿wc🔋 🌲

Regent Arcade

High St
Cheltenham, Glos., GL50 1JZ
☎ 0242 521345

Cheltenham

≋ 🚐 Cheltenham Spa

The world famous 'Wishing Fish Clock', designed by local artist, Kit Williams, is a feature in the shopping centre.

Mon–Sat: 9am–6pm

F🐕🅿️🅿️♿👜🏛️→▪️♿wc🐚 🍴🔋©

Bibury Trout Farm

Bibury
Nr Cirencester, Glos., GL7 5NL
☎ 0285 740215
Cirencester
🚆 Cirencester

See trout in various stages of development.
Plants, gifts, fresh and smoked trout for
sale. Feed the fish. Refreshments, fishing.

Summer: Mon–Sat: 9am–6pm
Sun: 10am–6pm
Winter: Mon–Sat: 9am–5pm
Sun: 10am–5pm

£©🚐🚌 ✕ 🅿 ♿ ➤ ⊣ wc ✕ 🕯
🏕🐾

The Robert Opie Collection

Albert Warehouse
Gloucester Docks, Glos., GL1 2EH
☎ 0452 302309
Gloucester
🚆 Gloucester

Museum of advertising and packaging.
Could be in temporary premises for 1992.

May–Sep: Mon–Sun inc BH 10am–6pm
Oct–Apr: Tue–Sun & BH 10am–6pm

£©🚐✕ 🅿 ♿ ➤ ⊣ ⊹ wc
✕ 🕯 🐾

The Wildfowl and Wetlands Trust

Slimbridge, Glos., GL2 7BT
☎ 0453 890065
Dursley (A4135)

You can feed rare and endangered ducks,
geese and swans. Explore a tropical
rainforest, watch dazzling pink flamingos
and view wild birds from comfortable hides.

Jan–Dec: 9.30am–5pm (summer)
9.30am–4pm (winter)

£©🚐🚌 ✕ 🅿 ♿ ➤ wc 🕯 ‖

Berkeley Castle

Berkeley, Glos., GL13 9BQ
☎ 0453 810332
Between Gloucester and Bristol
🚆 Gloucester

Owned by Berkeley family. Regrettably,
unsuitable for wheelchair occupants –
narrow passages and many steps. The

butterfly house is a modern building with
wheelchair facilities.

Apr: Tue–Sat: 11am–5pm
Sun: 2pm–5pm
May–Sep: Tue–Sat: 11am–5pm
Sun: 2pm–5pm

£©🚐🚌 ✕ 🅿 ♿ 🔔 ▬ 🏛 ⊹ wc ‖
🕯🏕 ♿

Batsford Arboretum

Estate Office
Moreton in Marsh, Glos., GL56 9QF
☎ 0608 50722
A44 1 mile from Moreton–in–Marsh
🚆 🚌 Moreton–in–Marsh

Most of Arboretum is on the side of a hill.

1 Mar–1 Nov: Mon–Sun 10am–5pm

£©🚐🚌 ✕ 🅿 ♿ 🔔 ▬ 🏛 ⊹ wc ‖
🕯🏕 ♿

National Waterways Museum

Llanthony Warehouse
Glos., GL1 2EH
☎ 0452 307009
A38 Gloucester
🚆 🚌 Gloucester

Within the historic port of Gloucester. An
area being redeveloped with shops,
refreshment areas. Plenty of car parking.

Winter: Mon–Sun 10am–5pm
Summer: Mon–Sun 10am–6pm

£©🚐🚌 ✕ 🛶 🔔 🅿 ♿ ➤ ⇒
wc 🕯 ‖ 🕯 🔄 👜 🖐 ⌀ ♿

Keynes Country Park

Shorncote
Cirecester, Glos., GL7 6DF
☎ 0285 861459
Cirencester

120 acres of landscaped lakes with picnic
sites and lakeside walks. Nature reserve
with access to hide, lakeside parking,
coarse fishing and picnic tables – all for
wheelchair users.

Fishing: 16 Jun–14 Mar
Park: All year 9am–9pm

£©🚐🚌 ✕ 🛶 🅿 ⊹ ♿ wc ‖ 🏕
♿ ⌀ ⌀

GLOUCESTERSHIRE

National Birds of Prey Centre

Newent, Glos., GL18 1JJ
☎ 0531 820286
Newent (B4215 off A40 or M50)
🚌 Newent

200 birds on display with 2nd largest collection of Birds of Prey in Europe after Berlin Zoo. 7 acres of countryside with fine views of the Cotswolds and the Malvern Hills. No guide dogs admitted
Feb–Nov: Mon–Sun 10.30am–5.30pm

£🚌 P ♿ ☞ → ⌐ ♿wc WC ‖ 🛉 🏕
♿ 🖐 ©

Gloucester City Museum & Art Gallery

Brunswick Road
Gloucester, GL1 1HP
☎ 0452 524131
Gloucester
�- 🚌 Gloucester

18th century walnut furniture, clocks, barometers, glass, silver, and landscape paintings; Romano–British and medieval carvings; wildlife, aquarium and beehive.
Mon–Sat: 10am–5pm

F 🚌 ⚹ P ⚲ ♿ 🏛 WC 🛉 © ©

Gloucester Antique Centre

1 Severn Rd
Gloucester
☎ 0452 529716
A40 on historical docks
🚌 Gloucester

A converted grain warehouse on 4 floors with passenger lift, restaurant, shops and showcases. Steps to lift.
Mon–Sat: 9.30am–5pm
Sun: 12 noon–5pm

F 🚌 ⚹ P♿ P ♿ ☞ ⬛ 🏛 🚻 ♿wc WC
‖ 🛉 🏕 🖐 © ©

Chedworth Roman Villa NT

Yanworth
Cheltenham, Glos., GL54 3LJ
☎ 024 289 256
Cirencester A429; Cheltenham A40

Best exposed Roman Villa in Britain. Three wings of the building enclose a large inner space; there are good 4th century mosaics in the bath suites and dining room. Water Shrine.
1 Mar–end Oct: Tue–Sun & BH Mon

10am–5.30pm
Closed Good Fri
1 Nov–8 Dec: Wed–Sun 11am–4pm

£© 🚌 P ♿ ☞ → ⌐ ♿wc WC ‖ 🛉
🏕 ♿ © ©

Hailes Abbey EH

Nr Winchcombe
Cheltenham, Glos., GL54 5PB
☎ 0242 602398
Cheltenham B4632
🚌 Cheltenham

Attractive wooded pastureland with the extensive remains of the cloisters and foundations, Examples of high quality sculpture and floor tiles in museum.
1 Apr–30 Sep: Mon–Sun – 10am–6pm
1 Oct–31 Mar: Tue–Sun – 10am–4pm

£© 🚌 ⚹ P♿ P ♿ 🛏 ♿wc WC 🛉 🎧

Folly Farm Waterfront

Bourton–on–the–Water
Nr. Cheltenham,
Glos. GL54 3BY
☎ 0451 20285
Cheltenham to Bourton on the Water A436
🚌 Cheltenham

Europe's largest conservation centre for rare domestic waterfowl. Friendly pets, small animals, well stocked garden centre and tea room.
Apr–Sept: 10am–6pm
Oct–Mar: 10am–4pm

£© 🚌 ⚹ P♿ P ♿ → ⌐ ♿wc WC ‖
🛉 🏕 © ©

Barnsley House Garden

Barnsley
Cirencester, Glos. GL7 5EE
☎ 0285 740 281
Cirencester: B4425 – Burford Rd
�-- Kemble

Spring bulbs, autumn colour, mixed borders, climbing and wall shrubs, Knot garden, herb garden, 18th century summerhouses, and laburnum walk (early June). House not open.
Mon/Wed/Thu/Sat: 10am–6pm

£© 🚌 ⚹ P ⚲ ☞ → ⌐ -‖ WC 🛉
🏕 ♿ 🖐 ©

Shambles Museum

16–20 Church St
Newent, Glos., GL18 1PP
☎ 0531 822144
Newent (Gloucester 10 miles)
⇌ 🚌 Gloucester

Recreated mini Victorian town fully
furnished and equipped house, shops,
cottage and workshops around cobbled
streets and square.

Mid Mar–Christmas: 10am–6pm (or dusk)

£ © 🚐 🐾 P 🅿 ♿ ⬛ 🏰 ⊹ ♿ WC
🍴 ⚓

Corinium Museum

Park St
Cirencester, Glos., GL7 2BX
☎ 0285 655611
Centre of Cirencester
⇌ Kemble Bus

One of the finest collections of Roman
antiquities mainly from Corinium.
Reconstructions of Roman dining room,
kitchen and craftsman's workshop.
Displays of Cotswold life and exhibitions.

Apr–Oct: Mon–Sat: 10am–5.30pm
Sun: 2pm–5.30pm
Nov–Mar: Tue–Sat: 10am–5pm
Sun: 2pm–5pm

£ © 🚐 🐾 P 🅿 ♿ ♿ WC ⚓
🐟 ☕

Cotswold Countryside Collection

Fosseway
Northleach, Glos., GL54 3JH
☎ 0451 60715
West end of Northleach
🚌 Northleach

Cotswold rural life museum housed in the
C18th Northleach House of Correction, with
preserved cells and restored court–room.
Role–play programmes available for groups.
The museum displays the Lloyd–Baker
Collection of agricultural history, plus
special exhibitions on country themes.

April–Oct: Mon–Sat 10.00am–5.30pm
Sun 2.00pm–5.30pm

Pittville Pump Room Museum

Pittville Park
Cheltenham, Glos., GL52 3JE
☎ 0242 512740
Cheltenham
⇌ 🚌 Cheltenham

A magnificent Regency building, where spa
waters are available, set in its own park,
with displays of original costumes from
Cheltenham's Regency heyday to the
Swinging Sixties.

Nov–Mar: Tues–Sat 10.30am–5.00pm
Apr–Oct Tues–Sun 10.30am–5.00pm

£ © 🚐 🐾 P ⬛ ⬛ ♿ WC ⚓ 🎪 ♿

Cheltenham Art Gallery & Museum

Clarence St
Cheltenham, Glos., GL50 3JT
☎ 0242 237431
Cheltenham
⇌ 🚌 Cheltenham

Important Art & Crafts Movement collection
including furniture, pottery and silver
inspired by William Morris. Also local history
and archaeology, rare Oriental porcelain,
Dutch & British paintings.

Jan–Dec Mon–Sat: 10am–5.20pm
May–Sep Sun: 2pm–5.20pm
Closed: BH's

F 🚐 🐾 ⬛ P 🅿 ♿ 🏰 ♿ WC 🍴 ⚓
🐟 ☕ ©

Holst Birthplace Museum

4 Clarence Rd
Cheltenham, Glos., GL52 2AY
☎ 0242 524846
Cheltenham
⇌ 🚌 Cheltenham

Regency house where the composer of 'The
Planets' was born, showing the 'upstairs-
downstairs' way of life of Victorian and
Edwardian times.

Jan–Dec: Tue–Fri: 12noon–5.20pm
Sats: 11am–5.20pm
Closed: Suns and BH's

F 🚐 🐾 P 🅿 ♿ ⬛ ⬛ 🏰 WC ⚓ ♿
☕ © 🎨

GLOUCESTERSHIRE

Gloucester Cathedral

17 College Green
Glos., GL1 2LR
☎ 0452 528095
Gloucester
⇋ 🚌 Gloucester
Built in 1089; Monastic site since 681
Jan–Dec: Mon–Sat 8.30am–6pm

F🚐🌲🛶 🅿 P ♿ 🏛 ➤ ⌐ ⬥ ♿ᵂᶜ
WC 🍴 🛒 🚼 ♿ 🦽 🐚 ♿ᴸ

Hidcote Manor Gardens NT

Chipping Campden
Glos., GL55 6LR
☎ 0386 438333

4m NE of Chipping Campden; 8m S of
Stratford–upon–Avon and signposted from
B4632

One of the most famous of modern gardens,
laid out by Major Lawrence Johnston over
forty years, starting in 1907. The many
formal gardens are grouped together like a
series of rooms.

Easter–31 Oct: Mon,Wed,Thur,Sat,Sun
11am–8pm

£🚐🌲P♿ 🅿 🦽🌿🛒➤ ⌐ ⬥♿ᵂᶜ
WC 🍴 ♿ ♿ᴸ

Westbury Court Gardens

Westbury–on–Severn, Glos.,
☎ 045 276 461

9m SW of Gloucester on A48

The earliest surviving Dutch water garden in
England. Formal canals, yew hedges and a
tall summerhouse dates from 1696–1705.
Garden restored since 1967 and planted
with species grown in England before 1700.

Easter: Sat/Sun/Mon
Apr–31 Oct: Wed–Sun & BH Mon
11am–6pm

£©🚐🌲🛶 P ♿➤ ⌐ ♿ᵂᶜ WC🚼
♿ ♿ᴸ

Crickley Hill NT

Nr Gloucester
Glos.,

Jointly managed by Gloucester County
Council and the National Trust, the park
provides spectacular views over the Severn
Vale towards the Welsh Mountains and
Malvern Hills. Information boards. The
Family Trail is suitable for wheelchair users.
Adapted WC.

Dovers Hill NT

Nr Chipping Campden
Glos.,

Car parking and wheelchair access path to
topograph; panoramic views over several
counties on a fine day. Leaflet available on
site.

Frocester Hill NT

Nr Nympsfield
Glos

Provides magnificent views from the
Cotswold scarp.

Nature in Art

The International Centre for Wildlife Art
Wallsworth Hall
Twigworth, Glos., GL2 9PA
☎ 0452 731422

Gloucester A38
🚌 Gloucester

The world's only award–winning museum
dedicated to wildlife art from any country,
any period and in any medium. Artists in
residence. 6 acres with paved and gravel
paths.

Jan–Dec: Tue–Sun & BH 10am–5pm

£©🛒🚐🌲🪶P♿ 🅿 🦽🏠➤ ⌐ ♿ᵂᶜ
WC 🍴 🛒 🏕 🐚 🅒

Dean Forest Railway

Forest Rd
Lydney, Glos., GL15 4ET
☎ 0594 843423

Lydney A48, then B4234
⇋ 🚌 Lydney

Steam trains are operated over 1½ miles of
former British Rail line in Forest of Dean. 2
acres with gravel paths.

Static Displays: Jan–Dec: Mon–Sun
In Steam: Easter–Sep: Sun & BH Mon
11am–5pm
Jun–July: Wed
Aug: Tue,Wed,Thur

£©🛒🚐🌲P♿ 🅿 🦽➤ ⌐ ♿ᵂᶜ WC 🍴
🛒 🏕 ♿ 🐚

Westonbirt Arboretum

Westonbirt
Tetbury, Glos., GL8 8QS
☎ 0666 88 220

Tetbury

Holds one of the largest collections of trees
and shrubs in Europe. 600 acres with gravel
paths.

Jan–Dec: Mon–Sun 10am–8pm or dusk

£©🚌✈🛏Ｐ🅿♿👜👈➤🚾
🚾🍴🛍🌲♿

Museum of the Manchesters

Ashton Town Hall
Market Place
Ashton–under–Lyne
Tameside
☎ 061 334 3078

Ashton, from Oldham A627 from
Manchester A635

≋ 🚌 Ashton

A social and regimental history of the
Manchester Regiment.

Jan–Dec: Mon–Sat 10am–4pm
Closed: BH

F🚌✈Ｐ🅿🖉👜👈➤⊓🔆♿
🚾🛍🌀©

The Manchester Museum

The University
Oxford Rd
Manchester, M13 9PL
☎ 061 275 2634

Manchester

≋ Oxford Rd 🚌 Piccadilly

A natural history museum with archaeology,
Egyptology, Botany, Ethnology,
Entomology, Geology, Zoology and
Numismatics.

Jan–Dec: Mon–Sat 10am–5pm

F🚌✈Ｐ🖉👜👈🔲🚾🛍🌲
♿🌀

The Whitworth Art Gallery

University of Manchester
Oxford Rd
Manchester, M15 6ER
☎ 061 273 4865

Central M/CR, opposite Royal Infirmary

≋ Oxford Rd 🚌 Piccadilly

Important collections of watercolours,
prints, textiles, wallpaper and contemporary
art. Temporary exhibitions and a
programme of regularly changing lively
displays from our collections.

Jan–Dec: Mon–Sat 10am–5pm
Thu 10am–9pm

F🚌✂Ｐ🅿👜♿🔲➤🚾wc🍴
🛍🌲🎧◆🌀©♿

Granada Studios Tour

Water St
Manchester, M60 9EA
☎ 061 833 0880

Manchester, A57

≋ Victoria or Picadilly

Take a fascinating look at the world of
television.

Apr–Sept: Tues–Sun 10am–4pm

£🚌✈🛏Ｐ🅿👜👈🔲➤🍴🔆
🚾🍴🛍🌀©♿

Salford Museum & Art Gallery

Peel Park
Salford, G.Manchester, M5 4WU
☎ 061 736 2649

On A6 Manchester to Preston

≋ 🚌 Manchester

Largest collection of works by L S Lowry,
the industrial painter. 'Lark Hill Place' is a
recreated period street. Victorian art gallery
with temporary exhibitions. Ramp up to
entrance.

Jan–Dec: Mon–Fri 10am–4.45pm
Sun 2pm–5pm
Closed Good Fri

F🚌✈🖉🛏Ｐ🅿👜🔲wc🏛🍴
🛍🌀

Portland Basin Industrial Heritage Centre

Portland Place
Portland St South,
Ashton–under–Lyne,
G.Manchester, OL6 7SY
☎ 061 308 3374

≋ 🚌 Ashton

Former canal warehouse at the junction of
three canals, now telling the social and
industrial history of Tameside.

Apr–Oct: Tue–Sat 10am–6pm
Sun 12noon–6pm
Oct–Apr: Tue–Sat 10am–4pm
Sun 12noon–4pm

F🚌✈Ｐ🖉👜👈🔲➤⊓🔆wc
🛍🌲🌀©

HAMPSHIRE

Andover Museum & Musuem of the Iron Age

6 Church Close
Andover, Hants., SP10 1DP
☎ 0264 366283

Andover M3, A303, A343

 Andover

Museum of the Iron Age: Exhibits focus on artefacts excavated from nearby Danebury Hillfort and includes dioramas, models, reconstructions and audio–visual displays.
Jan–Dec: Tue–Sat 10am–5pm
Apr–Sep: Sun 2pm–5pm

£©🚌 🛬 P 🦽 ☞ ♿ 🎞 🦽 👋 ©

Longdown Dairy Farm

Longdown
Ashurst
Nr Southampton, Hants., SO4 4UH
☎ 0703 293326

A35 from Totton to Lyndhurst

🚌 Southampton

Modern, working dairy farm, adapted to allow visitors to walk round. Also pigs, goats, chickens, ducks, guinea pigs. Adventure playground (for more able bodied). 200 acres with paved paths.
Easter–31 Oct
Other times by arrangement.

£🚌 🛬 P P ♿ → ⌐ ✦ ♿ wc ⌂
🎞 🏕 ♿

New Forest Butterfly Farm

Longdown
Ashurst
Southampton, Hants., SO4 4UH
☎ 0703 292166

A35 from Totton to Lyndhurst

🚌 Southampton & Lymington 🛬 Lyndhurst Rd, Ashurst.

A living display of butterflies and moths from all over the world, flying freely in large glasshouse. Also scorpions, tarantulas, praying mantids. 5 acres with gravel paths.
Easter–31 Oct: Mon–Sun – 10am–5pm

£🚌 🛬 P ♿ → ⌐ ✦ ♿ wc ⌂
🍴 🎞 🏕 🦽 ⚓

Winchester City Museum

The Square
Winchester, Hants
☎ 0962 863064

Winchester

🛬 🚌 Winchester

Museum illustrates the city's history from its prehistoric past to the present day.
Apr–Sep: Mon–Sat 10am–5pm
Sun: 2pm–5pm
Oct–Mar: Tue–Sat 10am–5pm
Sun: 2pm–4pm

F🚌 🛬 P ♿ 🎞 wc 🦽 🦽 © ©

West End Arts Centre

Queens Rd
Aldershot, Hants., GU11 3JD
☎ 0252 21158/330040

Aldershot A325

🛬 Aldershot

Provides entertaining drama, recent–release movies, dance & classical music. Holds classes, courses and workshops from aerobics to watercolour.
Mon–Sun: 9.30am–Midnight

£©🚌 🛬 P♿ P ♿ 🦽 → ⌐ ✦ ♿
wc ⌂ 🍴 © ©

Museum of Army Flying

Middle Wallop
Stockbridge, Hants., SO20 8DY
☎ 0264 384421

A343 nr Andover

🛬 🚌 Andover

Unique collection in exciting displays telling the story of Army flying from 19th century to present day. Aircraft fly daily. International Air Show 9–10 May 1992.
Mon–Sun: 10am–4.30pm

£©🚌 🛬 P♿ P ♿ ☞ 🎞 ⌐ ⇒ ♿
wc ⌂ 🍴 🎞 🏕 🎧 © ©

The Hawk Collection

Weyhill
Andover, Hants., SP11 8DY
☎ 0264 772252

Andover A303

🛬 🚌 Andover

The most comprehensive collection of birds of prey available to the public in the UK. 15 acres with grass and gravel paths.
1 Mar–31 Oct: 10.30am–5pm

£© 🛬 P♿ P ♿ → ⌐ ⇒ ♿ wc 🍴
🎞 🏕 🦽 ©

Finkley Down Farm Park

Finkley Down Farm
Andover, Hants., SP11 6NF
☎ 0265 352195

Andover A303 – A3093

≷ 🚌 Andover

One of Hampshire's leading tourist
attractions, the farm remains an example of
traditional Hampshire countryside. 6 acres
with grass and gravel paths.

1 Apr–1 Oct: 10.30am–6pm

£🚌 ⚹ P₀ P ♿ ➤ ⇒ ♿ WC ❙❙ ☒
👥 ♿ ✆

The Light Infantry Museum

Peninsula Barracks
Romsey Rd
Winchester, Hants., SO23 8TS
☎ 0962 885522 x 5130

Winchester, A3090

≷ 🚌 Winchester

Formed in 1968 from the former County
Light Infantry Regiments, (Somerset,
Cornwall, Shropshire, Yorkshire and
Durham). This museum depicts the modern
Light Infantrymen. See the Berlin Wall.

Tue–Sat: 10am–5pm
Sun: 12 noon–4pm

£© 🚌 ⚹ P P ♿ ⚑ ➤ ⊣ ♿ WC
☒ ♿ ✆

HMS Warrior 1860

Victory Gate
HM Naval Base
Portsmouth, Hants., PO1 3QX
☎ 0705 291379

Portsmouth A27, M2

 Portsmouth Harbour

The world's first and only surviving iron-
hulled warship, HMS Warrior, was the
largest, fastest and most formidable naval
vessel of her time. Ships ladders are
awkward but help is available. Lower decks
inaccessible to wheelchair users.

Mar–Oct: 10.30am–5.30pm
Nov–Feb: 10am–5pm

£© 🚌 ⚹ 🛏 P₀ P ♿ ⊣ ➕ ♿ WC
⚓ ❙❙ ☒ 👥 ♿ ✆ ✆ ♿ ♿

Rotherfield Park

Alton, Hants., GU34 3QL
☎ 042 158 204

A32

Victorian gothic family home since 1820.
Many original contents. Large garden. Fine
views. 8 acres with gravel and grass paths.

House & Gdn: Sun & Mons of BH weekends.
1–7 Jun; 1–7 Jul; 1–7 Aug: 2pm–5pm

Garden only: May–Sept Sun & Thurs
2pm–5pm

£© 🚌 ⚹ P₀ P ⚑ ✆ ➡ ➤ ⊣ WC
❙❙ ☒ 👥 ♿ ✆

Farley Mount Country Park

West of Winchester
On Sarum Road, Hants
☎ 0962 846034

Winchester

≷ 🚌 Winchester

1000 acre country park providing informal
access and pleasant walks. Roman road to
site of villa lie within the park plus an ancient
wood and downland.

Jan–Dec Mon–Sun

F🚌 ⚹ P ➤ ⊣ ♿ WC 👥 ♿

Exbury Gardens

Exbury
Nr Southampton, Hants., SO4 1AZ
☎ 0703 891203

Southampton A326/B3054 to Beaulieu

World famous de Rothschild selection of
Rhododendrons, Azaleas, Camellias,
Magnolias, etc. 250 acres with many
horticultural and landscape features. Gravel
and tarmac paths.

Mar–Oct Mon–Sun 10am–5.30pm

£© 🚌 ⚹ P₀ P ♿ ➤ ⊣ ⇒ ♿ WC
❙❙ ☒ 👥 ✆ ♿

Winchester College

Winchester, Hants., SO23 9NA
☎ 0962 868778

Winchester M3

≷ 🚌 Winchester

600 year old school with medieval chapel
and other buildings. Cobbled and paved
paths.

Mon–Sun 10am–5pm

£© 🚌 ⚹ P ♿ 🏛 ➤ ➕ WC ♿

HAMPSHIRE

The National Motor Museum Complex

The John Montagu Building
Beaulieu, Hants., SO42 7ZN
☎ 0590 612345

Beaulieu signed from the M27

Home of one of the finest collections of cars and motor cycles in the world. Palace House ancestral home of Lord Montagu. The Abbey ruins and exhibition of Monastic Life and many special features are all on a transport theme.

Guide dogs not allowed on the Monorail

May–Sep: Mon–Sun 10am–6pm
Oct–Apr: Mon–Sun 10am–5pm

£©🚌☀🌳🦮 Pᴬ P ♿⚓🏰
🔋🔌♿ WC ⛲ 🍴 ♨♿⛲ ♿

Wellington Country Park

Riseley
Reading
Berks., Hants., RG7 1SP
☎ 0734 326444

Reading/Basingstoke off A33
➤ 🚌 Reading

400 acres of woodland, lake and meadow with deer park, nature trails, miniature steam railway, childrens animals, boating, camping and caravaning, playground and gift shop. Woodchip paths.

Mar–Oct: Mon–Sun 10am–5.30pm
Winter: Sat/Sun 10am–dusk

£©🚌☀ Pᴬ P ♿➤ ⊢ ♿ WC ⛲
🍴 ♨♿⊘©♿

Stratfield Saye House

Stratfield Saye
Reading
Berks., Hants., RG7 2BT
☎ 0256 882882

Reading/Basingstoke on A33
➤ 🚌 Reading

Family home of the Dukes of Wellington since 1817 when the estate was presented to the Iron Duke. Many personal possessions and momentoes of this famous soldier/statesman. Funeral carriage, gardens and Wellington exhibition.

1 May–Last Sun in Sep: Sat–Thur 11.30am–4pm

£🚌☀ P ♪♿➤⊢♿ WC 🍴 ♨
♨♿⊙⊘

Moors Valley Country Park

Horton Road
Ashley Heath
Nr Ringwood, Hants., BH24 2ET
☎ 0425 470721

Ringwood A31 – Horton Road
🚌 Ringwood

Lakeside and forest walks in 300 acres with gravel paths suitable for wheelchair users. Easiriders available and 'wheelchair friendly' tables. Fishing, golf & narrow gauge steam railway.

Mon–Sun 6am–9pm

Bohunt Manor Gardens & Waterfowl

Liphook, Hants., GU30 7DL
☎ 0428 722208

On A3 in village
➤ 🚌 Liphook

Medium sized garden. Herbaceous border and lakeside walks. Rare shrubs and trees, rhododendrons, azaleas and bulbs in the spring. Grass paths surround the site.

Jan–Dec: Mon–Sun dawn–dusk

£🚌☀ Pᴬ P ♿➤⊢ WC ♨©♿

Lepe Country Park

Lepe
Exbury
Southampton, Hants., SO4 1AD
☎ 0703 899108

Between New Forest and Solent
🚌 Summer Sun & BH

Over a mile of beach offering superb views of the Solent and Isle of Wight. Good view point for disabled people.

Jan–Dec

£©🚌☀ Pᴬ P ♿⊢♿ WC 🍴 ♨
♨♿⊘

The Winchester Gallery

Park Avenue
Winchester, Hants., SO23 8DL
☎ 0962 852500

Winchester
➤ 🚌 Winchester

Gallery is a public exhibitions venue with a national reputation, located within the

School of Art.
Tue–Fri: 10am–4.30pm

F�... 📱 P ⚬ 🏠 ➤ ♿ WC ❙❙ 🖼 ⓒ

The Royal Marines Museum

Southsea, Hants., PO4 9PX
☎ 0705 819385

A2030

⇌ Portsmouth Harbour/Portsmouth or Southsea

History of the Royal Marines from 1664 to the present day. Includes dynamic Falklands audio visual and chilled artic display.

Easter–Aug: 10am–5.30pm
Sep–Easter: 10am–4.30pm

£ⓒ🚌... 📱 ⓟ ⚬ 🔥 🏠 ❙❙ WC ❙❙
🖼 🛗 ♿

Eling Tide Mill

The Toll Bridge
Eling
Totton, Hants., SO4 4HF
☎ 0703 869575

Southampton A35 to Lyndhurst

⇌ Totton

The only surviving tide mill still in regular production of wholeflour. Blind people, when accompanied by a helper, find the sounds, smells and feel for the mill a very satisfying experience. Guide dogs not allowed.

Wed–Sun: 10am–4pm

£ⓒ🚌✏📱 ⚬ 🔥 ▄ 🏠 WC 🖼 🛗
♿ 🖐 ✖

Hospital of St Cross

St Cross
Winchester, Hants., SO23 9SD
☎ 0962 851375

Winchester city centre ⅛ mile

⇌ 🚍 Winchester

England's oldest Almshouse with transitional Norman chapel and gardens. An extensive collection of medals, uniforms and many other interesting items connected with warfare.

Apr–Oct: 9.30am–5pm
Nov–Mar: 10.30am–3.30pm

£🚌 📱 P ⚬ ▄ 🏠 ❙ ❙ ♿ WC 🖼
🛗 ♿ ⓒ

Paultons Park

Ower
Romsey, Hants., SO51 6AL
☎ 0703 814445/814442

Just off exit 2, M27 near Southampton

⇌ 🚍 Southampton

Leisure park with extensive gardens and lake. Exotic birds, wildfowl and animals. Romany and village life museums, working watermill. Rio Grande railway, pets corner, childrens entertainments, clock maze and Japanese Garden. 140 acres with paved paths. Rio Grande railway does not take wheelchairs.

Mar–Oct: Mon–Sun 10am–4.30pm

£ⓒ🚌... 📱 📱 ⚬ ➤ ⊓ 🚲 ♿ WC
🌳 ❙❙ 🖼 🛗 🖐 ⓒ ♿

Staunton Country Park

Middle Park Way
Havant, Hants
☎ 0705 453405

Havant, B2149

⇌ 🚍 Havant

A beautiful Victorian estate with landscaped park and lake. Walled garden and ornamental farm with animals and exotic game birds. 152 acres with gravel paths.

Easter–Oct: Mon–Sun 10am–5pm
Nov–Apr: Sat/Sun 10am–4pm

£ⓒ🚌... 📱 📱 ⚬ ➤ ♿ WC ❙❙ 🖼
🌳 🛗 🖐 ⓒ ♿

Winchester Heritage Centre

52/54 Upper Brook St
Winchester, Hants., SO23 8DG
☎ 0962 864292

Winchester

⇌ 🚍 Winchester

Heritage centre set up by Winchester Preservation Trust in 1983 in 2 semi–detached Victorian (1830) cottages. A superb exhibition 'Discover the City' opened in 1986.

Easter–31 Oct Tues–Sat: 10.30–12.30, 2.00–4.00
Sun: 2.00–4.00

£ⓒ🚌... P ⚬ 🔥 ▄ 🏠 ➤ WC
🖼 🛗 🖐 ⓒ

HAMPSHIRE

Upper Hamble Country Park

Manor Farm
Postel Brook Lane
Botley
Southampton, Hants
☎ 0489 787055

Juntion 8 off M27

≋ 🚌 Botley

Working farm of bygone age with traditional buildings, farm animals, machinery and equipment, farmhouse, garden and church. 400 acres with gravel and grass paths.

Easter–Oct: Mon–Sun 10am–5pm
Nov–Easter: Sun 10am–dusk

£©🚌✕♿Ⓟ♿▬🏛➤🚻⇒
♿WC🏠¶️🗿♿◆🐟☕𝒸♿

The New Forest Owl Sanctuary

Crow Lane
Crow
Ringwood, Hants., BH24 3EA
☎ 0425 476487

A31, B3477

🚌 Ringwood

100 avaries and flying displays. Owl hospital. Lectures on birds of prey. Level and concrete paths.

Jan–Dec

£©🚌✕🗿♿Ⓟ♿⇒♿WC¶️
🗿♿♿

Marwell Zoological Park

Colden Common
Winchester, Hants., SO21 1JH
☎ 0962 777406

Winchester – take road to Bishop's Waltham

≋ 🚌 Eastleigh

One of Britain's largest collections of endangered wildlife set in 100 acres of beautiful Hampshire parkland. No guide dogs or dogs. Gravel and paved paths.

Jan–Dec: Mon–Sun: from 10am

£©🚌♿Ⓟ♿➤🚻⇒🚐▪️♿
WC🏠¶️🗿♿◆☕𝒸♿

Mary Rose Trust

College Road
HM Naval Base
Portsmouth, Hants., PO1 3LX
☎ 0705 750521

Portsmouth M275

 ≋ 🚌 Portsmouth Harbour

Henry VIII's great warship is an awe–inspiring sight. Discover her treasures in the exhibition. Mostly paved paths but some cobbled.

1 Jan–28 Feb: 10.30am–5pm
1 Mar–3 Oct: 10am–5.30pm
1 Nov–31 Dec: 10.30am–5pm

£©🚌✕☀️◗♿Ⓟ♿➤🚻⇒
♿WC🏠¶️🗿♿🎧◆☕𝒸♿

Gurkha Museum

Peninsula Barracks
Romsey Rd, Winchester
Hants., SO23 8TS
☎ 0962 842832

A33/M3

≋ Winchester

The Gurkha Musuem tells the exciting story of the Gurkhas from Nepal and their involvement in world wars up to the present day.

Tue–Sat & BH: 10am–5pm

£©🚌✕☀️◗♿Ⓟ🅿️♿▬🎏
➤🚻♿WC¶️🗿♿◆☕𝒸

Breamore House & Museums

Nr Fordingbridge, Hants., SP6 2DF
☎ 0725 22468

A338 Salisbury

🚌 Salisbury

Elizabethan Manor House 1583, with fine pictures and furniture. Countryside Museum gives an insight into the days when a village was self sufficient. Carriage museum. 4 acres with concrete and tarmaced paths.

Apr: Tue/Wed/Sun
May–Jul: Tue/Wed/Thu/Sat/Sun/All holidays
Aug: Every day
Sep: Tue/Wed/Thu/Sat/Sun/All holidays
Time: 2pm–5.30pm

£©🚌♿Ⓟ♿👐▬🏛➤▪️♿
WC🤸🗿♿♿☕

The Royal Hussars Museum

Peninsula Barracks
Winchester, Hants., SO23 8TS
☎ 0962 863751

Winchester, Romsey Road

≋ 🚐 Winchester

The museum tells the story of two Cavalry Regiments (10th & 11th Hussars) from their raising in 1715, through amalgamation in 1969 to form the Royal Hussars, to the present day.

Tue–Fri: 10am–4pm
Sat/Sun/BH: 12 noon–4pm

£©🚐✳ 🅿 P � 🙌 ➤ ⛼ WC

🥾

Jenkyn Place Gardens

Bentley
Nr Farnham, Hants., GU10 5LU
☎ 0420 23118

A31 between Farnham and Alton

≋ 🚐 Bentley

Beautiful and interesting 6 acre garden with paved paths. Only a few shallow steps. House not open.

9 Apr–6 Sep Thurs–Sun

£🚐 🅿 ✗ � ➤ ⌐ WC 🌳 🔵

Airborne Forces Museum

Browning Barracks
Aldershot, Hants., GU11 2BU
☎ 0252 349619

Aldershot

≋ 🚐 Aldershot

Displays, models and equipment of the Parachute forces from 1940 onwards. Paved paths.

Jan–Dec: Tue–Sun: 10am–4.30pm

£©🚐✳ 🅿 P �🍰 🙌 🏛 ➤ ⌐ ⇒

👁 ⛼ WC 🥾 🌳 🔵

Petersfield Physic Garden

High St
Petersfield, Hants

Petersfield on A3

≋ 🚐 Petersfield

A garden recreated into a C17th physic garden, using plants and layout as at that period. Gravel paths.

Jan–Dec: Mon–Sun: 9am–5pm

F🚐✳ P � ➤ ⌐ WC 🌳 🔵

Ocean Village

Canutes Pavilion
Southampton, Hants., SO1 1JS
☎ 0703 228353

Southampton

≋ 🚐 Southampton

Extensive waterfront speciality retail complex with numerous, restaurants, bars and cafes, all under glass. Largest multiplex cinema in the south, many weekend events throughout spring/summer. 75 acres with paved paths.

Jan–Dec: Mon–Sun: 10.30am–8pm

F🚐✳ P🔵 🅿 �🙌 ➤ ⌐ ⛼ WC ♿

🍽 🥾 🌳 🔵

Regimental Museum of the Royal Corps of Transport

Buller Barracks
Aldershot, Hants., GU11 2BX
☎ 0252 348837

Aldershot via M3–A325

≋ 🚐 Aldershot

The story of the Royal Corps of Transport, The Royal Army Service Corps and their predecessors from 1799 to the present day. Displays of uniforms, models, medals and militaria with photographs and models of military transport.

Jan–Dec: Mon–Fri: 9am–12.30pm and 1.30pm–4pm
Closed: BH's

F🚐✳ P �🍰 🙌 ➤ ⌐ 🍴 WC

🥾 🔵 🖐 ©

Fort Nelson

Down End Rd
Fareham, Hants., PO17 6AN
☎ 0329 233734

Fareham A27

≋ Portchester

Impressive Victorian artillery fort, restored and re-armed with correct ordnance and containing Royal armouries artillery collection. Grass, concrete, gravel and paved paths. Access being improved.

Easter–31 Oct: Sat/Sun/BH Mons/: 12noon–4.30pm

£©🚐✳ P🔵 🅿 ✗ À🍰 🏛 ➤ ⌐

🍴 ⛼ WC 🎭 🌳 ©

HAMPSHIRE

Army School of Physical Training Museum

Queens Ave
Aldershot, Hants., GU11 2LB
☎ 0252 347131

Aldershot

≋ 🚌 Aldershot/Farnborough

The museum covers fitness, sport, famous personalities, especially during world and other wars. 2 acres with paved paths.

Jan–Dec: Mon–Fri 8.30am–12noon
2.00pm–4.00pm
Term dates may vary please tel.

F🚐P 🗡 ⚓🔥➤wc ‖ ⚓ 🖐

The Sir Harold Hillier Gardens and Arboretum

Jermyns Lane
Ampfield
Nr Romsey, Hants., SO51 0QA
☎ 0794 68787

3 miles NE of Romsey off A31

🚌 Romsey/Winchester

The largest collection of different trees and shrubs in the British Isles, providing colour and interest throughout the four seasons. 160 acres with gravel, paved and grass paths.

Mar–Nov: Mon–Sun inc BH 10.30am–6pm
Dec–Feb: Mon–Fri 10.30am–5pm

£©🚐🅿 🅿 ⚓➤ ⌐ ⊹ ⚓ᵂᶜwc ‖

Yateley Common Country Park

The Rangers House
Cricket Hill Lane
Yateley
Camberley, Hants., GU17 7BB
☎ 0252 874346

N of A30, W of Blackwater

430 acres of heathland, woodland and lakes. Many rare and interesting species of wildlife. Fishing available by pre–booking.

Jan–Dec: Mon–Sun

F🚐☀ 🅿 ⌐ ⊹ wc⚓

Southsea Castle

Clarence Esplanade
Southsea, Hants., PO5 3PA
☎ 0705 827261

Portsmouth A3

≋ 🚌 Portsmouth

C16th fort built by Henry VIII (1545) to protect the coasts from foreign invasion.

Displays a variety of artillery. Exhibition on the Military History of Portsmouth and life in the castle. Audio–visual show. Underground tunnels and panoramic views of the Solent.

Jan–Dec: Mon–Sun 10.30am–5.30pm

£©🚐☀🗡🅿 P 🗡 ⚓🔺🏢 ⌐
⊹ 🆆🅲 ⚓⚗🎧🖐⚓

D–Day Museum & Overlord Embroidery

Clarence Esplanade
Southsea, Hants., PO5 3NT
☎ 0705 827261

Portsmouth A3

≋ The Hard 🚌 Palmerston Rd

Main feature is 'The Story of Portsmouth' exhibition which uses objects, paintings, video and series of room settings to show life in Portsmouth from the C17th to the 1950's. Furniture, ceramics and glass from the C16th–C20th and a contemporary crafts gallery with changing exhibitions.

Jan–Dec: Mon–Sun 10am–5.30pm

£©🚐☀🗡 �\ 🅿 🅿 ⚓➤ ⌐ ⚓ᵂᶜ
🆆🅲 ⚓🔺🎧⚗🖐

City Museum & Art Gallery

Museum Rd
Old Portsmouth, Hants., PO1 2LJ
☎ 0705 827261

Portsmouth A3

≋ The Hard 🚌 Cambridge Junction

Opened in 1984 to commemorate the D–Day landings. The centre–piece of the museum is the 'Overlord Embroidery', 34 panels long with personal Soundalive commentary. Award–winning audio visual show. Other displays of the 1944 period including weapons and military vehicles.

Jan–Dec: Mon–Sun 10.30am–5.30pm

£©🚐☀🗡🅿 🅿 ⚓🏢➤ ⌐ ⊹
⚓ᵂᶜ wc ⚓🖐⚓

Aldershot Military Museum

Evelyn Woods Rd
Queens Avenue
Aldershot, Hants., GU11 2LG
☎ 0252 314598

Off A325 1m S of Farnborough

≋ North Camp, Aldershot & Farnborough Bus

A look behind the scenes at the soldiers life in the home of the British Army. Local history gallery. Gallery of Canadian Army in Aldershot and Europe in two World Wars.

Mar–Oct: 10am–5pm
Nov–Feb: 10am–4.30pm

£©🚌⚹P♿➤♿wc🖼🌳

New Forest Museum & Visitor Centre
High Street
Lyndhurst, Hants., SO43 7NY
☎ 0703 283914
Lyndhurst, A35
Audio visual show and exhibition displays telling the story of the New Forest – it's history, traditions, characters and wildlife.
Jan–Dec: Mon–Sun 10am

£🚌⚹♿P♿➤♿wc🖼♿

Winchester Cathedral
The Close
Winchester, Hants., SO23 9LS
☎ 0962 853137
Winchester, A33/M3
≥ 🚌 Winchester
Founded in 1079, second longest nave in Europe. Treasures; C12th illuminated Winchester bible, Norman font, medieval wall paintings, Triforium Gallery, etc.
Jan–Dec: Mon–Sun 7.30am–6.30pm

F🚌⚹🎧P🏷♿🔊📺➤🔺
🍴wc🖼🎪♿🎨🎁♿

The Vyne
Sherborne St John
Basingstoke, Hants., RG26 5DX
☎ 0256 881337
Basingstoke
≥ Bramley & Basingstoke 🚌 Basingstoke
Early Tudor House of Diaper brickwork, built by William Sandys between 1500 and 1520. Important C18th alterations to interior. Fine peaceful gardens.
Apr–Oct: Mon–Sun 12.30pm–5pm

£©🚌⚹🔊🏷🔊📺➤🔺♿wc
🍴🖼🎪🎨🎁♿

Ludshott Common NT
Nr Grayshot, Hants.,
Off B3004 at Grayshott
Viewpoint with parking places for less able visitors in Dunelm car park.

The Watercress Line Steam Railway
The Railway Station
Alresford, Hants., SO24 9JG
☎ 0962 734200/733810
Alresford or Alton. Just off A31
≥ Alton
Full–size steam railway operating 10m from Alresford to Alton. Powerful steam locomotives hauling trains through beautiful Hampshire countryside.
Please ring for 1992 times

£©🚌⚹P♿P♿➤♿wc🍴🖼🎨🎁

Broadlands
Romsey, Hants., SO51 9ZD
☎ 0794 516878
Romsey A35 bypass
≥ 🚌 Romsey
Palladian mansion in beautiful landscaped setting on banks of River Test. Visitors may view House, Riverside Lawns, Mountbatten Exhibitions and audio–visual presentation. 27 acres.
Easter–30 Sep: Sat–Thu 10am–4pm

£©🚌⚹P♿P🔊📺➤♿wc🍴
🖼🎪♿🎨

Spetchley Park
Worcester, Worcs. WR5 1RS
☎ 090565 213/224
Worcester, A422 to Stratford–upon–Avon
≥ 🚌 Worcester
The Berkeley family have owned the house since 1605. House not open. The garden covers about 30 acres with gravel paths.
1 Apr–30 Sep: Tue–Fri – 11am–5pm
Sundays – 2pm–5pm
BH Mons – 11am–5pm

£©🚌⚹P♿➤🔺wc✖♿♿

Abbey Dore Court Garden
Nr Hereford, HR2 0AD
☎ 0981 240419
Hereford A465 to Abergavenny
River and walled garden with shrubs and hardy perennials. Pool & rock garden. Fern border and circular herb garden. 4 acres

with gravel and grass paths.
3rd Sat Mar–3rd Sun Oct: Thurs–Tues
11am–6pm

£🚐✖ 🅿 ♿➤ ⌐ ➕♿ᵂᶜ wc ‖ 🦞
🏕🖐

Wyre Visitor Centre FC

Callow Hill
Nr Bewdley
Hereford & Worcs
☎ 0299 266303

Bewdley – A456 to Callow Hill
≋ Bewdley (Severn Valley Railway connects)

The beautiful Wyre Forest provides a visitors centre, observation hide and all ability forest trail designed for wheelchair users. 2000 acres with rolled gravel paths.

Visitors Centre: Mon–Sun 11am–4pm
All Ability Trail: Always open

F🚐✖ 🅿 ♿➤ ⌐⇒♿ᵂᶜ wc ‖ 🦞
🏕♿🎧🐟🖐🄯

Hereford City Museum & Art Gallery

Broad Street
Hereford. HR4 9AU
☎ 0432 268121 x 207

Hereford
≋ 🚐 Hereford

Natural history, archaeology and local history. Art gallery includes collections of 19th century watercolours and works by local artists.

Tue/Wed/Fri: 10am–6pm
Thurs: 10am–5pm
Sat: 10am–5pm (summer)
10am–4pm (winter)

F🚐✖ P ♿ ⬛🏰♿ᵂᶜ wc 🦞🏕♿
🐟🖐🄯♿ᴸ

The Jubilee Park

Symonds–Yat West
Herefordshire, HR9 6DA
☎ 0600 890360

Between Monmouth, Ross–on–Wye and Forest of Dean
🚐

A unique 'hands–on' interactive Museum of Mazes provides touch, sound and vision experience of history, magic and mystery of mazes and puzzler.

Feb–Dec: Mon–Sun 11am–5.30pm

£🄯🚐✖ 🛶 🅿♿ ♿👉➤ ⌐♿ᵂᶜ wc
🏠‖🦞🏕🖐

Eastnor Castle & Deer Park

Nr Ledbury
Herefordshire, HR8 1RD
☎ 0684 567103

Ledbury A438
≋ Ledbury

Georgian castle in fairytale setting. Deer park, lake and arboretum. Tapestries, fine art, armour and furniture. Italianate and Gothic interiors.

May–Mid Oct: Sun & BH Mon 2pm–5pm
Jul–Aug: Tue–Thu 2pm–5pm

£🄯🚐✖ 🅿 ◢🏰 ⌐ ➕wc 🎎🦞
🏕♿ ♿ᴸ

Clent Hills NT

Nr Birmingham
Wheelchair path from Nimmings car park to viewpoint (½m)

Hergest Croft Gardens

Kington
Herefordshire, HR5 3EG
☎ 0544 230160

Kington A44

Rhododendron Valley and old fashioned kitchen garden with trees, shrubs and borders for the enthusiastic gardener. 50 acres with gravel and grass paths.

Jan–Dec: Mon–Sun 1.30pm–6.30pm

£🚐✖ 🅿 ♿🐾➤ ⌐➕‖ 🦞
♿🄯

Hereford & Worcester County Musuem

Hartlebury Castle
Hartlebury
Nr Kidderminster. Worcs., DY11 7XZ
☎ 0299 250416/250560

On B4193 from Stourport to Kidderminster
≋ 🚐 Hartlebury

The museum occupies the north wing of historic Hartlebury Castle, the home of the Bishop of Worcester. 2½ acres with gravel and paved paths.

1 Mar–30 Nov: Mon–Thu – 10am–5pm
Fri&Sun – 2pm–5pm
Closed Good Fri.

£ 🚐 ✕ ♿ 🅿 ♿ 🏛 ➔ ⊣ ⊹ wc ¶
♿ 🌲 ♿ 🖐 Ⓒ

Severn Steamboat Co
Riverside Walk
Stourport, Worcs., DY13 3AW
☎ 02993 71177
Kidderminster
≋ 🚌 Kidderminster
Travel up the river to Stoney Bottom then
downstream to the historic Red Stone
Caves. 3 acres with paved paths.
Apr–Sep

£Ⓒ🚐✕♿🅿♿⬛🏛➔⊣⊹
♿wc ¶ ♿🌲♿

Royal Worcester
The Royal Porcelain Works
Severn Street
Worcs. WR1 2NE
☎ 0905 23221
Worcester Centre
≋ Forgate Street
Britain's oldest manufacturer of china and
porcelain. World's largest collection of
Royal Worcester. Dyson Perrins Museum.
Factory tour not suitable for wheelchair
users.
Mon–Sat: 9am–5.30pm
Closed: Easter BH's and Christmas Day

F🚐✕♿🅿♿♿⊣⊹♿wc 🐚
¶ ♿♿◆Ⓒ♿

Treasures of Tenbury
Burford House Gardens
Tenbury Wells, Worcs., WR15 8HQ
☎ 0584 810777
Tenbury Wells, A456
≋ 🚌 Worcester & Ludlow
Plant centre offers one of the widest
selection of plants in the area. National
collection of Clematis with 200 varieties to
choose from. 4 acres with paved and gravel
paths in plant centre.
Gardens: 16 Mar–20 Oct: Mon–Sat
10am–5.00pm
Sun 1pm–5.00pm
Winter: Mon–Fri by appointment
Plant centre: Jan–Dec Mon–Sat 10am–6pm

£Ⓒ🚐🍃♿♿➔⊣♿wc ¶ ♿
♿Ⓒ

HEREFORD & WORCESTER

Areley Kings Parish Church & Church House
Stourport on Severn
Stourport, Worcs.
☎ 029 93 2868 or 2898
Stourport on Severn
≋ 🚌 Kidderminster
Church associated with early English writer,
Layamon. Beautiful hill top site with views of
Severn Valley. Church House has 15 steps
to main entrance. 5 acres with tarmaced
paths.
By appointment

F✕♿🅿♿◢➔⊣wc ✖♿♿
🖐♿

Stourport Steamer Co
56 Heightington Place
Stourport, Worcs., DY13 0BE
☎ 02993 2306
Next to Stourport Road Bridge
🚌 Stourport
River trips on the beautiful River Severn with
central heating.
Mar–Dec Tel. for times

£Ⓒ🚐✕♿🅿♿⊣wc ¶ ♿🖐

Kidderminster Parish Church
St Mary & All Saints'
Churchfields
Kidderminster, Worcs., DY10 2JN
☎ 0562 751923/823265
Off A456 in Kidderminster
≋ Kidderminster
Large town church mainly perpendicular
style with tower. Rebuilt Chantry adjacent.
Good C15th monuments and brasses.
Chancel recently reordered. Paved paths.
May–Sep: 9am–5pm

F🚐✕♿🅿♿➔⊣⊹wc🌲🖐

Droitwich Heritage Centre
St Richard's House
Victoria Square
Droitwich, Worcs., WR9 8DS
☎ 0905 774312
Worcester A38
≋ 🚌 Droitwich
A unique Spa town tracing 2000 years of
salt making history. Touring exhibitions,
souvenirs and brass rubbing. Paved paths.
Winter: Mon–Sat 9am–4pm
Summer: Mon–Sun 9am–5pm
Sat 9am–4pm

HEREFORD & WORCESTER

F🚌🖈🐾♿P♿P♿➤🚻WC🖼️👨‍👩‍👧
♿©

Wye Valley Farm Park
Goodrich
Ross–on–Wye
Herefordshire, HR9 6JN
☎ 0600 890296
Follow signs from Goodrich
Collection of rare farm animals in traditional stone farm buildings. No guide dogs. 30 acres with gravel paths.
Easter–31 Oct: Mon–Sun 10am–5pm

£🚌P♿➤🚻🍴WC🖼️👨‍👩‍👧©

Worcester Cathedral
10a College St
Worcester, WR5 2BJ
☎ 0905 28854
Worcester
🚆 Foregate Street
King Johns Tomb, Norman Crypt with Pilgrim exhibition, C14th Tower, C12th Chapter House, acclaimed choir, touch and hearing centre. Paved paths.
Jan–Dec: Mon–Sun: 7.30am–6pm
BH's: 10am–6pm

F🚌🖈🐾♿P♿🔉🔌🚻⇒👁️♿
WC🍴🖼️👨‍👩‍👧♿🎧◆🐕♿

West Midland Safari & Leisure Park
Spring Grove
Bewdley, Worcs., DY12 1LF
☎ 0299 402114
A456
195 acres of parkland with rare and exotic animals, pets corner, sealion show, reptile house, parrot show, and amusement area with fairground rides. Grassed car parking.
Jan–Dec: 10am–5pm

£©🚌🖈♿P♿➤🚻WC🍴🖼️
👨‍👩‍👧🎧🐕©

Bewdley Museum
The Shambles,
Load St
Bewdley, Worcs., DY12 2AE
☎ 0299 403573
Bewdley A456
🚌 Birmingham

The Shambles is an 18th Century row of butcher's shops, which is now a folk museum. The emphasis is on crafts and industries of Wyre Forest. Paved paths.
1 Mar–30 Nov: Mon–Sat: 10am–5.30pm
Sun: 2pm–5.30pm

£©🚌🖈🐾♿🚻🍴WC🖼️🐕

Harvington Hall
Kidderminster, Worcs., DY10 4LR
☎ 0562 777267
Kidderminster/Bromsgrove A448/450
🚆🚌 Kidderminster
Moated medieval and Elizabethan manor house with secret hiding places and rare wall paintings. ¾ of an acre with gravel paths.
1 Mar–31 Oct: Mon–Sun
Closed Good Fri

£©🚌🖈P♿🏛️➤🚻🍴♿WC
🍴🖼️👨‍👩‍👧♿🐕©

HERTFORDSHIRE

Fairlands Valley Park
Six Hills Way
Stevenage, Herts., SG2 0BL
☎ 0438 353241
Stevenage, A1M Junc 7 and A602
🚆🚌 Stevenage
The park contains paddling pools, cafe, licensed bar, sailing and fishing facilities . 150 acres with tarmac and paved paths through open grassland.
Jan–Dec: Mon–Sun 9am–1hr before dusk

F©🚌🖈P♿➤🚻♿WC🍴👨‍👩‍👧
🐕©

Standalone Farm
Wilbury Road
Letchworth, Herts., SG6 4JN
☎ 0462 686775
A1M (London/North) A505 (Luton/Royston)
🚆🚌 Letchworth
Small working farm. Two shire horses, sheep, cattle, pigs and poultry. Milking demonstrations. Wildfowl area and hide for disabled people. 170 acres with concrete areas, gravel and paved paths.
Easter–31 Oct: Mon–Sun 11am–5pm

£©🚌✈ P ♿👤☛➜ ⊓ ♿ WC
⛺ 🍴 🎣 ♿☎♿

Rye House Marsh Reserve RSPB

Rye House
Rye Rd
Hoddesdon, Herts., EN11 0EJ
☎ 0992 460031
Hoddesdon, A10
≋ Rye House

A site of special scientific interest alongside the River Lee, which is one of the main educational reserves for the RSPB. 13 acres with gravel paths. Some hides inaccessible.

Jan–Dec

£©🚌✈ P ♿ ⊓ ▪️ WC ♿ ♿

Watford Museum

194 High St
Watford, Herts., WD1 2HG
☎ 0923 32297
Watford A411 – close to M1 and M25
≋ 🚆 Watford

Watford museum concentrates on local history with special reference to the brewing and printing industries. It has an excellent art collection and a regularly changing programme of temporary exhibitions. Archaeological and art galleries inaccessible to wheelchair users.

Jan–Dec: Mon–Sat 10am–5pm

F🚌� P♿ P ♿☛ 🏛 ⊓ ▪️ ♿ WC
🎣 ♿🤲♿

St Albans Organ Museum

320 Camp Rd
St Albans, Herts., AL1 5PB
☎ 0727 51557/869693
St Albans
≋ 🚆 St Albans

A permanently playing exhibition of mechanical musical instruments: organs, pianos, musical boxes and two theatre organs.

Sun: 2pm–4.30pm
All other times by arrangement

£©🚌✈ P ♿👤☛➜ ⊓ WC 🍴
🎣🤲♿♿

Westminster Lodge Sports Centre

Holywell Hill
St Albans, Herts., AL1 2DL
☎ 0727 46031
St Albans
≋ 🚆 St Albans

Lesiure and track facilities situated next to large park, (lakes, playing fields, Roman wall remains, etc). Part of old Verulamia. 200 acres with paved and gravel paths

Mon–Sun: 8am–6pm

£©🚌✈ P♿ P 🏛➜ ⊓ ⇒ 👁 ▪️
♿ WC ⛺♿♿🤲♿♿

The Forum Entertainment Centre

Lemsford Rd
Hatfield, Herts., AL10 0EB
☎ 0707 271217
Hatfield
≋ 🚆 Hatfield

Public entertainment centre offering arts, cinema, pantomime, international artistes, dinner dances and drama in an all year round programme.

Box office: Mon–Sat 10am–6pm + ½ hour before performances

£©🚌✈ 🎣 P ♿➜ ⊓ ▪️ ♿ WC
♿♿ ©

Stevenage Museum

St George's Way
Stevenage, Herts., SG1 1XX
☎ 0438 354292
Stevenage
≋ 🚆 Stevenage

Displays which tell the history of Stevenage from the Stone Age to the present day.

Mon–Sat: 10am–5pm
Closed : Good Fri

F🚌✈ P♿➜♿ WC 🎣♿

Hitchin Museum & Art Gallery

Paynes Park
Hitchin, Herts., SG5 1EQ
A505, A602
≋ 🚆 Hitchin

Small museum with displays of social history and fashion. Reconstructed Victorian chemist shop, physic garden. Art exhibitions change monthly. Costume and chemist shop on first floor.

Jan–Dec: Mon–Sat 10am–5pm

HERTFORDSHIRE

Sun 2pm–4.30pm
Closed : BH's

F 🚌 🐕 P♿ P ♿ ⬛ 🏠 WC ♿ 🤝

Stevenage Gardens

Frobisher Drive
Stevenage, Herts., SG2 0HH
☎ 0438 725416

A1(M) Stevenage/Hitchin

≋ 🚍 Stevenage

Stevenage Lodge is intended to be a focus
for all residents of the town who have an
interest in Horticulture. 1½ acres with gravel
paths.

Jan–Dec: Mon–Fri 9am–5pm
Sat–Sun 2pm–4pm

F 🚌 🐕 P ♿ 🛏 ⬛ 🏠 → ⊣ ♿WC WC
♿ 🕐

Verulamium Museum

St Michael's
St Albans, Herts., AL3 4SW
☎ 0727 866100 x 2912

St Albans

≋ 🚍 St Albans

Site museum for Verulamium, major Roman
British city. Informative museum of
everyday life in Roman Britain.

Mar–Oct: Mon–Sat 10am–5.30pm
Sun 2pm–5.30pm
Nov–Feb: Mon–Sat 10am–4pm
Sun 2pm–4pm

£ © 🚌 🐕 P ♿ ♿WC WC ♿ 🌳 ♿ 🤝

Aldenham Country Park

Park Office
Dagger Lane
Elstree, Herts., WD6 3AT
☎ 081 953 9602

Boreham Wood

≋ 🚍 Elstree

Fields and woodland surrounding an old
British waterway compensating reservoir.
Rare breeds of farm animals. 175 acres with
gravel paths around the lakeside and
headbank walk.

Jan–Dec: Mon–Sun 9am to 6pm Summer
9am to 4pm Winter

£ © 🚌 🐕 P♿ P ♿ → WC 🌳 🕐

Shaw's Corner NT

Ayot St Lawrence
Nr Welwyn, Herts., AL6 9BX
☎ 0438 820307

Welwyn Garden City A1

Home of playwright George Bernard Shaw,
where he lived for 46 years. The small house
remains exactly as he left it with literary and
personal relics. 3½ acres with gravel paths.

Jan–Dec: Wed–Sat: 2pm–5.30pm
Sun: 12noon–5.30pm

£ 🚌 🐕 P 🛏 ⬛ ⊣ ♿WC WC ♿ ♿ 🌿

Mill Green Museum & Mill

Mill Green
Hatfield, Herts., AL9 5PD
☎ 0707 271362

Between Hatfield and Welwyn Garden City
at the junction of the A1000 and A414

≋ Hatfield

A fully restored and operating C18th waterpowered corn mill. In the Miller's house next
door, is a small local history museum.

Jan–Dec: Tue–Fri 10am–5pm
Sat,Sun & BH 2pm–5pm

F 🐕 P♿ P ♿ 🏠 → ⊣ ⬛ WC ♿ 🌳
♿ 🤝

Welwyn Roman Baths

The By Pass
Old Welwyn, Herts., AL6 9HT
☎ 0707 271362

In a vault under the A1(M). Access from the
central roundabout off Welwyn by pass.

≋ Welwyn North

A C3rd AD bath house, the only visible
feature of a Roman Villa. The site is
remarkably well preserved. Finds from the
villa and other local sites are also on display.

Jan–Dec: Thu–Sun & BH 2pm–5pm
Other times by appointment

£ © 🚌 🐕 P ♿ 👉 → ⊣ WC ♿
🌳 ♿

Paradise Wildlife Park

White Stubbs Lane
Herts., EN10 7QA
☎ 0992 468001

A1170 Broxbourne

≋ 🚍 Broxbourne

Compact leisure park and zoo. Various
facilites include woodland railway.

Jan–Dec: Mon–Sun 10am–6pm or dusk

£ © 🚌 🐕 P♿ 🅿 ♿ ➤ ⊣ ♿ᵂᶜ WC ⛪
🍴 🛅 🧑‍🦽 🅱 🎧 ⊙ ♿ᴸ

Ashridge NT
Nr Berkhamstead
Herts.,

Nearly 4000 acres of wood, heath and down on the eastern part of the Chilterns. Near the Bridgewater Monument are walks suitable for wheelchair users. Improvements are planned, as some access routes are difficult in bad weather.

➤ ⇒ ♿ᵂᶜ 🍴 🛅 ♿ᴸ

The Gardens of the Rose
The Royal National Rose Society
Chiswell Green
St Albans, Herts., AL2 3NR
☎ 0727 50461

2m S of St Albans on B4630

≈ 🚉 St Albans

The world famous gardens contain some 30,000 roses of all types. Holds the International Rose Trials and other demonstrations and displays. 20 acres with Hoggin paths.

13 Jun–18 Oct: Mon–Sat 9am–5pm
Sun & BH Mon 10am–6pm

£ © 🚌 🐕 P♿ 🅿 ➤ ⊣ ♿ᵂᶜ WC 🍴 🛅
🧑‍🦽 ⊙ 🐕

HUMBERSIDE
Normanby Hall Country Park
Normanby
Scunthorpe, S. Humbs., DN15 9HU
☎ 0724 720588

Scunthorpe

350 acres of parkland and countryside. Regency mansion and farming museum. Special events. Guided walks and tours available. Nature trails planned for elderly and disabled people in 1992.

Park: Jan–Dec Mon–Sun Dawn–Dusk
Hall: Mar–Nov Mon–Fri 11am–5pm
Sat/Sun 1pm–5pm
Farm Museum: Mar–Nov Mon–Sun
1pm–5pm

F 🚌 P♿ 🅿 ♿ 🦮 🚾 🏚 ➤ ⊣ ⇒ ♿ᵂᶜ
WC ⛪ 🍴 🛅 🧑‍🦽 🅱 🎧

Elsham Hall Country Park
Elsham
Nr Brigg, S. Humbs., DN20 0QZ
☎ 0652 688698

Brigg, A15

≈ Barnaby

Park facilities include 2 special restaurants; working craft centre; animal farm; carp lake; wild butterfly walkway for wheelchairs; falconry centre with courses for handicapped people. 36 acres with gravel and paved paths. Special wooded walkway

Easter Sat–Mid Sep: Mon–Sun 11am–5pm
Mid Sep–Easter: Sun 11am–4pm

£ © 🚌 🐕 👓 P♿ 🅿 ♿ ➤ ⊣ ⇒ 👁
♿ᵂᶜ WC ⛪ 🗡 🛅 🧑‍🦽 🅱 🎧 🐟 🖐 ⊙

Burton Agnes Hall
Estate Office
Burton Agnes
Driffield, Humbs., YO25 0ND
☎ 0262 89 324

Bridlington or Driffield A166

≈ 🚌 Bridlington or Driffield

Elizabethan House containing carvings, furniture, impressionist and modern paintings. Potager and jungle gardens. Campanula collection, shrub and herbaceous borders. Maze.

1 Apr–31 Oct: Mon–Sun: 11am–5pm
Groups by app. outside these times

£ © 🚌 🐕 🅿 ♿ 🦮 🚾 🏚 ➤ ⊣ ⇒
🍴🔥 ♿ᵂᶜ WC 🍴 🛅 🧑‍🦽 🖐 ⊙

Thornton Abbey
Ulceby, S. Humberside, DN39 6TU
☎ 0469 540357

Barton–upon–Humber, A1077

≈ Thornton Abbey

Features one of the largest Gatehouses in the country. Founded in 1139 by Augustinian Order. Closed 1539 in the suppression of Monastries. 5 acres with gravel paths.

Oct–Maun Thu: Sat–Sun 10am–4pm
Gd Fri–Sep: Mon–Sun 10am–6pm pls.tel.to check

£ © 🚌 🐕 🅿 ◣ ◢ 🏚 ➤ ⊣ 🆆🅲 🛅
🧑‍🦽 🧑‍🦽 🖐

HUMBERSIDE

Humber Bridge Country Park

Hessle, N. Humbs.
☎ 0482 641989

Hull A63

≋ Hessle 🚌 Hull

Situated next to Humber Bridge – 48 acres of meadows, woodland, ponds, cliffs and an old mill from when the area was a chalk quarry. Compacted limestone paths.

Jan–Dec: Mon–Sun

Bempton Cliffs RSPB

Nr Bridlington
Humbs.

Signposted from Bempton village on B1229 from Flamborough to Filey.

Wheelchair access along surfaced path from car park to seabird observation points on cliff-top. Special disabled access days are arranged each summer: dates on application.
Warden: c/o The Post Office, Bempton, Nr.Bridlington.

Blacktoft Sands RSPB

Goole,
Humbs.
☎ 040 584 294

Signposted from Goole by–pass off Junc.36 of M62

Four hides overlooking the waterfowl lagoons and reedbeds. Accessible to wheelchair users. Cars may be driven to them by arrangement.

ISLE OF WIGHT

St Helen's Duver NT

Isle of Wight

A wide spit of sand and shingle, previously a golf course, stretching across the mouth of Bembridge Harbour, popular for its plants and birds. There is a ½m nature trail around the Duver suitable for accompanied wheelchair users which begins and ends at the car park. An information board and leaflet about the nature trail are planned.

Hanover Point & Afton Down NT

Isle of Wight

Viewpoints at car parks, but wheelchair users are advised that the car park surface at Afton Down is not ideal. The car park at Hanover Point is tarmaced, but there is no wheelchair access to the beach.

Ventnor Heritage Centre

11 Spring Hill
Ventnor, IoW., PO38 1PE
☎ 0983 855407

Centre of town

🚌 Ventnor

Built in 1904 as high class furniture showroom. In June 1987, it was opened as a Heritage centre. New exhibition annually.

Jan–Dec: Mon–Sat: 10am–12noon & 2pm–4pm
Closed: Wed & Sat pm & Sun
Jul–Sep: Tue & Thur only 2pm–9pm

Arreton Country Craft Village

Arreton
Newport, IoW., PO30 3AA
☎ 0983 528353

Newport–Sandown Road

🚌 Newport

The Island's oldest established working craft centre within a picturesque 'village' setting, where more than a dozen local craftsmen have their workshops. 3 acres with paved paths.

Jan–Dec: Mon–Sun 9.30am–5pm

Alum Bay Glass Ltd

Alum Bay, IoW., PO39 0BL
☎ 0983 753473

Yarmouth, B3322

🚌

Visitors may watch the glassmaking and purchase handmade glassware from the extensive shop. There is also an historical display of glassmaking. Paved paths.

Oct–Easter: Mon–Sun – 9.30am–5pm
Easter–Oct: Mon–Sun – 9.30am–5.30pm
No glassmaking on Saturdays

Flamingo Park

Springvale
Seaview, IoW., PO34 5AP
☎ 0983 612153

Ryde & Seaview

Flamingo Park overlooks the Solent and contains many hundreds of birds, including breeding flamingos. Many birds are tame and will feed from the hand. No dogs allowed. 10½ acres with gravel paths.

Easter–Apr: 2pm–5.30pm
May–30 Sep: 10am–5.30pm
Oct: 2pm–5pm

£©🚐🚌🐕‍🦺 P ♿ ➔ ⊓ ⇒ ♿ wc ⛲ 🍴
🌳🏕♿🤝♿

Brickfields Horse Country

Newnham Road
Binstead, IoW., PO33 3TH
☎ 0983 615116/66801

Ryde, A3054

🚌 during season

Working shire horses, miniature horse stud, parades, carriage rides, guided tours of heritage museums/carriage collection and more. 10 acres with concrete and gravel paths.

Jan–Dec: Mon–Sun 10am–5pm

£©🚐🐕‍🦺 P♿ P ♿ ➔ ⊓ ♿ wc ⛲
🍴🌳🏕♿🤝◎♿

Ventnor Botanic Garden

Undercliffe Drive
Ventnor, IoW., PO38 1UL
☎ 0983 855397

Ventnor A3055

🚆 Shanklin 🚌 Ventnor

22 acres of palm, mediterranean, New Zealand, medicinal and scree gardens; temperature house including many plants endangered in the wild. Gravel and paved paths.

Temperate House: Good Fri–Oct: Mon–Sun 10am–5pm
Nov–Good Fri: Tue–Thu 11am–3pm
Sun 1pm–4pm
Garden: Jan–Dec Mon–Fri

£©🚐🐕‍🦺 P♿ P ♿ ➔ ⊓ ♿ wc ⛲
🍴🌳🏕♿

Golden Hill Fort

Freshwater, IoW., PO40 9TF
☎ 0983 753380

Newport

Local buses

One of Lord Palmerston's historic forts, built 1863–1872, to help protect the Solent harbours against attack from the French. The Fort houses a military museum, craft and shops. Chair lift available.

Easter–Oct: Mon–Sun 10am–5pm
Nov–Easter: Sat &Sun 10am–5pm
Historic fort never closes

£©🚐🐕‍🦺 P♿ P ♿ ♿🏛➔ ⊓ ✚
♿ wc 🍴 🌳♿🤝◎♿

IOW Rare Breeds and Waterfowl Park

St Lawrence
Undercliffe Drive
Ventnor, IoW., PO38 1UW
☎ 0983 852582/855144

Ventnor, A3055

🚆 🚌 Shanklin

A survival centre for rare breeds of domestic animals, poultry and waterfowl. One of the largest in UK. Given first class status by Rare Breeds Survival Trust. No dogs or guide dogs. 30 acres with gravel, tarmac & grass paths.

Easter–31 Oct: Mon–Sun 10am–5.30pm

£©🚐 P ♿ ♿☛➔ ⊓ ♿ wc 🍴
🌳🏕♿◎

KENT

Blean Bird Park

Honey Hill
Blean
Canterbury, Kent, CT2 9JP
☎ 0227 471666

A290 Whitstable–Canterbury

🚆 🚌 Whitstable or Canterbury

Macaws, cockatoos, owls, peacocks, pheasants, jays, parakeets and pets corner. Gravel and paved paths.

Mar–Nov: Mon–Sun 10am–6pm

£©🚐🐕‍🦺 P ♿ ➔ ⊓ ♿ wc 🍴 🌳
🏕♿◎

KENT

White Cliffs Experience

Market Square
Dover, Kent, CT16 1PB
☎ 0304 214566

Town centre location well signposted

≥ 🚌 Dover Priory

The history of Roman Dover, the maritime story and 1940's Dover featured in audio–visual and high tech displays.

Apr–Jul: Mon–Sun 10am–6.30pm
Jul–Sept: Mon–Sun 10am–7.30pm
Last admissions 1 hr before closing.
Pls tel. for winter openings.

£©🚌☆✕🌳P🅿♿🏛➤⌐&ᵂᶜwc
⌂¶️🏆👫🏿

St Nicholas of Ash Vineyard

Moat Farm
Moat Lane
Ash
Canterbury, Kent, CT3 2DG
☎ 0304 812670

A257 Canterbury–Sandwich

🚌 Canterbury–Deal

Vineyard and winery in picturesque setting with C15th farmhouse (not open), large lily pond and attractive garden. 3 acres with tarmac paths.

Easter–31 Oct: Mon–Sun 10am–6pm

F🚌✕🅿♿➤✚🛗ᵂᶜwc🏆👫🌳🏿

Penshurst Place

Penshurst
Tonbridge, Kent, TN11 8DG
☎ 0892 870307

Tunbridge Wells and Tonbridge A26/A21

≥ Penshurst 🚌 T. Wells

Stately home and gardens. The magnificent Great Hall was built in 1340. Ten acres of walled gardens. Toy museum, venture playground. Gravel and paved paths.

House and Grounds 1 Apr–4 Oct: Tue–Sun 12.30–5.00pm
Grounds only Mar and Oct: Sat–Sun 12.30–5.00pm

£©🚌✕♿🅿🏛➤⌐✚&ᵂᶜ
wc⌂🍴👫🏆♿

Ramsgate Library, Museum and Art Gallery

Guildford Lawn
Ramsgate, Kent, CT11 9AY
☎ 0843 593532

Ramsgate

≥ 🚌 Ramsgate

Permanent exhibition in musuem of local interests. Gallery on first floor.

Jan–Dec: Mon–Wed: 9.30am–6pm (Closed BH's)
Thurs: 9.30am–5pm
Fri: 9.30am–8pm
Sat: 9.30am–5pm

F🚌✕🌳🅿♿📶🏛➤🛗ᵂᶜ
🏿♿

Hythe Local History Room

Oaklands
Stade St
Hythe, Kent, CT21 6BQ
☎ 0303 67111

Hythe

≥ Sandling

Local history room adjoining public library. Material of interest to local residents includes Cinque Ports and Small Arms School.

Mon: 9.30am–1pm & 2pm–6pm
Tue–Thu: 9.30am–1pm & 2pm–5pm
Fri: 9.30am–1pm & 2pm–7pm
Sat: 9.30am–1pm & 2pm–4pm

F✕🌳🅿♿wc👫🏿🌳

Philippine Village Craft Centre

The RAF Camp
Brookland
Romney Marsh, Kent, TN29 9TF
☎ 06794 616

Brookland 1 mile towards Rye

A unique site with a vast range of Philippine handicrafts. Five shops, each with its own unique identity.

Whitsun–30 Sep: Mon–Sun 10am–6pm
Other times ring for details

F🚌✕🅿🛗✚wc🍴🏆🏿🌳©

Whitbread Hop Farm

Beltring
Paddock Wood, Kent, TN12 6PY
☎ 0622 872068

Maidstone–Paddock Wood

≥ Paddock Wood & Beltring Heath

Venue houses the longest collection of Victorian Oast Houses in the world and is the country home of the famous Whitbread Shire Horses. The Rural Museums Centre is a famous piece of English Heritage. The horse and dray rides are suitable for the disabled but not wheelchair users.

Mar–Dec: Mon–Sun 10am–6pm

£ⓒ🚌⚡🐎🅿♿🅿♿➤⌐⟹🚻
🚻wc🔥🍴📷♿🎧🛍🎨ⓒ♿

The Canterbury Tales

St Margarets St
Canterbury, Kent, CT1 2TG
☎ 0227 454888

Canterbury A2/A28/A29C

⇌ 🚌 Canterbury

Extraordinary recreation of life in medieval England, conjured up by using the latest presentation technology in light, sound and smells.

Jan–Dec: Mon–Sun 9.30am–5.30pm

£ⓒ🚌⚡🐎🅿♿🅿🚻wc🍴
📷♿🎧🛍🎨

Parsonage Farm Rural Heritage Centre

North Elham
Nr Canterbury, Kent, CT4 6UY
☎ 0303 840766/840356

Canterbury A2 and Folkestone A20

⇌ 🚌 Folkestone & Canterbury

Family run working farm with farm trail, rare breeds, old buildings and implements and a musuem illustrating farm's history.

Easter–30 Sep: Tue–Sun & BH Mon 10.30am–5pm

£ⓒ🚌⚡ 🅿♿➤🍴wc🍴📷
♿

Cobham Hall

Cobham, Kent, DA12 3BL
☎ 0474 82 3371

Gravesend A2 B2009

⇌ Sole Street

Spacious C16th Grade 1 house, interior by James Wyatt. 150 acres of Reptons landscape gardening with gravel, paved and tarmaced paths. Now an independent girls school.

Apr: 5/8/9/12/17/19/20/22/23
Jul: 26/29/30
Aug: 5/6/9/12/13/16/19/20/23/26/27/31
2pm–5pm

£ⓒ🚌⚡ 🅿♿🔥🏛➤🍴🚻wc
🔥🍴📷♿🎨ⓒ♿

KENT

Bleak House Dickens Museum

Fort Rd
Broadstairs, Kent, CT10 1HD
☎ 0843 62224

M2 and A299 signpost Broadstairs

⇌ 🚌 Broadstairs

Formerly known as Fort House; the holiday home of Charles Dickens where he wrote 'David Copperfield'. Smuggling cellars and exhibits.

Mar–Jun: 10am–6pm
Jul–Sep: 10am–9pm

£ⓒ🚌⚡🅿♿🔥🔥🏛➤⌐WC
📷♿🛍

Margate Old Town Hall Local History Museum

Margate, Kent, CT9 1XD
☎ 0843 225511 Ext 2520

Margate Market Square

⇌ 🚌 Margate

Museum dates from late C17th. Contains old Victorian Police Station. Main theme is history of Margate from C18th to present day.

May–Sep: Mon–Sat 10am–5pm

£ⓒ🚌⚡🅿🔥🔥🏛🍴WC📷♿
🛍♿

Badsell Park Farm

Hatfield
Tonbridge, Kent, TN12 7EW
☎ 0892 83 2549

Tonbridge A21 to Pembury, then B2015

⇌ 🚌 Paddock Wood

Animal park with old breeds of farm animals and fowl. Pet area, butterfly house. C17th Farmhouse. 1 acre with gravel paths.

Apr–31 Oct: 10am–5.30pm

£ⓒ🚌⚡ 🅿🅿♿🔥🍴⌐⟹🍴
🚻wc🍴📷♿🏛🛍ⓒ

Marle Place Gardens and Nursery

Marle Place Road
Brenchley, Kent, TN12 7HS
☎ 0892 72 2304

A21 Lamberhurst; follow signs to 'Sprivers' on B2162

Scented walled garden, plantlovers borders, Victorian Gazebo, herb and wild flower nursery, Bantam collection. Peaceful

KENT

family owned gardens. 5 acres with gravel and grass paths.

Apr–Oct: Mon–Sat 10.30am–5pm
Closed on BH's

£©🚐🐕 P 👤 🚻 🚻 ⛲ 👤👤 👤👌

Falstaff Antiques & Motor Museum

63–67 High Street
Rolvenden, Kent, TN17 4LP
☎ 0580 241234

Tenterden A28

🚄 Tenterden

Unique motoring collection specialising in Morgan 3–wheel cars. Bicycles, motorcycles, toy and model cars, displayed with much automobilia. Concrete paths.

Jan–Dec: Mon–Sat 10am–6pm

£🚐🐕 P 👤 🚻 🚻 👤👤👤 👌🏃

Hever Castle

Edenbridge, Kent, TN8 7NG
☎ 0732 865224

Edenbridge (B roads only)

≽ 🚄 Hever & Edenbridge

Moated castle, childhood home of Anne Boleyn. Italian garden, maze, topiary and lake. 46 acres with gravel, tarmac and grass paths.

Mid Mar–Early Nov: Gardens Mon–Sun 11am–6pm
Castle Mon–Sun 12noon–6pm
Last admissions 5pm

£©🚐🐕👀 P 👤👤👤→👤👤
👤🚻 👤👤 👤👤👤©👌👌

The Roman Painted House

New St
Dover, Kent, CT17 9AJ
☎ 0304 203279

≽ 🚄 Dover

Exceptionally well preserved Roman building with unique early C3rd Frescos and elaborate underfloor heating system. Touch– table of archaeological finds.

Apr/Sep/Oct: Tue–Sun: 10am–5pm
May & Jun: Tue–Sun: 10am–6pm
Jul & Aug: Mon–Sun: 10am–6pm

£©🚐🐕 P 👤 👤 🚻 👤👤👤👤👌

Royal Engineers Museum

Brompton Barracks
Chatham, Kent, ME4 4UG
☎ 0634 406397

Gillingham, Kent

≽ Gillingham

A surprising insight into the lives and work of Britain's soldier engineers from the Norman Conquest to the end of World War II.

Spring/Summer: Tue–Fri & BH Mon: 10am–5pm
Sun: 11.30am–5pm

£🚐🐕 👤 P 👤→👤👤🚻🚻 👤 👤👤👤👤©©

Chiddingstone Castle

Nr Edenbridge, Kent
☎ 0892 870347

Near A21 and M20

≽ 🚄 Edenbridge

Neo–gothic, late Georgian mansion in 30 acres with gravel and grass paths.

Apr–Oct Tel for times

£🚐🐕 P 👤👤👤→👤👤👤🚻
👤👤👤👤

Finchcocks Musical Museum

Goudhurst, Kent, TN17 1HH
☎ 0580 211702

Tunbridge Wells A21 and A262

≽ Marden 7 miles

C18th house containing magnificent collection of historical keyboard instruments in concert condition. Beautiful gardens. Musical tours whenever house is open. Gravel and paved paths with some grass.

Apr–Oct: Sun & BH's 2pm–6pm
Most days by appointment
Aug : Wed–Sat 2pm–6pm

£©🚐🐕👀 P 👤👤→👤🚻👤
👤👤👤👤👤👌

Squerryes Court

Westerham, Kent, TN16 1SJ
☎ 0959 562345/563118

Westerham

≽ Oxted or Sevenoaks

Manor house built in 1681. Home of Warde Family since 1735. Fine pictures and furniture. Very attractive garden with lake. 15 acres with gravel and grass paths.

March: Sunday only
Apr–Sep: Wed/Sat/Sun/BH Mon

£🚌✖️ 🅿️ 👓🤚🏛️➤ 🚻 ⊹ ♿ ᵂᶜ wc
🍴 🎿🧑‍🤝‍🧑♿ 🐚

Rochester Cathedral

The Cathedral Office
Garth House
The Precinct
Rochester, Kent, ME1 1SX
☎ 0634 843366

Chatham A229, A2

≈ Rochester or Stroud

Fourteen centuries of Pilgrimage and prayer continue in England's second oldest cathedral. Magnificent Norman structure merging with majestic gothic architecture. Paths are brick and York stone.

Jan–Dec: Mon–Sun 7am–6.30pm

F🚌✖️♘P👓👓🤚🚜🖼️➤🚻⇒
⊹♿ᵂᶜwc🍴🎿🧑‍🤝‍🧑🎧🐚♿ᴸ

The Historic Dockyard

Chatham, Kent, ME4 4TE
☎ 0634 812551

Chatham

≈ Chatham then taxi/bus

400 years of naval shipbuilding history in 8 museum galleries including working ropery, flag and sail loft and award winning 'Wooden–Walls' exhibition. Heavy horse wagon rides unsuitable for wheelchair users.

Easter–31 Oct: Wed–Sun & BH's: 10am–6pm
Nov–Easter: Wed/Sat/Sun: 10am–4.30pm

£©🚌✖️🛍️P👓♿🤾➤🚻⊹♿ᵂᶜ
wc🐣🍴🎿🧑‍🤝‍🧑♿🐚♿ᴸ

Headcorn Flower Centre & Vineyard

Grigg Lane
Headcorn, Kent, TN27 9LY
☎ 0622 890250

Maidstone South on A274

≈ Headcorn

The country's only vineyard and flower centre. Breathtaking displays of chrysanthemums and orchid lilies. Guided tours through acres of heated flowerhouses ending with tutored wine tasting. Vineyard and reservoir trail. 40 acres with paved and grass paths.

Jan–Dec: Mon–Sun 10.30am–4.30pm

£©🚌✖️🅿️♿➤🚻⇒⊹♿ᵂᶜwc
🍴🎿🧑‍🤝‍🧑♿🐚

St Martins Plain Exhibition Centre

Cheriton High Street
Folkestone, Kent, CT19 4QD
☎ 0303 270111

Junction 12 off M20

≈ Folkestone

The centre has many special features including a 32m long N–gauge model railway, floor to ceiling illuminated map, full-sized shuttle interior model, a 21m observation tower overlooking the Folkestone Terminal site.

Summer: Tue–Sun: 10am–6pm
Winter: Tue–Sun: 10am–5pm
Closed: Mondays except BH Mons

£🚌✖️P👓🅿️♿🤾🏛️♿ᵂᶜwc🐣🍴
🎿🧑‍🤝‍🧑🐚☾

Bedgebury National Pinetum FC

Goudhurst
Cranbrook, Kent, TN17 2SL
☎ 0580 211044

B2079 to A21 at Flimwell or Broad to Goudhurst

Europe's best collection of conifers started by Kew Gardens, but now owned and administered by the Forestry Commission. Set in 300 acres of hilly ground with level areas. Paths are gravelled and paved.

Visitors centre & shop: Easter–31 Oct Mon–Sun 11am–5pm
Pinetum: Jan–Dec Mon–Sun 10am–8pm/dusk

£©🚌✖️P👓🅿️♿➤🚻⇒👁️♿ᵂᶜ
wc🎿🧑‍🤝‍🧑♿🐚

Biddenden Vineyards

Little Whatmans
Biddenden
Ashford, Kent, TN27 8DH
☎ 0580 291726

A274 Maidstone–Tenterden Road

≈ Headcorn

Kent's oldest commercial vineyards,

KENT

producing fine English wines, strong
Kentish ciders and apple juice. 22 acres
with tarmac and grass paths.

Jan–Feb: Mon–Sat
Mar–Dec: Mon–Sun
Closed: 24 Dec–1 Jan

F ✻ P ⟍ ▦ ➔ ⊓ ⇒ wc ¶¶ ♜
▲▲ ⟍

Church Wood RSPB

Blean, Nr Canterbury
Kent
☎ 0227 462491

¼ mile from A290

A surfaced track from the car park along the
southern boundary is easily negotiable by
wheelchair users, providing 1 mile of views
up rides and over glades for bird and
butterfly watching. Cars may be driven
down by arrangement. The Green Trail may
be negotiated entirely by wheelchair users.

Eurotunnel Exhibition Centre

St Martin's Plain
Cheriton High St
Folkestone, Kent, CT19 4QD
☎ 0303 270111

Junction 12 off M20

≋ Folkestone Central

Displays and models to explain the design
and engineering of the three tunnels. Has
many special features including a railway,
floor to ceiling illuminated map and a 21m
observation tower. Paved paths. No lift in
the viewing tower.

Summer: Tue–Sun & BH 10am–6pm
Winter: Tue–Sun & BH 10am–5pm

£© ➟ ✻ P⟍ P ⟍ ▦ ⟍ʷᶜ wc ⋔ ¶¶
♜ ▲▲ ⬭ ©

Crabble Corn Mill

Lower Rd
River
Dover, Kent, CT17 0UY
☎ 0304 823292

Dover, A256

≋ Kearnsey ⟺ Dover

Restored working mill built 1812 to provide
flour for troops stationed nearby. Unique
collection of Victorian milling machinery.

Jan–Dec: Sat 10am–5pm
Sun 12noon–5pm
Easter–31 Oct: Wed–Mon 10am–5pm
Aug: Mon–Sat 10am–5pm

Sun 12noon–5pm

£© ➟ ✻ P ⟋ ⟍ ▰ ▦ ➔ ⊓ ʷᶜ
wc ¶¶ ▲▲ ⟍ ⋒ ⬭ ©

Leeds Castle

Nr Maidstone, Kent, ME17 1PL
☎ 0622 765400

Maidstone A20, junction 8 of M20

≋ Bearsted ⟺ Maidstone

Originally a Saxon fortress – now a
beautifully furnished Castle in 500 acres of
rolling parklands and gardens. Aviary and
Dog Collar Museum.

16 Mar–Oct: Mon–Sun 11am–5pm
Nov–14 Mar: Sat–Sun 11am–4pm

£© ➟ ✻ ⟍ P⟍ P ⟍ ▰ ▦ ⊓ ⊣⊢
⟍ʷᶜ wc ⋔ ¶¶ ♜ ▲▲ ⟍ ⬭ ©

Herne Windmill

Mill Lane
Herne
Nr Canterbury, Kent
☎ 0227 368511

Herne Bay A291

≋ ⟺ Herne Bay

Kentish Smock Mill built 1789, fully restored
by KCC in 1986. Maps, photos, displays
and equipment.

Apr–Sep: Sun & BH Mon 2pm–5pm
Mid Jul–Mid Aug: Thur & Sat 2pm–5pm

£➟ ✻ ⟋ P ⟋ ▰ ▰ ▦ WC ♜ ▲▲
⟍ ⬭ ⬮ ⥁

A Day at the Wells

The Corn Exchange
The Pantiles
Tunbridge Wells, Kent, TN2 5QJ
☎ 0892 546545

Tunbridge Wells

≋ ⟺ Tunbridge Wells

Recreation of Tunbridge Wells in the C18th
– complete with sights, sounds and smells
of the period.

Easter–Oct: Mon–Sun 9.30am–5pm
Nov–Easter: Mon–Sun 10am–4pm

£© ➟ ✻ ⟋ ⟍ P⟍ P ⟋ ⟍ ⟍ʷᶜ wc
¶¶ ♜ ⋒ ⬭ ⬮ © ⟍ᴸ

92

Dungeness Nature Reserve RSPB

Nr Lydd, Kent
☎ 0679 20588

Entrance off Lydd to Dungeness road.

4 hides overlooking lakes, with wildfowl and terns, accessible by wheelchair – up to 400 yards from car park. Cars may be driven to them by arrangement. Toilets reasonably accessible. New observatory (with wheelchair access) under construction.

Tunbridge Wells Museum & Art Gallery

Civic Centre
Mount Pleasant
Tunbridge Wells, Kent, TN1 1NS
☎ 0892 26121

A26/A267

⇌ Tunbridge Wells Central

Displays of local history, archaeology, natural history, Tunbridge ware, dolls, toys, and regularly changing art exhibitions.

Jan–Dec: Mon–Sat 9.30am–5pm
Closed BH

Dover Museum

Market Square
Dover, Kent, CT16 1PB
☎ 0304 201066

Dover

⇌ ▭ Dover Priory

Dover's new 3 floor museum of local history and archaeology. Gallery shows regularly changing displays of temporary exhibitions.

Nov–Feb: Wed–Sun 10am–5pm
Mar–Oct: Mon–Sun 10am–5pm

Chislehurst Caves

Old Hill
Chislehurst, Kent, BR7 5NB
☎ 081 467 3264

Bromley, A222

⇌ ▭ Chislehurst

22 miles of caves, parts dating from 4000 BC. World War II exhibits.

Easter–30 Sep: Mon–Sun 11am–5pm
1 Oct–Easter: Sat–Sun 11am–5pm

Fleur De Lis Heritage Centre

13 Preston St
Faversham, Kent, ME13 8SU
☎ 0795 534542

Faversham, A2

⇌ ▭ Faversham

The story of one of Britain's finest historic towns, told in colourful displays.

Jan–Dec: Mon–Wed & Fri–Sat 10am–1pm & 2pm–4pm

Brogdale Horticultural Trust

Brogdale Rd
Faversham, Kent
☎ 0795 535286

Faversham

⇌ Faversham

Formerly the National Fruit Trials. Largest collection of apples, pears, plums, cherries, nuts, quinces, and other soft fruit. 2,300 different varieties of apple. Only suitable when ground is dry.

Easter–Christmas: Wed–Sun 11am–5pm

Langdon Cliffs NT

Dover, Kent

A wheelchair accessible viewpoint overlooks the docks and harbour, with extensive views along the coast and to the coast of France on a clear day.

LANCASHIRE

Fleetwood Pier

The Esplanade
Fleetwood, Lancs., FY7 6HB
☎ 0253 874563

A584 Blackpool to Fleetwood

⇌ ▭ Blackpool

Fleetwood Pier has a variety of entertainments.

Mar–31 Oct: Mon–Sun 9.30am–10.45pm
Nov–Mar: Mon–Sun 12noon–10pm

LANCASHIRE

Medlock Valley Country Park

The Stables
Park Bridge
Ashton–under–Lyne, Lancs., OL6 8AQ
☎ 061 330 9613

A627 Oldham–Ashton

≉ 🚐 Ashton–under–Lyne

The base for the Medlock Valley Warden
Service. A visitor centre with information
about the surrounding countryside. 5 acres
with hard earth paths.

Park: Jan–Dec Mon–Sun 10.30am–5pm
Centre: Jan–Dec Tue–Fri 1pm–4pm
Sat–Sun 10.30am–5pm

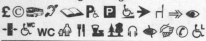

The Wildfowl and Wetlands Centre

Martin Meke
Burscough
Nr Ormskirk, Lancs., L40 0TA
☎ 0704 895181

Ormskirk 6 miles A59 (10 miles from
Southport)

≉ Burscough Bridge or Junction 🚐
Ormskirk to Martin Meke

See rare and exotic birds from all over the
world & feed them by hand. In winter
thousands of Whooper and Bewick swans
flock from Siberia and Iceland to this 360
acre centre. No guide dogs.

Brewery Arts Centre

Highgate
Kendal, Lancs., LA9 4HE
☎ 0539 725133

Kendal town centre

≉ 🚐 Kendal

A modern multi–purpose arts venue
(theatre, cinema, concert hall, photographic
gallery, visual arts gallery and workshops) in
a converted 150 year old former brewery,
with its own landscaped garden. 'Stairmate'
wheelchair access to other floors. Certain
areas being refurbished, check for details.

Jan–Dec: Mon–Sat
Closed: BH's

Lancaster Maritime Museum

St Georges Quay
Lancaster, Lancs., LA1 1RB
☎ 0524 64637

Just out of Lancaster city centre

≉ Lancaster

1764 custom house and adjacent
warehouse containing displays on
Lancaster's maritime history, port, canal,
warehousing, etc.

Easter–31 Oct: Mon–Sun 11am–5pm
Nov–Easter: Mon–Sun 2pm–5pm

Blackpool Zoological Gardens

East Park Drive
Blackpool, Lancs., FY3 8PP
☎ 0253 65027

Blackpool A583

≉ Blackpool 🚐 summer only

The 32 landscaped acres of Blackpool Zoo
are home to over 400 animal species from
all over the world. No guide dogs. Paved
and tarmaced paths.

Winter: 10am–dusk
Summer: 10am–5.15

Rufford Old Hall NT

Rufford
Nr Ormskirk, Lancs., L40 1SG
☎ 0704 821254

7 miles north of Ormskirk on A59

≉ Rufford (not Sun) 🚐 Rufford

One of the finest timber framed houses in
Lancashire. Magnificent Great Hall,
collections of C16th arms and armour, fine
oak furniture. 14 acres of gardens with
gravel paths.

1 Apr–31 Oct: Sat–Thurs 1pm–5pm

Camelot Adventure Theme Park

Charnock Richard
Chorley, Lancs., PR7 5LP
☎ 0257 453044

Chorley

≉ 🚐 Chorley

Medieval world of Camelot brought to life
with hundreds of rides and attractions. Live

entertainment for 4–14 year olds and adults. 40 acres with paved paths.

Mar–Oct: Mon–Sun 10am–⅚/7pm

£ © 🚐 ✕ 🄿 🅿 ಸ ➤ ♿ WC ⛲ ❢
🏛 🎪 ಸ 🤚 ♿

Leighton Moss RSPB

Nr Silverdale
Lancs., LA5 0SW
☎ 0524 701601

Entrance near Silverdale station, reached from M6 via Yealand Redmayne.

Surfaced path leads to a wheelchair-accessible hide with panoramic views overlooking mere and reedbeds with waterfowl, bitterns, otter, etc. Public hide on the causeway, 400 yards from roadside parking, is accessible at all times. Good views of reedbed birds from firm path beyond hide.

Jan–Dec: Wed–Mon 9am–9pm

£ ♿ WC 🏛

Frontierland – Western Theme Park

Morecombe, Lancs., LA4 4DG
☎ 0524 410024

Morecombe
≈ Morecambe

Western Theme Park with over 30 rides including log flume, 3 rollercoasters and fun house. Also 2 live shows and western gunfights. 12 acres with paved and tarmaced paths.

Easter: Sat–Sun only
Apr–Sep: Mon–Sun
Oct: Sat–Sun only

£ © 🚐 ✕ 🅿 ಸ ➤ 🄿 ╫ ♿ WC ⛲
❢ 🏛 🎪 ಸ

The British Commercial Vehicle Museum

King St
Leyland, Preston,
Lancs., PR5 1LE
☎ 0772 451011

Preston A49 or Junction 28 off M6 motorway
≈ Leyland

Museum devoted to the history of the British commercial vehicle industry. Exhibits from 1896 to present day.

Apr–Sep: Tue–Sun & BH 10am–5pm

Oct–Nov: Sat–Sun 10am–5pm

£ © 🚐 ✕ 🅿 🄿 ಸ ➤ 🄿 ╫ ♿ WC
❢ 🏛 🤚 🄿 ಸ

East Lancashire Railway

Bolton St Station
Bury, Lancs., BL9 0EY
☎ 061 764 7790/705 5111

Bury A56, A58
≈ Bury Interchange

A preserved railway of 8 miles running between Bury, Ramsbottom & Rawtenstall. Steam and diesel engines. Wheelchair users can be assisted into guards van.

Jan–Dec: Sat–Sun Sat 10am/Sun 11am–5pm
Easter–Aug: BH

£ © 🚐 ✕ 🄿 🅿 ಸ 🚂 🄿 ╫ ♿ WC
❢ 🏛 🎪 🤚

Pilkington Glass Museum

Prescot Rd
St Helens, Lancs., WA10 3TT
☎ 0744 692014

A58 1½m from St Helens Centre
≈ 🚍 St Helens Central

4000 years of glassmaking. Outstanding glass collection. Glass & its uses in building, transport, science and technology. Working models & interactive exhibits. Stair lift.

Jan–Dec: Mon–Fri 10am–5pm
Sat,Sun & BH 2pm–4.30pm
Closed Xmas–New Year

F 🚐 ✕ 🅿 🄿 ಸ 🦮 🄴 🏛 🄿 ╫ ♿
WC 🏛 🤚 🄿

Lancaster Priory

Castle Hill
Lancaster, Lancs.,
☎ 0524 65338

A6 & M6

Founded in 1094 – Medieval, Georgian and later alterations. Magnificent oak canopied stalls carved in 1340, reputed to be the finest in the country.

Summer: Mon–Sun 9.30am–6pm
Winter: Mon–Sun 9.30am–5.30pm

F 🚐 ✕ 🅿 ಸ 🄴 ➤ 🄿 ♿ WC 🎪 🏛 🎪
🤚 🄿 🄴

LEICESTERSHIRE

Staunton Harold Hall

Sue Ryder Home
Ashby De La Zouch
Leics., LE6 5RT
☎ 0332 862798

Melbourne B587 or Ashby A453

C18th Hall now used for hospice care. Ground floor tours arranged. Next to NT C16th church. 30 acres with gravel, tarmac and grass paths.

Jan–Dec: Tue–Sun 10am–5pm

Foxton Locks

Foxton Boat Services
Market Harborough
Leics., LE16 7RA
☎ 0533 792285

Market Harborough A6

≈ Market Harborough

Unique flight of 10 staircase locks and site of inclined plane boat lift, on well–used canal in beautiful countryside. Museum not easily accessible.

Jan–Dec: Mon–Sun

Lyddington Bede House EH

Blue Coat Lane
Lyddington, Leics., LE15 9LZ
☎ 057282 2438

Uppingham A47

The Bede house is located in a beautiful village; originally a palace for the Bishops of Lincoln, later an Almshouse. 1 acre with gravelled and cobbled paths. Main areas are via stairs.

Summer: 10am–6pm

Rutland Water

Sykes Lane
Empingham
Oakham, Leics., LE15 8PX
☎ 0780 86 321

Oakham/Stamford A606

 Oakham/Stamford

Largest man–made lake in Western Europe – cycling, fishing, sailing, passenger cruiser, nature reserve, Normanton Church museum and drought garden. Steps into Normanton Church. 4,000 acres with paved paths. Rutland Belle suitable for wheelchair users.

Jan–Dec

The City Gallery

90 Granby St
Leicester, Leics., LE1 1DJ
☎ 0533 540595/3

Leicester

≈  Leicester

Craft gallery, foyer showcases and 2 exhibition areas. Chairlift available.

Jan–Dec Tue–Fri: 11am–6pm
Sat: 10am–5pm

Belvoir Castle

The Estate Office
Belvoir
Nr Grantham, Leics., NG32 1PD
☎ 0476 870262

Grantham A607 towards Melton Mowbray

≈ Grantham

Home of the Duke and Duchess of Rutland. Many exquisite state rooms, paintings and furniture. Guide dogs by appointment only. Upstair rooms inaccessible. Gravel and rough cobbled paths.

Apr–Sep: Tue/Wed/Thur Sat/Sun/BH Mon

Tropical Bird Gardens

Linbridge Lane
Desford, Leics., LE9 9GN
☎ 0455 824603

A47 out of Leicester

≈ St Margarets

Aviarys and free flying parrots in natural woodland. 6 acres with gravel and paved paths.

Jan–Dec: Mon–Sun 10am–5.30pm or dusk

£©🚌🚶🐕 🅿 ♿ ⌐ ⇒ ⊢ ♿ WC 🍴 👥 🐾 ✋

Rutland County Museum

Catmos St
Oakham
Rutland, Leics., LE15 6HW
☎ 0572 723654

Oakham
≋ Oakham

Rural life collections illustrating history and archaeology of Rutland. Indoor riding school of 1794. History of the volunteer soldiers.

Jan–Dec: Mon–Sat & BH Mon 10am–1pm & 2pm–5pm
Sun 2pm–5pm

F🚌🚶🐕 🏇 P 🅿 🔔🤚 🏛 ♿ WC 🦮

Great Central Railway

Loughborough, Leics.,
☎ 0509 230726

Loughborough
≋🚌 Loughborough

8 miles of steam railway between Loughborough and Leicester. Wheelchair users by appointment.

Jan–Dec: Sat–Sun
Mid week by appointment

£©🚌🚶🐕 🅿 🅿 ⌐🤚◀➤ ⌐ ⌐ ⊢ WC 🍴 🦮 👥 🐾 ✋

Gorse Hill City Farm

Anstey Lane,
Leicester, Leics., LE4 0FL
☎ 0533 537582

Leicester, A50
≋🚌 Leicester

9 acres of land, which was disused allotments and has been developed since 1985. Cattle, goats, donkeys & organic garden.

Summer: Thu–Tue 10am–6pm
Winter: Thu–Tue 10am–4pm

F🚌🚶🐕 🅿 🅿 ♿➤ ⌐ ♿ WC 🦮 🍴 👥 🐾 ✋

Farmworld

Stoughton Farm Park
Gartree Rd
Leicester, Leics., LE2 2FB
☎ 0533 710355

A47 or A6 from Leicester
≋🚌 Leicester

Based on working dairy farm. Rare breeds, childrens playgrounds, farmyard, lake, woodlands in 27 acres of landscaped parkland. Compact granite dust paths.

Jan–Dec: Mon–Sun 10am–5pm

£©🚌🚶🐕 🅿 🅿 ♿➤ ⌐ ♿ WC 🦮 🍴 🐾 👥 🐾 ✋

Battlefield Line Steam Railway

Shackerstone Station
Shackerstone
Nuneaton, Leics., CV13 6NW
☎ 0827 715790

Nuneaton/Hinkley

Standard gauge preserved passenger steam railway, linking up with the site of the Battle of Bosworth Field (1485).

Apr–Oct: Sun & BH Mon 11am–5.30pm

£©🚌🚶🐕 🅿 ♿🤚➤ ⌐ ⊢ WC 🍴 🐾 👥 🐾 ✋

LINCOLNSHIRE

Tattershall Castle NT

Tattershall
Lincoln, Lincs., LN4 4LR
☎ 0526 42543

On A153 – Horncastle 10 miles
≋🚌 Boston

Large fortified house built in 1440 for the Lord Treasurer of England. 100ft high keep, tower containing state apartments. Four great chambers with ancillary rooms. Spiral staircase to upper floors. 7½ acres with gravel and brick paved paths.

Apr–Oct: Mon–Sun: 10.30am–5.30pm
Nov–Mar: Mon–Sun: 12 noon–4pm

£©🚌🚶🐕 🅿 🔔◀🏛 ⌐ ⊢ ♿ WC 🐾 ♿

Museum of Lincolnshire Life

Burton Rd
Lincoln, Lincs., LN1 3LY
☎ 0522 528448

Near city centre, cathedral and castle
≋🚌 Lincoln

This is one of the largest of its kind in East Midlands with everything from thimbles to tanks. 90% of museum is on ground floor.

One acre with paved paths.
May–Sep: Mon–Sun 10am–5.30pm
Oct–Apr: Sun 2pm–5.30pm

£©🚐⭑ʔ🅿🅿🅿💰🛍📷➔
🚻⚡🚾 WC 🍴♿👫♿🐟🌳⭕©♿

Usher Gallery

Lindum Rd
Lincoln, Lincs., LN2 1NN
☎ 0522 527980

Lincoln A46

⇌ 🚉 Lincoln Central

Collections include clocks and watches,
miniatures, porcelain, silver, glass, Peter De
Wint Paintings, topographical paintings of
Lincolnshire, coins and Tennyson material.
5 acres with tarmaced paths.

Mon–Sat 10am–5.30pm
Sun 2.30pm–5pm

£🚐⭑ʔ🅿🅿💰🛍🛍🏛➔🚻
🚾 WC 🍴♿👫♿⭕©

Hemswell Antique Centres

Caenby Corner Estate
Hemswell Cliff
Gainsborough,
Lincs., DN21 5TJ
☎ 042 773 389

Lincoln

⇌ 🚉 Lincoln or Gainsborough

Former Lancaster Bomber base, RAF
Hemswell, now houses 300 antique dealers
and licensed restaurant. 5 acres with paved
paths.

Jan–Dec: Mon–Sun 10am–5pm

£©🚐⭑⛵🅿🅿♿➔🚻⇒🚾
WC 🍴♿👫🌳⭕©♿

Doddington Hall

Lincoln
Lincs., LN6 4RU
☎ 0522 694308

Lincoln and A46 Lincoln by–pass

Late Elizabethan mansion with gatehouse,
walled gardens and superb flowers. Varied
contents of home reflect 400 years of
unbroken family occupation. 5 acres with
gravel and grass paths. All areas accessible
if using guide.

May–Sep & Easter Mon: Wed/Sun/BH
Mons: 2pm–6pm

£©🚐⭑⛵🅿♿⚡🏭➔🚻🚾
WC 🐟🍴👫♿

Gibraltar Point Nature Reserve

Gibraltar Road
Skegness, Lincs., PE24 4JU
☎ 0754 2677

Skegness A52

⇌ Skegness 3 miles away

1100 acres of coastal sand dunes and
saltmarshes, with gravel, paved and chalk
paths. Good for bird watching, botany and
natural history.

Jan–Dec

F🚐⭑🅿♿➔🚻⚡🚾 WC 👫👫

Northcote Heavy Horse Centre

Great Steeping
Spilsby, Lincs., PE23 5PS
☎ 0754 86 286

Spilsby on A16 – take B1183 East 3 miles

A nostalgic journey to the world of the
Working Horse. The centre opened in 1989
and located on part of the ex bomber airfield
RAF Silsby. Guide dogs by prior
arrangement as Dalmation dogs work here.
4 acres with gravel, paved and part grass
paths. Horse drawn dray rides; stepped
access to dray only very severley disabled
people cannot manage. ' We aim to
accomodate the elderly rather than the
young'. The site is tranquil and disabled
people can benefit just as much as the able–
bodied.

Mar–Jun: Sun/Wed/Thu 11.30am–4.30pm
Jul–Aug: Sun–Fri 11.30am–5pm

£©🚐⭑🅿🅿♿➔🚻⚡🚾 WC
🍴👫👫♿🎧

Rutland Cottage Mechanical Music and Fairground Museum

Millgate
Whaplode St Catherine
Nr Spalding, Lincs
☎ 040 634 379

On B1165 at Whaplode St Catherine

A trip through the history of entertainment
as visitors listen to music boxes, fairground
organs, church organs, cinema organs,
edison phonographs, early gramaphones,
barrel organs, pianolos, etc. 6 acres with
gravel and grass paths.

Easter–Sep: Sat/Sun/BH: 10am–6pm
Jul/Aug/Sep: Mon–Fri: 1pm–5pm

Other times by appt.

£©🚐☀🐕 P🅿 ♿➔ ⊣ wc ⅋ 🛥 🌲♿⊕

Manor Stables Craft Workshops

Fullbeck
Grantham, Lincs., NG32 7JN
☎ 0400 72779

A607 Lincoln to Grantham

Old stables converted to craft workshops. Eight different workshops & showroom of other local crafts. ½ acre with gravel paths.

15 Jan–23 Dec: Tue–Sun & BH Mons 10.30am–4.30pm

F🚐☀ 🅿 🚶 🏛➔ ⊣ ⊥ ♿wc ⅋ 🛥🌲♿✋©

The Lawn Visitor Centre

Union Rd
Lincoln, Lincs., LN1 3BL
☎ 0522 560306/560330

Lincoln, A46, A15, A57, A158

≷ 🚐 Lincoln Central

First purpose built lunatic assylum, built 1820. Converted to conference centre/visitor centre by Lincoln County Council. Officially opened 20 November 1990 by HRH Prince Charles. 9¼ acres with gravelled areas (soon to be changed to a more suitable surface).

Mon–Fri: 9am–5pm
Sat–Sun: 10am–4pm

F🚐☀ P🅿 ♿ ▱🏙➔ ⊣ ♿wc ⅋ 🛥🌲♿♿

Ayscoughfee Hall & Gardens

Churchgate
Spalding, Lincs., PE11 2RA
☎ 0775 761161

Spalding

≷ 🚐 Spalding

C15th Manor House on side of River Welland set in gardens – contains local history museum and tourist information centre. 4 acres.

Gardens: Mon–Sat: 8am–dusk
Sun: 10am–dusk
Closed w/ends: Mar–Oct and 25 Dec
Museum: Mon–Thu: 10am–5pm
Fri: 10am–4.30pm
Sat: 10am–5pm
Sun: 11am–5pm

F🚐☀🐕 P🅿 ♿⊣ ⊥wc ⅋ 🛥 🌲♿

Grantham Museum

St Peters Hill
Grantham, Lincs., NG31 6HG
☎ 0476 68783

Between Nottingham and Stamford A1

≷ 🚐 Grantham

The comprehensive set of displays, presenting the town's history and background.

Apr–Sep: Mon–Sat: 10am–5pm
Sun: 2pm–5pm
Oct–Mar: Mon–Sat: 10.30am–12.30pm & 1.30pm–5pm

£🚐☀🐕 P 🚶 🏛➔ ⊣ wc 🛥 ♿✋

Stamford Steam Brewery Museum

All Saints St
Stamford, Lincs., PE9 2PA
☎ 0780 52186

Stamford A1

🚐 Stamford

Genuine Victorian Steam Brewery with mash tuns, coppers and fermenting vessels. Automatic sound system describes brewery in use. ½ acre with paved paths.

1 Apr–30 Sep: Wed–Sun & BH Mon 10am–4pm
Closed Wed in BH weeks

£©🚐P 🚶 ♿▱▱🏛➔ ⊣ ♿ wc 🛥🌲♿🎧✋✋©

Stamford Shakespeare Company

Tolethorpe Hall
Nr Stamford
Lincs., PE9 1PJ
☎ 0780 54381/56133

Stamford A6121

≷ 🚐 Stamford

Rutland open air theatre. All seats covered – no performance is ever cancelled because of rain. Paved and gravel paths.

Mid Jun–31 Aug

£🚐☀ P🅿 ♿➔ ⊣ ⇒ ♿wc ⅋ 🛥🌲♿✋©

LINCOLNSHIRE

Whisby Nature Park

Thorpe–on–the–Hill
Lincoln, Lincs
☎ 0522 500676

From A46 Lincoln, into Moor Lane

160 acres of disused gravel pits supporting marsh, woods and grassland, with numerous plant and animal species. Gravel paths.

Jan–Dec: Mon–Sun 9am–dusk

Springfields Gardens

Camelgate
Spalding, Lincs., PE12 6ET
☎ 0775 724843

Spalding A151

⇌ 🚌 Spalding

Opened in 1966 showing magnificent displays of tulips & daffodils in spring & bedding and roses in summer. Exhibitions and shows held all year round. 25 acres with paved paths.

Apr–Sep: Mon–Sun: 10am–6pm

£ 🚐 ✳ P ♿ ➔ ┤ ♿ WC ♨ ᚦᚸ ᚻ
🌳 ⟲ ♿

Louth Museum

4 Broadbank
Louth, Lincs., LN11 6EQ
☎ 0507 604717

Just off A16, just east of church

Natural history, geology, bygones, posters, photographs, scrapbooks of Louth and district.

Jan–Nov: Wed/Fri/Sat/Sun: 2pm–4pm

£ © 🚐 ✳ P ♿ ➔ ┤ WC ♿ ⟲

Woodhall Spa Cottage Museum

Iddesleigh Rd
Woodhall Spa, Lincs., LN10 6SH
☎ 0526 53775

Woodhall Spa B1191

Museum to preserve the community history. Based on a collection of photographs and memorabilia of the Wield family, whose home was the Museum. ¼ acre with gravel paths.

Easter–Sep: Mon–Sun 10am–5pm

£ © 🚐 ✳ P ♿ ➔ WC ♿

Hartsholme Country Park & Nature Reserve

Skellingthorpe Rd
Lincoln, Lincs.,
☎ 0522 686264

SW Lincoln off A46 by–pass

⇌ 🚌 Lincoln

96 acre park with beautiful, mature, landscaped grounds and level path around lake. 150 acre nature reserve with trail suitable for wheelchair users.

Jan–Dec: Mon–Sun 10am–6pm

F 🚐 ✳ P ♿ P ♿ ➔ ┤ ♿ WC ᚻ ᚸ
♿ ⟲

The Pearoom Craft Centre

Station Yard
Heckington
Sleaford, Lincs., NG34 9JJ
☎ 0529 60765

6m from Sleaford on A17 to Boston

⇌ Heckington

A converted pea–sorting warehouse, The Pearoom, now houses ten workshops for resident craftspeople. Two galleries for craft exhibitions.

Jan–Dec: Mon–Sat 10am–5pm
Sun 12noon–5pm

F 🚐 ✳ P ♿ P ♿ 🤚 🏛 ➔ ┤ ♿ WC
♿ ⟲

Burghley House

Stamford, Lincs., PE9 3JY
☎ 0780 52451

Just off the A1 Stamford

⇌ 🚌 Stamford

Largest and grandest house of the First Elizabethan Age, situated within a beautiful Deer Park, landscaped by Capability Brown.

17 Apr–4 Oct: Mon–Sun 11am–5pm

£ © 🚐 ✳ P ◀ ◀ 🏛 ┤ ┃ ♿ WC
ᚻ ♿ ᚸ ♿ ⟲ © ♿

Stamford Museum

Broad St
Stamford, Lincs., PE9 2BN
☎ 0780 66317

In the centre of Stamford

Interprets the historic town of Stamford. Archaeological and local history displays.

Apr–Sep: Mon–Sat 10am–5pm
Sun 2pm–5pm
Oct–Mar: Mon–Sat 10am–12.30pm & 1.30pm–5pm

£ © 🚐 ✳ ♿ P P ♿ ♿ 🏛 ♿ ♿ ⟲

LONDON

SYMBOL DESCRIPTIONS

£   Admission charge

F   No admission charge but donation in some places

©   Special concession charge for disabled people, elderly people, carers and children

    Groups must book in advance – special rates may apply

    Guide dogs accepted except in certain areas

    Sympathetic Hearing Scheme participated in or Loop System

    Special information available for disabled people

PARKING

P   Designated disabled parking space

P   Own car park with a dropping off point within 50 yards

P   Public car park nearby and/or street parking within 200 yards

P   Dropping off point or disabled parking place by telephone appointment

MAIN ENTRANCE

    Entrance level or ramped and over 30″ wide

    Steps into building 1–5 or bumpy

    Steps into building 6 or more

    More suitable entrance freely available, telephone for details or help. Temporary ramps to be made available.

    Steps within the buildings that cannot be overcome by ramps

    More than one floor level and no lift

    More than one floor level and suitable lift/stairclimber/stairlift for wheelchair users

OUTSIDE

→   Routes around the site are free of steps or steps can be avoided

    Seats available around the site

⇒   Routes indicated for wheelchair users

    Routes indicated for visually handicapped people

    Transport around the site suitable for disabled people and wheelchair users – telephone in advance

    Transport around the site not suitable for disabled people or elderly people

    There are limited areas that cannot be reached due to steps or doorways less than 30″

TOILETS

&ᵂᶜ   Unisex toilets designed or adapted for disabled people or public toilets within 50 yards. Radar key required in some

WC   Ordinary toilets with level access

WC   No toilets on site but public ones nearby

⛲   Baby changing/parents room available

GENERAL

✕   Restaurant/tea room/cafe/ not accessible due to steps/narrow doorway/first floor with no lift

¶   Restaurant/tea room/cafe/vending accessible by ramp or level or lift with 30″ doors

⬛   Shop not accessible due to stairs but may be accessible with help

⬛   Shop/sales area accessible by ramp or level and 30″ doorway

⚑   Picnic area only, or nearby

♿   Wheelchair users are advised to come accompanied

🎧   Taped guides available/or person

👁   Facilities for visually handicapped/braille or by request

✋   People available to help (telephone beforehand if you require help)

☏   Telephone accessible for wheelchair users

♿   This site is suitable for elderly people but unsuitable for wheelchair users

♿ᴸ   Wheelchairs/batricars for loan or hire – telephone for advance booking

NT   The National Trust

EH   English Heritage

NTS   National Trust for Scotland

RSPB Royal Society For the Protection of Birds

FC   Forestry Commission

⇌   British Rail

🚌   Bus

☎   Telephone

⊖   Underground

NOTES

LONDON

Royal Festival Hall

South Bank Ctr
London, SE1 8XX
☎ 071 921 0639

Between Waterloo & Hungerford bridges, central London

≋ Waterloo ⊖ Waterloo/Embankment

Three concert halls with constantly changing performances. Hayward Gallery with exhibitions.

Jan–Dec: Mon–Sun 10am–11pm

£F©☀🐾𝒥🗨️P♿P♿▟🗃️⌐
⇒👁️🖐️♿WC🐕🍴♿👫♿🎧⚓
🗨️©♿

Public Record Office

Chancery Lane
London, WC2 1LR
☎ 081 876 3444

Central London

⊖ Temple/Chancery Lane/Holborn 🚌 to Fleet St or Holborn

The PRO in Chancery Lane houses central Government and court records of England and Wales.

Jan–Dec: Mon–Fri 9.30am–5pm
Closed: BH/Sep 30th–Oct 11th

F🚐🗨️♿𝒫▟🖐️🗃️♿WC🐕
♿🗨️©

St Katherine by the Tower

Ivory House
St Katherine by the Tower
London, E1 9AT
☎ 071 488 2400

Adjacent to Tower Bridge

⊖ Tower Hill

Docks built in 1825–28; now private estate; open to the public.

Jan–Dec

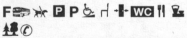

F🚐☀P P♿⌐🖐️WC🍴♿
👫©

The Horniman Museum & Gdns

100 London Rd
Forest Hill
London, SE23 3PQ
☎ 081 699 1872

Forest Hill on the S.Circular

≋ 🚌 Forest Hill

Sets out to illustrate the world we live in, through its cultures, arts, crafts, music and national environment.

Jan–Dec: Mon–Sat 10.30am–5.50pm
Sun 2pm–5.50pm

F🚐🐾🗨️P▟🐕▟🗃️➤⌐⇒
🖐️♿WC🌳🍴♿👫♿🎧⚓♿

Serpentine Gallery

Kensington Gardens
London, W2 3XA
☎ 071 402 6075

End of Exhibition Rd, past Albert Memorial, in park

⊖ Lancaster Gate/South Ken.

Originally built as a tea pavilion, in 1912, by the architect Sir Henry Tanner. In 1970, it was launched as an art gallery by the Arts Council.

Jan–Dec: Mon–Sun 10am–6pm

F🚐☀P♿▟➤⌐🖐️WC WC♿
👫♿🗨️♿

Cutty Sark

King William Walk
Greenwich
London, SE10 9HT
☎ 081 853 3589

Greenwich

≋ Greenwich/Maze Hill

Only remaining example of Tea Clipper in world, built in 1869. Ship with 3 decks. Lower deck accessible by chair lift, upper deck inaccessible.

Jan–Dec: Mon–Sat 10am–5pm
Sun: 12noon–5pm

£©☀P𝒫♿▟🗃️🖐️♿WC♿
♿♿

LONDON

National Gallery

Trafalgar Square
London, WC2N 5DN
☎ 071 839 3321

Trafalgar Square
≋ ⊖ Charing Cross

One of the finest collections of art in the world.

Jan–Dec: Mon–Sat 10am–6pm
Sun 2pm–6pm
Mid July–Mid Aug: Mon–Fri 10am–8pm

F🚌✕ P 🖉 ☞ 🏠➤♿wc ⛲ 🍴
♿ ♨⚓ⓒ ♿

Greenwich Park

Greenwich
London, SE10 8QY
☎ 081 858 2608

Lewisham – Blackheath – Greenwich
≋ Blackheath/Maze Hill

Royal residence since 1300. Old Royal Observatory, National Maritime Museum. Deer herd, flower gardens, colour all year round. Good views of London.

Jan–Dec: Mon–Sun dawn–dusk

F🚌✕ P♿ P 🏠 ♿wc 🍴 ♨♿ ⌨

Dulwich Picture Gallery

College Rd
London, SE21 7AD
☎ 081 693 5254

Dulwich
≋ West Dulwich

The paintings are a fine collection of Oldmasters, originally bought for the King of Poland. The building was designed by Sir John Soane.

Jan–Dec: Tue–Fri 10am–1pm & 2pm–5pm
Sat 11am–1pm & 2pm–5pm
Sun 2pm–5pm

£©🚌✕ P P 🖉 ♿☞➤ 🏠♿
wc ⛲ ♨⚓ⓒ

Kew Bridge Steam Museum

Green Dragon Lane
Brentford, London, TW8 0EN
☎ 081 568 4757

M4, junc.2, A315
≋ Kew Bridge

Victorian steam engines, workshops, waterworks, railway and water supply displays.

Jan–Dec: Mon–Sun 11am–5pm

£©🚌✕ P ♿🏛➤ 🏠➤ 🍴 wc 🍴
⛲ ♨⚓📞🐶ⓒ

The Wallace Collection

Hertford House
Manchester Square
London, W1M 6BN
☎ 071 935 0687

Manchester Square
⊖ Bond St

Permanent collection of paintings, porcelain, furniture, arms and armour in impressive house which belonged to the Marquess of Hertford and was left to the Nation by Lady Wallace in 1897.

Jan–Dec: Mon–Sat 9am–5pm
Sun 2pm–5pm

F🚌✕ P 🖉 ⚓☞⬛🏠wc ⛲ ♿
🐶

Bethnal Green Museum of Childhood

Cambridge Heath Rd
London, E5 8PY
☎ 081 980 3204/4315

London
⊖ Bethnal Green

Collection of dolls, dolls houses, teddies & train sets. Children clothes, puppets and paper toys.

Jan–Dec: Mon–Thu/Sat 10am–6pm
Sun 2.30pm–5.30pm

F🚌✕ ⟨⟩ P ⚓☞⬛🏠➤♿
♿wc ⛲ ⛲ ♨🐶♿

Royal Academy of Arts

Burlington House
Piccadilly
London, W1V 0DS
☎ 071 439 7438

Central London
⊖ Green Park & Piccadilly Circus

Founded in 1768; famous for major loan exhibitions and summer ones in particular.

Jan–Dec: Mon–Sun 10am–6pm

£©🚌✕ ⟨⟩ P 🖉 ♿⚓🏠♿wc
🍴 ⛲ ♨◆🐶ⓒ♿

Design Museum

Butlers Wharf
London, SE1 2YD
☎ 071 403 6933

Butlers Wharf

≋ London Bridge ⊖ Tower Hill/Tower Gateway

Museum of everyday things: the first to explain how mass–produced consumer objects work, why they look the way they do and how the design contributes to the quality of our lives.

Jan–Dec: Tue–Sun & BH 11.30am–6.30pm

Bruce Castle Museum

Lordship Lane
Tottenham
London, N17 8NU
☎ 081 808 8772

North London

≋ Bruce Grove

Dates from the late C16th, with later additions. Rowland Hill, who invented the Penny Post, lived here. Middlesex Regimental Gallery.

Jan–Dec: Tue–Sun 1pm–5pm

Sir John Soane's Museum

13 Lincoln's Inn Fields
London, WC2A 3BP
☎ 071 430 0175

Central London

⊖ Holborn

Houses his collection of antiquities, books and works of art; these include two sets of paintings by William Hogarth.

Jan–Dec: Tue–Sat 10am–5pm
1st Tue of each month 6pm–9pm

Tower Bridge

London, SE1 2UP
☎ 071 403 3761

Central London

⊖ Tower Hill/London Bridge

Unique world famous bridge; exhibitions in the main towers; impressive panoramic views from enclosed, high walkways. Victorian steam machinery in museum.

Wheelchair users wishing to visit the bridge, advise the Head Supervisor prior to arrival by telephoning 071 407 5247

Apr–Oct: Mon–Sun 10am–6.30pm
Nov–Mar: Mon–Sun 10am–4.45pm

National Portrait Gallery

St Martins Place
London, WC2H 0HE
☎ 071 306 0955

St Martins Place

⊖ Leicester Sq/Charing X

Founded to collect the likenesses of famous British men and women who created and are still creating, the history and culture of the nation.

Jan–Dec: Mon–Fri 10am–5pm
Sat 10am–6pm
Sun 2pm–6pm

Westminster Cathedral

Victoria St
London, SW1P 1QW
☎ 071 834 7452

Victoria–London

≋ ⊖ Victoria

Largest Catholic church in Britain – Byzantine architecture – excellent marbles and mosaics. Home of Westminster Cathedral Choir.

Jan–Dec: Mon–Sun 7am–8pm
BH: 8am–4.30pm

Alexandra Palace & Park

Wood Green
London, N22 4AY
☎ 081 365 2121

On north circular rd.

≋ Alexandra Palace ⊖ Wood Green

Opened 1873; main attraction the Wills Concert Organ. Exhibitions, conferences, banquets and concerts.

Jan–Dec: Mon–Sun 10am–10pm

LONDON

Guiness World of Records

Trocadero Centre
Piccadilly Circus
London, W1V 7FD
☎ 071 439 7331

Piccadilly Circus

⊖ Piccadilly Circus

Brings the Guiness Book of Records to life using life size models, computer data banks and the latest audio visual technology.

Jan–Dec: Mon–Sun 10am–10pm

Imperial War Museum

Lambeth Rd
London, SE1 6HZ
☎ 071 416 5000

London

⇌ Waterloo ⊖ Lambeth North

Museum of the Year in 1990. Covers all aspects of C20th warfare from Flanders to the Gulf – wars which are part of family history.

Jan–Dec: Mon–Sun 10am–6pm

Florence Nightingale Museum

2 Lambeth Palace Rd
London, SE1 7EH
☎ 071 620 0374

A23, A22

⊖ Westminster/Waterloo

Opened in February 1989. Devoted to the life and work of Florence Nightingale, 'The Lady with the Lamp'. Won the London Tourist Board President's Marketing Award in 1991.

Jan–Dec: Tue–Sun 10am–4pm

The Queen's House

Romney Rd
Greenwich, London, SE10 9NF
☎ 081 858 4422

A2/A206

⇌ Maze Hill

A Royal Palace built for wife of Charles I. Restored to period of 1662. Contains a treasury and art collection of Dutch marine paintings. Royal apartments on 1st floor.

Apr–Sep: Mon–Sat 10am–6pm
Sun 12noon–6pm
Oct–Mar: Mon–Sat 10am–5pm
Sun 2pm–5pm

Old Royal Observatory

Greenwich Park
Greenwich, London, SE10 9NF
☎ 081 858 4422

A2

⇌ Maze Hill or Greenwich

Designed by Christopher Wren, these buildings housed the Royal Observatory from 1675 until 1947. It is the site of Longitude and origin of GMT. Beautiful Royal park, gardens and spectacular views.

Apr–Sep: Mon–Sat 10am–6pm
Sun 12noon–6pm
Oct–Nov: Mon–Sat 10am–5pm
Sun 2pm–5pm

National Maritime Museum

Romney Rd
Greenwich
London, SE10 9NF
☎ 081 858 4422

A2/A206

⇌ Maze Hill/Greenwich

Museum of maritime history of Britain. Many types of boats. Items from explorations of Captain Cook. Nelson memorabilia.

Apr–Sep: Mon–Sat 10am–6pm
Sun 2pm–6pm
Oct–Mar: Mon–Sat 10am–5pm
Sun 2pm–5pm

Rock Circus

London Pavilion
Piccadilly Circus
London, W1V 9LA
☎ 071 734 8025

Piccadilly Circus

⊖ Piccadilly Circus

Exhibition created by the Tussauds Group, telling the story of rock and pop music using

waxworks, animatronics, lasers and video.
Summer: Mon–Sun 10am–10pm
Winter: Mon–Sun 11am–9pm

£©🚌🚶P🅿♿🚗🏨→🚾🚾 WC♿♿

Cabinet War Rooms

Clive Steps
King Charles St
London, SW1A 2AQ
☎ 071 930 6961

Westminster

🚊 Victoria/Charing Cross ⊖ Westminster

The underground HQ used by Winston Churchill and the British Government in World War II.

Jan–Dec: Mon–Sun 10am–6pm

£©🚌🚶🛶🅿🚶🍴🚗🏨♿WC
🛒🎧♿©♿

The London Dungeon

28–34 Tooley St
London, SE1 2SZ
☎ 071 403 0606

Under London Bridge station

World famous medieval horror museum. Scenes of torture, disease and death in spine–chilling detail.

Apr–Sep: Mon–Sun 10am–5.30pm
Oct–Mar: Mon–Sun 10am–4.30pm

£©🚌🚶P🅿♿♿WC🍴🛒©

William Morris Gallery

Lloyd Park, Forest Rd
Walthamstow
London, E17 4PP
☎ 081 527 3782

Walthamstow

Boyhood home of William Morris; designer, poet and socialist. Collections of his work in arts and crafts movement. Scented garden within 4 acre Lloyd Park.

Jan–Dec: Tue–Sat 10am–1pm & 2pm–5pm
1st Sun each mth 10am–12noon &
2pm–5pm

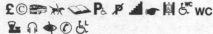

F🚌🚶🅿P♿🍴🚗🏨→♿
WC🛒♿♿©

Victoria & Albert Museum

Cromwell Rd
South Kensington, London, SW7 2RL
☎ 071 938 8500

South Kensington

🚊🚌 South Kensington

Britain's largest museum of design and the decorative arts. 10 acres with paved paths.

Jan–Dec: Mon–Sun 10am–6pm

F🚌🚶🛶🅿🍴🚗🏨🏨♿
WC♿🍴🛒♿🚗©♿

HM Tower of London

Tower Hill, London, EC3N 4AB
☎ 071 488 5695

London

🚊🚌 Fenchurch St ⊖ Tower Hill

900 years of history are encapsulated in this world–famous castle. Home of the Crown Jewels, Royal Armouries, Yeoman Warders and Ravens. 18 acres with cobbled and paved paths.

Mar–Oct: Mon–Sat 9.30am–6pm
Sun 2pm–6pm
Nov–Feb: Mon–Sat 9.30am–5pm

£©🚌🚶🛶P🅿♿🏨🏰
♿WC♿🍴🛒👥♿♿

Madame Tussaud's

Marylebone Rd
London, NW1 5LR
☎ 081 935 6861

West London

🚌 ⊖ Baker St

Wax exhibition of the famous and infamous with new themed areas throughout the exhibitions.

Jan–Dec: Mon–Sun 10am–5.30pm

£©🚌P♿🏨♿WC♿🍴🛒👥
♿🚗©©

Whitechapel Art Gallery

Whitechapel High St
London, E1 7QX
☎ 071 377 0107

Whitechapel High St

🚊 Liverpool St ⊖ Aldgate

Gallery opened in 1901 & administered by a charitable trust. Shows diverse range of temporary exhibitions & is known as one of the key galleries in Europe.

Jan–Dec: Tue–Sun 11am–5pm
Wed 11am–8pm

F� ✕ 𝒫 P ♿ ⬆ 🏨 ♿WC WC 🐕 🍴
🎫 🤲

Museum of the Moving Image

South Bank
Waterloo, London, SE1 8XT
☎ 071 928 3535
Underneath Waterloo Bridge
≥ 🚇 Waterloo

Museum about the history of cinema and television. Emphasis on hands–on participation.

Jan–Dec: Mon–Sun 10am–6pm

£ © 🚌 ✕ 𝒫 🔍 P♿ P ⬆ 🏨 ♿WC WC
🍴 🗺 ♿ 🤲 🎫

The Natural History Museum

Cromwell Rd
London, SW7 5BD
☎ 071 938 9123
South Kensington
≥ Victoria ⊖ South Kensington

Home of the national collections of natural history, including the dinosaurs. Housed in a splendid Victorian building.

Jan–Dec: Mon–Sun 9am–5pm

£ © 🚌 ✕ P♿ P ⛴ ⛵ 🏨 🔌 ♿WC WC
🐕 🍴 🗺 ♿ 🎫 © 🎫

Royal Air Force Museum

Grahame Park Way
London, NW9 5LL
☎ 081 200 1751
M1 (southbound) A1/A41/A5
⊖ Colindale

On the site of the historic Hendon Aerodrome, 3 large exhibition halls display 70 full size aircraft.

Jan–Dec: Mon–Sun 10am–6pm

£ © 🚌 ✕ P ♿ 🏨 ➤ 🔌 ⇒ ♿WC WC
🐕 🍴 🗺 ♿ ♿ 🎧 ✈ ♿ © 🎫

Kensington Palace State Apartments

Kensington
London, W8 4PX
☎ 071 937 9561
Kensington High St, Kensington Rd
⊖ High St Kensington & Queensway
William–de–Orange and Queen Victoria

lived at Kensington in the past; now the home of the Prince and Princess of Wales.

Summer: Mon–Sat 9am–5pm
Sun 11am–5pm
Winter: Mon–Sat 9am–dusk

£ © 🚌 ✕ P♿ P ♿ 🔍 🏛 🔌 ⬅ ♿
WC 🍴 🗺 🎪 ♿ ♿

London Transport Museum

The Piazza
Covent Garden, London, WC2E 7BB
☎ 071 379 6344
Covent Garden, London
≥ Charing Cross 🚇 Strand/Holborn ⊖
Covent Garden

Formerly the site of the Covent Garden Flower Market, the museum houses London Transport's collection of historic vehicles and memorabilia. Zimmer available.

Jan–Dec: Mon–Sun 10am–6pm

£ © 🚌 ✕ 𝒫 P ♿ ♿WC WC 🐕 🗺
🤲

Tate Gallery

Millbank, London, SW1P 4RG
☎ 071 821 1313
Millbank
≥ Vauxhall ⊖ Pimlico

Houses the national collections of British painting from the C16th, including the Turner Bequest and C20th foreign painting and sculpture.

Jan–Dec: Mon–Sat 10am–5.50pm
Sun 2pm–5.50pm
Closed Good Fri, Xmas Eve & May Day BH

£ F © 🚌 ✕ 𝒫 🔍 P P ♿ ⛴ ⛵
🏨 ♿WC WC 🍴 🗺 🎪 🎧 ✈ © ♿

The Iveagh Bequest, Kenwood EH

Hampstead Lane
London, NW3 7JR
☎ 081 348 1286
Between Hampstead and Highgate villages
🚇 Hampstead Lane

Standing in its own splendid grounds on the edge of Hampstead Heath, Kenwood contains one of the most important private collections of paintings to be given to the nation this century.

1 Apr–30 Sep: Mon–Sun 10am–6pm
1 Oct–31 Mar: Mon–Sun 10am–4pm

Do you know about The Talking Book Service for those who aren't visually impaired?

Thousands of people who are unable to read because of accident, illness, disability, or learning difficulties can benefit from our library which offers a special tape player and unlimited access to over 2,500 unabridged books, postage paid both ways, for an annual subscription of £15.

NATIONAL LISTENING LIBRARY

12 Lant Street, London SE1 1QH.
Tel: 071 407 9417

LONDON

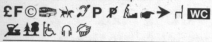

Westminster Abbey

20 Dean's Yard
Westminster, London, SW1P 3PA
☎ 071 222 5152

≋ Victoria and Waterloo ⊖ Westminster

An architectural masterpiece of the C13–16th, Westminster Abbey also presents a unique pageant of British history.

Jan–Dec: Mon–Sat 9am–5pm

£F©🚌✕✎P✗🔦☞➜⊣WC
🎿🌲👥🎧🐾

Science Museum

Exhibition Rd
London, SW7 2DD
☎ 071 938 8000

Kensington

⊖ South Kensington

World firsts in profusion: including steam engines, steam turbines and 600 working exhibits. Many encourage the visitor to experience science and technology 'hands on'.

Jan–Dec: Mon–Sat 10am–6pm
Sun 11am–6pm

£©🚌✕👓P↕P🔦⊣➾
⊱WC🐑¶🎿🌲👥🐾⊙↕

Rangers House EH

Chesterfield Rd
Blackheath, London, SE10
☎ 081 853 0035

Blackheath

≋ Maze Hill 🚌 Plumstead

A handsome red brick villa built 1700 on the edge of Greenwich Park, with a splendid bow–windowed gallery. It houses a remarkable series of Jacobean portraits and a collection of musical instruments.

Jan–Dec: Mon–Sun 10am

F🚌✕P✗↕◢☞🔦↕WC🐑🎧
🐾⊙

Chiswick House EH

Burlington Lane
London, W4
☎ 081 995 0508

Hammersmith

≋ Chiswick 🚌 Hammersmith–Staines ⊖
Turnham Green

One of the first English Palladian villas dating from 1725, which was built for Lord Burlington. The interior decoration is by William Kent, as are the beautiful Italianate gardens, with classical statues and neoclassical temples. Exhibition on the ground floor with a film telling the story of the house and gardens.

1 Apr–30 Sep: Mon–Sun 10am–6pm
1 Oct–31 Mar: Tue–Sun 10am–4pm

£©🚌✕P P🔦🔦➜↕WC¶
🎿🎿🐑🎧

The M.C.C. Museum

Lord's Cricket Ground
London NW8
☎ 071 289 1611

⊖ St.John's Wood

Collection of cricket memorabilia, sporting paintings and extensive cricket library.

Open match days Mon–Sat 10.30am–5pm & Sun Noon–5pm to visitors who have paid ground admission.
Tour of Lord's most days 12noon & 2pm.
Prior booking advisable.

£©🚌✕P🔦◢☞🔦⊣↕⊱
WC🎿🐑🐾🐾

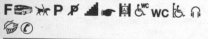

NOTES

NOTES

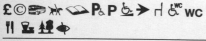

MERSEYSIDE

Southport Zoological Park

Princes Park
Southport, Merseyside, PR8 1RK
☎ 0704 538102

Town centre

⇌ 🚌 Southport

The home of over 800 exotic animals living and breeding in family groups. Many endangered in the wild, all dependent on people who care for them.

Jan–Dec: Mon–Sun 10am

£ © 🚌 🐾 🗺️ P P ♿ ✈ ⊣ 🚾 WC
🍴 🎿 🌲 🐾 🦆

NORFOLK

Sheringham Park NT

Gardeners Cottage
Upper Sheringham
Sheringham, Norfolk, NR26 8TB
☎ 0263 823778

Sheringham Junction A148/B1157

to entrance

Greatest work of Humphrey Repton – landscape designer. 50 acres of wild garden featuring Rhododendrons (May/June). 770 acres with dressed tar surfaces and woodland tracks.

Jan–Dec: Mon–Sun Dawn–Dusk

£ P P wc

wc

Thetford Forest Park FC

Santon Downham
Brandon, Norfolk, IP27 0TJ
☎ 0842 810271

Thetford/Brandon

Britain's largest lowland forest, first planted from 1922. Arboretum with daffodils in spring. High Lodge Centre provides walks. 50,000 acres with sand and grass paths.

Forest: Jan–Dec
High Lodge: Easter–Oct

£ © P P wc wc

The North End Trust – Fishing Heritage Ctr

True Yard's
King's Lynn
Norfolk, PE30 1QW
☎ 0553 770479

King's Lynn

King's Lynn

A visual record of a unique community. Shop, tea rooms, museum, restored fishing cottages and an old Lynn fishing smach, 'The Activity'. The whole area has been designed with disabled people very much in mind. Paved paths.

Jan–Dec: Mon–Sun 9.30am–4.30pm

£ © wc

wc ©

Titchwell Marsh Nature Reserve RSPB

Titchwell
King's Lynn, Norfolk, PE31 8BB
☎ 0485 210432

King's Lynn/Hunstanton A149

Lagoons and reed bed created by the RSPB from flooded farmland. Breeding Avocet, Bittern, Marsh Harrier, Passage Waders and Wildfowl. 520 acres with gravel paths. One hide is only accessible via the beach.

Reserve: Jan–Dec Mon–Sun
Visitor Centre: 1 Apr–31 Oct: Mon–Sun: 10am–5pm
1 Nov–31 Mar: Mon–Sun: 10am–4pm

£ © P wc wc

Norfolk Lavender

Caley Mill
Heacham
King's Lynn, Norfolk
☎ 0485 70384

King's Lynn 12 miles on A149 to Hunstanton

King's Lynn Hunstanton

Lavender farm with gardens of lavender, herbs and roses. Guided tours available. 7 acres with paved paths.

Jan–Dec: Mon–Sun 10am–5pm

F P P wc wc

©

Thrigby Hall Wildlife Gardens

Filby
Great Yarmouth, Norfolk, NR29 3DR
☎ 0493 369 477

Between Acle and Caister off A1064

Specialist collection of Asian animals in the 250 year old landscaped grounds of Thrigby Hall. Tigers, gibbons & crocodiles. 11 acres with smooth concrete and some gravel paths.

Jan–Dec: Mon–Sun from 10am

£ © P P wc wc

©

NORFOLK

Norwich Castle Museum

Castle Meadow
Norwich, Norfolk, NR1 3JU
☎ 0603 223624

Centre of Norwich

≷ 🚐 Norwich

Varied museum housed in Norman Castle and Victorian Prison. Specialities are Norwich school paintings, natural history, archaeology, and world's largest collection of teapots. Paved paths.

Jan–Dec: Mon–Sat 10am–5pm
Sun 2pm–5pm

£ © 🚌 🕱 🅿️ P ♿ 🚻 ➤ ⊣ ⊢ ♿ WC
🛝 ❚❚ 🧺 🎪 🏛 🐾 🄯 ♿

The Norfolk Shire Horse Centre

West Runton Stables
West Runton, Norfolk, NR27 9QH
☎ 026 375 339

A149

≷ 🚐 West Runton

Shire horses demonstrated working daily. Native ponies, small animals, rural collection and bygones, photographs and video. 8 acres with concrete and short grass paths.

Good Fri–31 Oct: Sun–Fri 10am–5pm

£ © 🚌 🕱 🅿️ 🕱 ♿ ➤ ⊣ ♿ WC ❚❚
🧺 🎪 🄯

Kingdom of the Sea – Hunstanton

Southern Promenade
Hunstanton, Norfolk
☎ 0485 533576

Hunstanton A10 from King's Lynn

🚐 Hunstanton

British marine life on a breathtaking scale. All year, all weather marine attraction. Over 20 natural settings with sea creatures in their own environment. Seal hospital.

Jan–Dec: Mon–Sun from 10am

£ © 🚌 🕱 P ♿ ♿ WC 🛝 ❚❚ 🧺 🎪
🐾 🄯

Kingdom of the Sea – Great Yarmouth

Marine Parade
Great Yarmouth, Norfolk
☎ 0493 330631

Great Yarmouth A12

🚐 Great Yarmouth

British marine life on a breathtaking scale; all year, all weather attraction. Over 25 natural settings with sea creatures in their own environment. Includes a display of sharks.

Jan–Dec: Mon–Sun: from 10am

£ © 🚌 🕱 P 🕱 ♿ ♿ WC 🛝 ❚❚ 🧺
🎪 🐾 🄯

Cathedral of St John the Baptist

Earlham Road
Norwich, Norfolk, NR1 2PA
☎ 0603 624615

Norwich, A11, A47

Built in early English style in 1880 by the Duke of Norfolk. Cathedral for Roman Catholic Diocese of East Anglia. Paved paths.

Mon–Fri: 8am–3.30pm
Sat–Sun: 8am–7.30pm

F 🕱 🕱 P 🍴 🍲 ⊣ WC ❚❚ 🧺 ♿

Fritton Lake & Country Park

Fritton
Great Yarmouth, Norfolk, NR31 9HA
☎ 0493 488208

Lowestoft A143

≷ 🚐 Great Yarmouth

250 acre landscaped park overlooking beautiful tree–lined lake. Waterfowl reserve, barbeque area, old world garden and fishing. Specially designed boat for wheelchair users. Pottery workshop. Gravel paths.

1 Apr–28 Sep:

£ © 🚌 🕱 🅿️ P ♿ ➤ ⊣ ⇒ 👁 ♿
WC 🛝 ❚❚ 🧺 🎪 🐾 🄯 ♿

Banham Zoo & Appleyard Craft Court

The Grove
Banham, Norfolk, NR16 2HB
☎ 095 387 476

Attleborough A11

🚐 Norwich

Over 20 acres of monkey sanctuary & spectacular wildlife, specialising in rare and endangered species. Ice cream parlour, zoo train, bakery, craft court and cidery. Gravel paths surround.

Jan–Dec: Mon–Sun 10am–6pm or dusk

£ © 🚌 🕱 🚢 🅿️ P ♿ ➤ ♿ WC 🛝
❚❚ 🧺 🎪 🐾 🄯 ♿

Walsingham Abbey Grounds & Ruins

c/o Walsingham Estate Co
Estate Office
Walsingham, Norfolk, NR22 6BP
☎ 0328 820259

Fakenham

≋ 🚌 King's Lynn

Site of Walsingham Priory: now known as Walsingham Abbey with its Great Arch. Ruins and gardens. 10 acres with gravel paths.

Apr: Wed/Sat: 2pm–5pm
May–Jul: Wed/Sat/Sun: 2pm–5pm
Aug: Mon/Wed/Fri/Sat/Sun: 2pm–5pm
Sep: Wed/Sat/Sun: 2pm–5pm
BH's: Easter–Sep

£ © 🚌 ⚡ 🅿 ⚡ ➤ ⊓ ⇒ 🚾 WC
⚡ ⚡

Sainsbury Centre for Visual Arts

University of East Anglia
Norwich, Norfolk, NR4 7TJ
☎ 0603 56060

Earlham/Watton Road (B1108) out of Norwich

≋ 🚌 Thorpe

The Sainsbury Centre for visual arts, and its recently opened crescent wing, were designed by Sir Norman Foster to house the Robert and Lisa Sainsbury Collection. 700 paintings, sculptures and ceramics are on permanent display with Picasso, Moore, Bacon and Giacometti, shown alongside art from Africa, the Pacific and the Americas.

Jan–Dec: Tue–Sun 12 noon–5pm

£ © 🚌 ⚡ 🅿 🅿 ⚡ ⚡ 🚾 WC ⚡
⚡ ⚡ ⚡ ⚡ © ⚡

Langham Glass

The Long Barn
North St
Langham
Holt, Norfolk, NR25 7DG
☎ 0328 830511

Holt

Glassmakers working with molten glass in lovely flint faced Norfolk barn. Complex dated 1722. Play area. 3 acres with paved paths.

Jan–Dec: Mon–Sun
Closed: 25 Dec–1 Jan

£ © 🚌 ⚡ 🅿 🅿 ⚡ ➤ ⊓ ⚡ ⚡
WC ⚡ ⚡ ⚡ ⚡ © ⚡

Houghton Hall

Houghton
King's Lynn
Norfolk, PE31 6UE
☎ 0485 528569

King's Lynn 14 miles – Fakenham 10 miles

Superb state rooms with many of the original furnishings by William Kent and others. Beautiful parkland containing a herd of white fallow deer. Stables with heavy horses, shetland ponies and Llamas. One of the most important collections of 20,000 model soldiers and militaria in the world. Cobbled paths.

Easter Sun–Last Sun in Sep: Thu/Sun/BH: 12.30pm–5.30pm

£ © 🚌 ⚡ 🅿 🅿 ⚡ ⚡ ➤ 🚾 WC
⚡ ⚡ ⚡ ⚡ ⚡

The Bygone Village

Fleggburgh
Gt Yarmouth, Norfolk, NR29 3AF
☎ 0493 369770

Gt Yarmouth A1064

Reconstruction of a C19th village in 40 acres of parkland. Collections of steam engines, vintage vehicles, motor cycles, gypsy wagons, street organs and the magnificent set of Savage Galloping Horses.

Apr–Sep: Mon–Sun 10am–6pm (Reduced facilities on Sat)
Oct–Mar: grounds only Please check.

£ © 🚌 ⚡ 🅿 ⚡ ➤ ⚡ 🚾 WC ⚡ ⚡
⚡ ⚡

Forge Museum

Church St
North Creake
Fakenham, Norfolk, NR21 9AD
☎ 0328 738910

Fakenham B1355

Working forge with blacksmith working in the old original way. Small museum alongside, which is of great historical interest. 114 acres with gravel paths.

May–30 Sep: Mon–Sun 12noon–5pm

£ ⚡ 🅿 ⚡ ⚡ ⇒ 🚾 WC ⚡ ⚡

NORFOLK

Norfolk Rural Life Museum and Union Farm

Gressenhall
Dereham, Norfolk, NR20 4DR
☎ 0362 860563

East Dereham A47

C18th workhouse, with extensive displays on Norfolk life. Edwardian cottage and garden, Craftsmen's Row. Working 1920's farm with rare breeds. 30 acres. Sympathetic Hearing Scheme and information for disabled people to be introduced in 1992.

Easter Sun–31 Oct: Tue–Sat 10am–5pm
Sun 2pm–5.30pm

£ © 🚌 ✈ ⟡ P♿ P ♿ ✈ ⊣ ♿ WC 👥
🍴 ⚓ 👥 🎧 ♿

Strumpshaw Fen RSPB

Nr Norwich
Norfolk
☎ 0603 715191

Signposted from Brundall off A47 Norwich–Gt Yarmouth road.

Accessible hide nearby (50yds) affords views of the main broad and reeds. Wheelchairs can be pushed with effort for further half mile through woodlands to a point overlooking grazing marshes, colourful with flowers in mid–summer. Bean geese, wigeon etc, may be watched from a car from Dec–Feb on nearby Buckenham Marshes.

£ 🅿 ♿ WC

Titchwell Marsh RSPB

Nr Hunstaton
Norfolk
☎ 0485 210432

On A149 between Thornham and Titchwell villages.

Access along firm, if a little uneven, bank to two hides adapted for wheelchair users, overlooking large lagoon and reedbed. Distances 500 and 900 yards with benches 450, 700 and 850 yards.

£ ♿ WC ♿

Snettisham RSPB

Nr King's Lynn
Norfolk
☎ 0485 542689

Signposted from A149 King's Lynn–Hunstanton road in Snettisham village.

Cars with disabled visitors are permitted to drive down private road through holiday chalets and on to the first hide adapted for wheelchair access. Excellent wader watching on a rising tide. Please contact Warden in advance.

WC ♿

The Muckleburgh Collection

Weybourne
Holt, Norfolk, NR25 7EG
☎ 026 370 210

Sheringham A149

The largest private military collection in the UK. 3000 exhibits. Norfolk Yeomanry history, tanks, guns, Gulf War, aircraft, life boats, radar, etc. 500 acres.

Easter–31 Oct: Mon–Sun 10am–5pm
Nov–Xmas: Sun

£ © 🚌 ✈ ⟡ P♿ P ♿ ♿ WC 🍴
⚓ 👥 ☕ ⊘ ♿

Great Yarmouth Museums' Galleries

Central Library
Tolhouse St
Great Yarmouth, Norfolk, NR30 2SH
☎ 0493 858900

A12 and A47

 Great Yarmouth

Galleries built 1961 as part of Library; adjoins Tolhouse Museum. Temporary exhibition programme, mostly paintings. Includes Great Yarmouth Museums' own pictures. Paved paths.

Jan–Dec: Mon–Fri 9.30am–5.30pm
Sat 9am–12.30pm
Sun 1.30pm–5pm
Closed: between exhibitions

F 🚌 ✈ P ♿ 🚽 ✈ WC ♿ ☕

Pettitts Crafts & Gardens

Camphill
Reedham, Norwich, NR13 3UA
☎ 0493 700094

Great Yarmouth A47

≈ Reedham

Birds of prey, pheasants, peacocks & waterfowl in gardens. Miniature horses and adventure playground with miniature railway.

Easter Sun–31 Oct: Mon–Fri 10am–6pm

Sun 1pm–5.30pm

£©⛟✳️♿🅿️⚓➜⌐🚾♿
🍴🎪⛺♿🐟☉♿

The Fairhaven Garden Trust

2 The Woodlands
Wymers Lane
South Walsham, Norfolk, NR13 6EA
☎ 060549 449

9m NE Norwich on the B1140

🚌 Norwich

Opened in 1975. 30 acres of Broad with
woodland walk. 900 year old oak,
candelabra primulas, primroses, native wild
flowers, rhododendrons and azaleas.

Apr–May: Sun/BH's 11am–6pm
May–Sep: Wed–Sun 11am–6pm
& BH's: Sat 2pm–6pm
Sep 20/27: Sun 11am–6pm

£©⛟✳️🅿️⚓➜⌐🚾🍴🎪♿

Felbrigg Hall NT

Roughton
Norwich, Norfolk, NR11 8PR
☎ 026375 444

2m S of Cromer off A148

� Cromer 2m

One of the finest C17th houses in Norfolk.
Original C18th furniture and pictures.
Outstanding walled garden. Walks in mature
woodland and around lake. 1,770 acres with
gravel paths.

Mar–Nov: Mon/Wed/Thu/Sat 11am–5.30pm
(Garden)
1.30pm–5.30pm (House)

£©⛟✳️⚲📷🅿️♿🔌🏯➜
⌐🚂♿🚾⛟🍴🎪♿🐟☉

Blakeney Point NT

Holt, Norfolk
☎ 0263 740080

3½ mile long sand and shingle spit, summer
home for over eleven species of seabird.
Please contact Warden well in advance of
visit.

♿🚾 ♿

Brancaster NT

Nr Hinstanton
Norfolk

On N coast, between Hinstanton and Wells.
Access to Brancaster Beach and Staithe.

NORTHAMPTONSHIRE

Sheringham Park NT

Upper Sheringham, Norfolk
☎ 0263 823778

90 acre landscaped park on the North
Norfolk coast near Cromer. Boarded
walkway for wheelchair users from the car
park to three viewpoints, including a section
of rhododendron drive. Main drive to Hall
(not open to vehicles) resurfaced, but uphill
back to car park. Adapted WC.

NORTHAMPTONSHIRE

Wicksteed Leisure Park

Kettering
Northants. NN15 6NJ
☎ 0536 512475

A6 South of Kettering Town Centre

≈ Kettering

A park of 150 acres with a 30 acre boating
lake and tarmac paths. Paid for rides and
amusements. Large free playground with
safety surfaces.

Good Fri–30 Sept: from 10.30

F⛟✳️🅿️🅿️♿➜⌐🏯♿🚾⛟
🍴🎪⛺☉☉

Central Museum and Art Gallery

Guildhall Road
Northampton, Northants. NN1 1DP
☎ 0604 39415

Northampton town centre

≈🚌 Northampton

Largest collection of boots and shoes in the
world; Northampton's history from Stone
Age to present; Fine and decorative arts;
Temporary exhibitions.

Mon–Sat: 10am–5pm
Thurs: 10am–8pm
Sun: 2pm–5pm

F⛟✳️🅿️✏️♿🏯♿🚾🍴⛺
♿☉

Canal Museum

Stoke Bruerne
Towcester, Northants. NN12 7SE
☎ 0604 862229

Northampton A508/Towcester A5

200 years of colourful canal history, housed
in a restored canalside mill building. One
acre with solid towpaths.

Easter–Oct: Mon–Sun: 10am–6pm
Nov–Easter: Tue–Sun: 10am–4pm

£⛟✳️🅿️📖🏯➜⌐🏯♿⛺🎪♿

NORTHAMPTONSHIRE

Derngate Arts Centre

19/21 Guildhall Rd
Northants. NN1 1DP
☎ 0604 26222

Northampton M1 Junction 15,15a and 16
⇌ 🚌 Northampton

Multi–purpose theatre/arts/entertainments facility. Also used for conferences/exhibitions and product launches. Marble and carpeted floors.

Sept–July Mon–Sun

Southwick Hall

Southwick
Peterborough, Northants., PE8 5BL
☎ 0832 274064

3 miles north of Oundle off A605

Manor house dating from C14th with Elizabethan and Georgian additions. Exhibitions of Victorian and Edwardian costumes and country bygones. 5 acres with grass paths.

BH Mon & Suns: Easter–Aug
Weds only: May–Aug

Hunsbury Hill Ironstone Railway Museum

Danes Camp Road
Northampton
☎ 0858 89216

Northampton A43 to Danes Camp Rd
⇌ 🚌 Northampton

History of Iron Ore quarrying and transport in Northants. 2 mile passenger carrying railway, designed to take wheelchair users. 7½ acres with gravel, grass and crushed ore paths.

Museum: Jan–Dec Sun 11am–5pm
Railway: May BH–30 Sep Sun 2pm–5pm

Stoke Park Gardens

Stoke Bruerne
Towcester, Northants., NN12 7RZ
☎ 0604 862172

Off A508 Milton Keynes–Northampton
⇌ Northampton

Two C17th pavilions attributed to Inigo Jones, set in extensive gardens. 8 acres with gravel, grass and paving.

Jun/Jul/Aug: Sat–Sun 2pm–6pm

Barnwell Country Park

Oundle, Northants., PE8 5PB
☎ 0832 273435

Oundle
🚌 Oundle

Restored gravel workings now a haven for wildlife. 37 acres with gravel and grass paths. Free fishing for disabled people.

Jan–Dec: Mon–Sun

Brigstock Country Park

Lyveden Road
Brigstock
Kettering, Northants., NN14 3HS
☎ 0536 373625

A6116
🚌 Kettering

Offers informal countryside recreation, picnics, walks, wildlife observation, childrens playarea. Visitor centre and ranger service. 37 acres with crushed stone paths.

Jan–Dec: Mon–Sun 8.30am–6pm

Sywell Country Park

Washbrook Lane
Ecton, Northants., NN6 0QX
☎ 0604 810970

Off A4500 Northampton–Wellingborough

The park consists of pastureland around a disused reservoir and a butterfly garden and arboretum area below the dam. Two car parks.

Summer: Mon–Sun 8.30am–6pm
Winter: Mon–Sun 8.30am–5pm

Irchester Country Park

Gypsy Lane

Little Irchester,
Northants., NN9 7DL
☎ 0933 276866

Wellingborough B570 off A509

≽ Wellingborough

Mixed woodland and meadows on former ironstone workings. Larch, pine & alder. Goldcrest, sparrowhawk & all three woodpecker species. 200 acres with crushed stone and compact earth paths.

Summer: Mon–Sun 8.30am–6pm
Winter: Mon–Sun 8.30am–5pm

Museum of Leathercraft

Bridge St
Northampton, Northants., NN1 1PA
☎ 0604 39415

Northampton

≽ 🚌 Northampton

Collections of fine leathercraft from Ancient Egypt to present day. Highlights include drinking vessels, gilt leather, furniture and American Indian costume.

Jan–Dec: Mon–Sat 10am–5pm

NORTHUMBERLAND

Tower House Pottery

Tower Rd
Tweedmouth
Berwick, Northumberland, TD15 2BD
☎ 0289 307314

A1 road Berwick

≽ 🚌 Berwick

Pottery and showroom making traditional slipware. Hand thrown decorative coloured earthenware. Personalised orders made.

Jan–Dec: Sun–Fri

Woodhorn Colliery Museum

Woodhorn
Ashington, Northumberland
☎ 0670 856968

Just off A189 east of Ashington

This new museum, situated within the Queen Elizabeth II Silver Jubilee Park, is the first phase of an exciting venture to develop some of the original Woodhorn colliery

buildings into a centre for the mining heritage of South East Northumberland. Paved paths around the museum.

Sep–Apr: Wed–Sun & BH 10am–4pm
May–Aug: Wed–Sun & BH 11am–5pm

Woodhorn Church Museum

Woodhorn
Ashington, Northumberland
☎ 0670 817371

Just off A189 east of Ashington

Although still consecrated, the Church hosts a lively programme of temporary exhibitions with supporting demonstrations, talks and children's workshops. Sales area of local crafts.

Sep–Apr: Wed–Sun & BH 10am–12.30pm & 1pm–4pm
May–Aug: Wed–Sun & BH 11am–12.30pm & 1pm–5pm

Hexham Herbs

Chesters Walled Garden
Chollerford
Hexham, Northumberland
☎ 0434 681483

6 miles north of Hexham, off B6318

≽ 🚌 Hexham

Unique herb collection in 2 acres of walled garden. Beautifully laid out with wide gravel paths and box–edged beds. National collection of thyme, Roman garden and woodland walk. Gold medal winning nursery sells plants.

Mar–Oct: Mon–Sun 10am–5pm
Nov–Feb: Mon–Sun pls tel.

Meldon Park

Morpeth, Northumberland, NE61 3SW
☎ 067 072 661

Morpeth A1 then B6343 west to Hartburn

≽ 🚌 Morpeth

Built for Cookson Family in 1832 by John Dobson, the famous architect. Tour of main downstair rooms and garden. The Wild Garden is spectacular with several different coloured rhododendrons in June. 10 acres with gravel paths.

NORTHUMBERLAND

Kirkley Hall College Garden

Ponteland
Newcastle-on-Tyne
Northumberland, NE20 0AQ
☎ 0661 860808

Ponteland

35,000 different species and varieties.
Ornamented boarders, Sunken Garden,
greenhouses, displays and garden trails. 6
acres with gravel, paved and some lawn
paths. All areas can be seen from level
route.

Jan–Dec: Mon–Sun 10am–dusk

The Maltings Arts Centre

Eastern Lane
Berwick upon Tweed
Northumberland, TD15 9DT
☎ 0289 330 999

Centre of Berwick–upon–Tweed, access via
A1

� 🚌 Berwick

The Maltings is the country's newest Arts
Centre in the delightful setting of a historic
border town. There is a year round
programme of outstanding events to suit all
ages. Paved paths.

Jan–Dec: Mon–Sun

Prudhoe Castle EH

Prudhoe
Northumberland, NE42 6NA
☎ 0661 33459

Prudhoe A695 Hexham–Blaydon

≈ 🚌 Prudhoe

Early C12th castle with later additions.
Exhibition of castle's history and video
presentation on ground floor of C19th
manor house. Gravel paths. Moat, outer
Bailey and Pele Yard are inaccessible.

Apri–Sep: Mon–Sun 10am–6pm
Oct–Mar: Wed–Sun 10am–4pm

Warkworth Castle EH

Nr Amble
Morpeth, Northumberland, NE65 0UJ
☎ 0665 711423

Amble A1068

≈ Alnmouth

C15th keep, dominating the village of
Warkworth. Owned by the Percy family
since 1332. 2 acres of hilly ground.

1 Apr–30 Sep: Mon–Sun 10am–6pm
1 Oct–31 Mar: Tue–Sun 10am–4pm

Heatherslaw Corn Mill

Ford & Etal Estates
Berwick–upon–Tweed
Northumberland, TD12 4TJ
☎ 089 082 338/297

Between Wooller and Coldstream A697

≈ 🚌 Berwick

A restored and working C19th
waterpowered corn mill, producing pearl
barley and wholemeal flour. Demonstrations
and exhibitions daily. 4 acres with paved
paths.

Easter–31 Oct: Mon–Sun 10am–6pm
Winter: By prior arrangement

Wallington House NT

Cambo
Nr Morpeth
Northumberland, NE61 4AR
☎ 067 074 283

A696, 6 miles NW of Belsey, then B6342

≈ 🚌 Morpeth

Built on site of castle in 1688, altered in
1740's. C19th hall, paintings by William Bell
Scott. Dolls house collection, walled garden
and conservatory. 100 acres of woodlands
and lakes with tarmac and gravel paths.

HOUSE: 1 Apr–31 Oct: Wed–Mon
1pm–5.30pm
GROUNDS: Jan–Dec: Mon–Sun Daylight
hours

Kielder Castle

Kielder Village
Hexham
Northumberland, NE48 1ER
☎ 0434 250209

30 miles north of Hexham

Kielder Castle has a forestry commission visitor centre and an art gallery. Dukes trail has a 1km forest walk through trees and fields. Gravel and paved paths.

Easter–30 Sep: Mon–Sun 10am–5pm

Northumberland Wildlife Trust

Hauxley Nature Reserve
Hauxley–Amble
Alnwick, Northumberland
☎ 0665 711578

Amble A1068
⇌ Acklington (4 miles)

Created after opencast mining by British Coal and developed by the trust. Visitor centre. 60 acres including islands, lakes and rare species of wildfowl.

Jan–Dec: Mon–Sun 9am–dusk

Norselands Gallery

The Old School
Warenford
Belford, Northumberland, NE70 7HY
☎ 0668 213 465

Belford A1

Converted school to gallery of British crafts and ceramic workshop including Bonsai House Aviary. Paved paths.

Summer: Mon–Sun 9am–9pm
Winter: Mon–Sun 9am–5pm

Chantry Bagpipe Museum

Bridge St
Morpeth, Northumberland
☎ 0670 519466

Morpeth, off A1
⇌ Morpeth

Specializes in the history and development of Northumbrian small pipes and their music, set in the context of bagpipes

around the world.

Jan–Feb: Mon–Sat 10am–4pm
Mar–Dec: Mon–Sat 9.30am–5.30pm

House of Hardy Museum

Willowburn
Alnwick, Northumberland, NE66 2PG
☎ 0665 510027

Alnwick
⇌ Alnmouth

Shows House of Hardy products from 1872, mainly fishing tackle, but includes golf clubs, guns, archery bows and tennis rackets.

Jan–Dec: Mon–Fri 9am–5pm
Sat 10am–5pm
Sun 1.30pm–5pm

The Chantry Craft Centre

Bridge St
Morpeth, Northumberland, NE61 1PJ
☎ 0670 511217

Morpeth A192 or A197, just off A1
⇌ Morpeth

Stone building dating from C13th. Variety of goods produced by over 40 local craftsmen.

Jan–Feb: Mon–Sat 10am–4pm Closed BH
Mar–Dec: Mon–Sat 9.30am–5.30pm
Jun–Aug: Mon–Sat 9.30am–5.30pm
Sun 10am–5pm

Redesdale Dairy & Riding Centre

Soppitt Farm
Otterburn, Northumberland
☎ 0830 20506

Otterburn – A696 on B6341

Farmhouse cheese making, farm shop, riding centre and sculptoress. 3 acres with gravel and paved paths.

Easter–1st Oct: 10am–5.30pm
2nd Oct–Easter: 10am–2.30pm (shop only)

Cragside House & Country Park

Rothbury
Morpeth, Northumberland, NE65 7PX
☎ 0699 20333

15 miles NW of Morpeth, off A697

Morpeth/Tropton to Reivers Gate

Victorian mansion in 900 acre park with tarmac and gravel paths. Created by the first Lord Armstrong. First house in the world to be lit by hydro–electricity.

House: Easter–31 Oct: Tue–Sun & BH Mon 1pm–5.30pm
Country Park: 29th Mar–end Oct: Mon–Sun 10.30am–7pm
Nov–Mar Sat–Sun 10.30am–4pm

Berwick Barracks

The Parade
Berwick–upon–Tweed
Northumberland, TD15 1DQ
☎ 0289 330933

Berwick town centre

Berwick

Earliest purpose built infantry barracks in UK, dating from 1721. Now houses 3 museums: Kings Own Scottish Borderers Regimental Museum, English Heritage and Berwick Borough Museum. 1½ acres with paved paths.

Summer: Mon–Sun 10am–6pm
Winter: Tue–Sun 10am–4pm

Berwick Museum & Art Galleries

Berwick KOSB Museum

Berwick Barracks EH

Corbridge Roman Site

Corbridge, Northumberland, NE45 5NT
☎ 0434 632349

Corbridge, A69 Newcastle–Carlisle

Corbridge

Series of excavated remains providing evidence of a succession of forts. A military depot and town includes well preserved

granaries. 4 acres with grass and paved paths.

Gd Fri or 1 Apr–30 Sep: Mon–Sun 10am–6pm
1 Oct–Maun Thu: Mon–Sun 10am–4pm

Chesters Roman Fort

Chollerford
Humshaugh
Hexham, Northumberland, NE46 4EP
☎ 0434 681379

Hexham, A69

Hexham

Finest example of Roman military bath house in Britain. Museum houses a collection of Roman artifacts. Also remains of Cavalry Fort. 5¾ acres with gravel paths.

Gd Fri–30 Sep: Mon–Sun 10am–6pm
1 Oct–Mau Thu: Mon–Sun 10am–4pm

Norham Castle EH

Norham
Berwick–upon–Tweed
Northumberland, TD15 2JY
☎ 0289 382329

Berwick–upon–Tweed, A698

Built c.1160 by the River Tweed guarding the river ford. The castle, now a ruin, was the major border stronghold to defend the English border, mainly against the Scots. 2½ acres with mainly grassed areas.

Summer: Mon–Sun 10am–6pm
Winter: Wed–Sun 10am–4pm

Eyemouth Museum Trust Ltd

Auld Kirk
Manse Rd
Berwick–upon–Tweed
Northumberland, TD14 5HE
☎ 08907 50678

Berwick–upon–Tweed

Berwick–upon–Tweed

A memorial to the local fishermen lost in the Great Fishing Disaster in 1881. Displays record local history on land and sea.

Easter–31 Oct: Mon–Sat 10am–12noon & 1.30am–4.30pm
Jul–Aug: Sun 1pm–5.30pm

Druridge Bay Nature Reserves

Low Hauxley
Amble, Northumberland
☎ 0661 711578

Amble – A1068–Newcastle

 Amble

Three wetland sites behind the dunes, each attracting different types of birds and overlooked by hides.

Jan–Dec: Mon–Sun 9am

Ayton Castle

Ayton
Berwick, Northumberland, TD14 5RD
☎ 08907 81212

Eyemouth

≈ Berwick–upon–Tweed

Fully lived–in family home, built in early Victorian era and recently, completely restored.

Jan–Dec: Sun 2pm–5pm

Allen Banks NT

Nr Bardon Mill
Northumberland
☎ 0434 344218

1½m SE of Bardon Mill off A69

Car park and picnic area accessible for less able visitors, and the first ¼m of the woodland walk is suitable for wheelchair users. Adapted WC with NKS lock.

Newton Pool NT

Low Newton
Northumberland
☎ 066 576 365 or 439

Purpose built bird hide for disabled visitors linked to Low Newton by 400yd pathway for wheelchair users. Reserved parking in Newton Square. The lane behind the NW side of Newton Square is cobbled and difficult for wheelchair users; improved access is planned. A wheelchair is available.

NOTTINGHAMSHIRE

Thrumpton Hall

Nottingham,
Notts., NG11 0AX
☎ 0602 830333

Nottingham A453

Jacobean and Elizabethan house. Carved Jacobean staircase, fine pictures and furniture. Lovely garden with water, trees and large lawns. 2 acres with gravel paths.

By appointment only for groups of 20 or more.

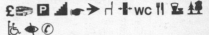

Clumber Park NT

Worksop, Notts., S80 3AZ
☎ 0909 476592/476653

Worksop & Retford A1 and A57

≈  Retford

Originally owned by the Dukes of Newcastle. 4000 acres of parkland to explore. Classical bridge, fine Gothic revival chapel. 2 childrens wheelchairs. 13 miles of tarmac roads.

Jan–Mar: Mon–Sun 10.30am–5pm
Apr–Oct: Mon–Sun 10.30am–6pm
Nov–Dec: Mon–Sun 10.30am–5pm

St Mary's Church

Church Street
Edwinstone
Mansfield, Notts., NG21 9QA
☎ 0623 822430

Mansfield A6075

≈ Worksop Mansfield

C12th church where it is said Robin Hood and Maid Marion were married. 2 acres with paved paths.

Apr–Sep: Mon–Fri 10am–5pm
Most Sunday's afternoons: 2pm–5pm

Newark Aviation Museum

The Airfield
Winthorpe
Newark, Notts., NG24 2NY
☎ 0636 707170

Newark A46 towards Lincoln

≈ Newark

Based on original 2nd World War bomber dispersal. Nearly half of the 40 aircraft are now displayed undercover. 2 acres with major concrete area.

Apr–Oct: Mon–Fri 10am–5pm
Sat–Sun 10am–6pm
Nov–Mar: Mon–Sun 10am–4.30pm

NOTTINGHAMSHIRE

Closed: 24–26 Dec

£©🚌🦮 🅿 ♿👜➔ ⌐🚹♿ WC 🍴
🎎🌿🖼

Ruddington Village Museum

St Peters Rooms
Church St
Ruddington, Notts., NG11 6HA
☎ 0602 211545

Nottingham A60

🚆 Nottingham 🚌 Ruddington

A small museum with a row of Edwardian
shops. Disabled people please give notice
of arrival.

Sun/Tue/Thu/Fri: 2.30pm–4.00pm

£🚌🦮🅿♿👜👨‍🦽 WC 🍴 🐟🖼

Castle Museum & Art Gallery

Nottingham, Notts., NG1 6EL
☎ 0602 483504

Nottingham city centre, off Maid Marion
Way

🚆 🚌 Nottingham

Magnificent mansion on the site of a
Norman castle, now a popular museum and
art gallery within a small park. 4 acres with
paved paths. Dog water bowl available.

Easter–Oct: 10am–5.45pm
Oct–Easter: 10am–4.45pm

£F©🦮🛍🅿♿👜🏭➔⌐
🎠🍴♿ WC 🐕🍴🐟🎧🖼🕐♿

Canal Museum

Canal St
Nottingham, Notts., NG1 7EH
☎ 0602 598835

In city centre A6005

🚆🚌 Broadmarsh

Restored canal warehouse with displays on
all aspects of the River Trent; canals,
bridges, floods and natural history. Paved
and cobbled paths. Dog water bowl
available.

Wed/Thu/Sat: 10am–12noon &
1pm–5.45pm
Sun: 1pm–5.45pm

F🦮🛍🅿♿👜🍴🏭➔⌐WC🐕🍴
♿🐟🖼♿

Natural History Museum

Wollaton Park
Nottingham,
Notts., NG8 2AE
☎ 0602 281333

A609 Ilkeston Road out of Nottingham

🚆🚌 Nottingham

One of the most spectacular and ornate
tudor buildings in Britain. Now home of the
natural history museum with displays of all
aspects of the natural world. 500 acres of
park with lakes, deer herds and adventure
playground. 2 battery cars available for
loan. Stairmate.

Summer: Mon–Sat 10am–7pm
Sun: 2pm–5pm Grounds open all year
Winter: Mon–Sat: 10am–dusk
Sun: 1.30pm–4.30p

£F©🦮🅿🏭👜🏰➔🎠🍴♿ WC
🍴♿🐟🖼♿

Newstead Abbey

Linby, Notts., NG15 8GE
☎ 0623 793557

12 miles north of Nottingham on A60
Mansfield Rd. Near to M1 exit 27.

🚆 Nottingham

A beautiful house set in extensive gardens
and parklands. Best known as the home of
the poet Lord Byron, who made the house
and its ghostly legends famous.

Easter–Oct: 12noon–6pm (house)
All day (grounds)
Oct–Easter: Grounds open
house closed except tours by arrangement

£©🚌🦮🅿♿👜🏭🏰➔🍴
♿ WC 🍴🐟♿🎧🖼

Costume Museum

51 Castle Gate
Nottingham,
Notts., NG1 6AF
☎ 0602 483504

Nottingham city centre off Maid Marion Way

🚆🚌 Nottingham

Situated in a row of C18th houses, the
museum holds the city's collection of
fashion through the ages, in particular, an
excellent lace collection. Dog water bowl
available.

Jan–Dec: Mon–Sun 10am–5pm

F🦮🛍🅿♿🅿🏭👜🍴WC♿
🖼🚫

Greens Mill Science Museum

Windmill Lane
Sneinton, Nottingham,
Notts., NG2 4QB
☎ 0602 503635

Nottingham

≋ 🚌 Nottingham

Restored Victorian working windmill plus interactive science centre. Exhibits exploring light, magnetism, and electricity. Displays on windmills and milling. Windmill inaccessible.

Jan–Dec: Wed–Sun & BH Mon: 10am–5pm

F ⚹ 𝒫 P ⓟ ◢ ☛ ◣ ᖬ ✚ 💧 🅦🅒 wc 🛶 🎪 ᕼ 🖐 Ⓒ ᕼ

Holme Pierrepont Hall & Gardens

Holme Pierrepont
Nottingham,
Notts., NG12 2LD
☎ 0602 332371

Westbridgford, Nottingham, A52

One of the rare houses open to the public today, where the presence of the family is strongly in evidence. Crossing the threshold, you walk into a family home, filled with very personal possessions.

Jun/Jul/Aug: Tue/Thu/Fri/Sun: 2pm–6pm
Easter, Spring & Summer BH: Sun/Mon/Tue 2pm–6pm
May Day: 2pm–6pm

£ 🚌 ⚹ P ⓟ ◣ 🏠 ➤ ✚ 🅦🅒 wc 🛶 ᕼ 🖐 Ⓒ

Brewhouse Yard Museum

Castle Boulevard
Nottingham,
Notts., NG7 1FB
☎ 0602 483504 x 3600

Nottingham city centre

≋ 🚌 Nottingham

Museum of Nottingham daily life in period room, shops and display cases. Touchable exhibits in C17th cottages.

Jan–Dec Mon–Sun: 10am–5pm

F 🚌 ⚹ 𝒫 🕶 P ⓟ ᒫ ➤ ᕼ ✚ 🅦🅒 wc 🎪 ✦ 🖐 ᕼ

Patchings Farm Art Centre

Oxton Road
Calverton
Nottingham,
Notts., NG14 6NU
☎ 0602 653479

Nottingham A614

≋ 🚌 Nottingham Midland

Studios, shops, galleries and restaurant converted from C19th farm, plus new 38 acre Painters Paradise Gardens with special facilities for disabled people. Variety of paths.

Jan–Dec: Mon–Sun 9am–10pm

F 🚌 ⚹ Pⓙ P ⓟ ☛ 🏠 ➤ ᕼ ᕼ wc 🍴 🛶 ✦ 🖐 Ⓒ ᕼ

The Tales of Robin Hood – Visitor Attraction

Maid Marian Way
Nottingham,
Notts., NG1 6GF
☎ 0602 483284

Maid Marian Way, Notts city centre, A52

≋ 🚌 Nottingham

Relive the Robin Hood legend in sight, sound and smell. Travel in an adventure car though medieval Nottingham. Specially adapted for wheelchairs.

Jan–Dec: 10am–3.30(winter)
10am–4.30(summer)

£ Ⓒ 🚌 ⚹ P ⓟ 🅗 🅦🅒 wc 🍴 ᕼ 🖐 Ⓒ

Creswell Crags Visitor Ctr

Crags Rd
Welbeck
Worksop, Notts., S80 3LH
☎ 0909 720378

Worksop A60

≋ Worksop 🚌 Creswell or Whitwell

Caves containing sediments relating to 100,000 years ago. Remains of early man and associated animals from the Ice Age, including woolly mammoth, woolly rhino and reindeer.

Feb–Oct: Mon–Sun 10.30am–4.30pm
Nov–Jan: Sun 10.30am–4.30pm

F 🚌 ⚹ P ⓟ ➤ ᕼ wc 🛶 🎪 ᕼ 🖐 Ⓒ ᕼ

Mansfield Museum & Art Gallery

Leeming St
Mansfield, Notts., NG18 1NG
☎ 0623 663088

Mansfield town centre

🚌 Mansfield

Exhibitions, images of Mansfield past and present, the nature of Mansfield, watercolours of old Mansfield and a wide

NOTTINGHAMSHIRE

variety of temporary exhibitions.
Jan–Dec: Mon–Sat 10am–5pm

F 🚌 ⚞ P ⚟ ♿ WC 🎋 🌳

Longdale Rural Craft Centre

Longdale Lane
Ravenshead, Notts., NG15 9AH
☎ 0623 791858

Mansfield/Nottingham

Incorporates The Gordon Brown Collection.
Set within a re–created mid–1800's village
street, this collection includes many
examples of tools and equipment from a
wide range of old crafts and trades.

Jan–Dec: Mon–Sun 9am–6pm

£ © 🚌 ⚞ P♿ P ♿ ➤ ⌐ ⇒ 👁 🍴
♿WC WC 🍴 🎋 🌳 🎧 ©

The Model Aviation Centre

Goosedale Farm
Moor Rd
Bestwood
Notts., NG6 8UJ
☎ 0602 632175

Nottingham A611, then B683

🚆 Nottingham Victoria

The only flying model aviation museum in
the world. Models up to half scale, some,
including 'Memphis Belle', from films. 150
acres with tarmac, gravel and grass paths.

Jan–Dec: Mon–Sun 10am–6pm

£ © 🚌 ⚞ P ♿ ➤ ⌐ ♿WC WC 🍴 🎋
🌳 🌿 ©

Nottingham Industrial Museum

Courtyard Buildings
Wollaton Park, Notts., NG8 2AE
☎ 0602 284602

A609 Ilkeston Rd out of Nottingham

🚃 🚆 Nottingham City Centre

Housed in C18th stable block of Wollaton
Hall, the industrial museum reflects the
history of Nottingham's industries from
curtains to computers. Enormous Victorian
steam engines, transport, etc. 500 acres
with paved paths.

Summer: Mon–Sat 10am–6pm
Sun 2pm–6pm
Winter: Thu & Sat 10am–6pm
Sun 1.30pm–4.30pm

£ F 🚌 ⚞ 🐾 P♿ P ♿ ➤ ⌐ 🍴 ♿WC
WC 🍴 🎋 🌳 🌿 ♿

H.Merry Weather & Sons Garden Centre

Halam Rd
Southwell, Notts., NG25 0AH
☎ 0636 813204

Newark

Old established nursery and garden centre
with exhibitions indicating the history of the
Bramley Apple in C19th office.

Jan–Dec: Mon–Sun 9am–5.30pm

F 🚌 ⚞ P ♿ ➤ ⌐ WC 🍴 🎋 🌳
© ♿

OXFORDSHIRE

Cotswold Wildlife Park

Burford
Oxon. OX18 4JW
☎ 0993 823006

Burford A361

Exhibits a wide variety of animals and birds
from all over the world. 200 acres of
gardens and woodland with gravel and
grass paths.

Jan–Dec: Mon–Sun 10am–6pm

£ © 🚌 ⚞ P♿ P ♿ ➤ ⌐ ♿WC WC 🐾
🍴 🎋 🌳 🎋 © ♿

Ashmolean Museum

Beaumont St
Oxford, Oxon. OX1 2PH
☎ 0865 278000

A4260 to Banbury/A34 to Abingdon

🚃 🚆 Oxford

Neo–classical building designed by Charles
Robert Cockerell, houses the University's
collection of European and Oriental fine and
applied art, artefacts from Ancient Greece
and Rome. The original collection dates
from 1683. No guide dogs.

Jan–Dec: Tue–Sat 10am–4pm
Sun 2pm–4pm

F P ⚟ 🔨 📷 WC 🎋 ♦ 🌿 © ♿

Banbury Museum

8 Horsefair
Banbury, Oxon. OX16 0AA
☎ 0295 259855

Banbury town centre

🚃 🚆 Banbury

Displays tell the story of 'Banburyshire' with
programmes of temporary historical and

contemporary exhibitions. Radar key
required for alt. entrance.

Jan–Mar: Tue–Sat 10am–4.30pm
Apr–Sep: Mon–Sat 10am–5pm
Oct–Dec: Tue–Sat 10am–4.30pm

F🚌✳️P♿P🦽☞🏠♿wc🦽♿

Sulgrave Manor & Gardens

Manor Rd
Sulgrave
Banbury, Oxon. OX17 2SD
☎ 0295 76205

6 miles NE of Banbury & M40; 12 miles from
M1

≋ Banbury

Tudor manor house of Shakespeare's time,
built by Lawrence Washington in 1539.
House furnished in period style. Beautiful
gardens. 5 acres with gravel paths. No dogs
inside house.

Apr–Sep: Thu–Tue 10.30am–1pm &
2pm–5.30pm
Oct–Dec: Thu–Tue 10.30am–1pm &
2pm–4pm
Feb–Mar: Thu–Tue 10.30am–1pm &
2pm–4pm
Closed: Jan and Weds

£©🚌✳️P P♿🦽🏛️🗂️wc
✖️🦽♿⦿♿

Aynhoe Park Residential Stately Home

Aynho
Banbury, Oxon. OX17 3BQ
☎ 0869 810636

Banbury B4100 exit A41

House dates from 1600's and Cromwellian
times. Architecture by Sir John Soane and
Thomas Archer. 4 acres with gravel paths.

First Wed in May–last Thu in Sep

£✳️P♿🗂️wc

Edgehill Battle Museum

The Estate Yard
Farnborough Hall
Farnborough, Banbury
Oxon. OX17 1DU
☎ 0926 332213/4/5

Banbury A432 or A41 (B4100)

≋ Banbury

Musuem of first battle of English Civil Wars,
with models, weapons, flags, music,
costumes and large battlefield nearby.
Battlefield unsuitable for wheelchair users.

Apr–Oct: Wed and Sat 2pm–6pm

Great Western Railway Centre

Didcot
Oxon. OX11 7NJ
☎ 0235 817200

Didcot M4–A34

≋ Didcot Parkway

16 acre working museum reflecting the
Great Western Railway. Workshops and
locomotives. Paved paths and ramps to
platform. Special steam day for disabled
people in early July.

Apr–Sep: Mon–Sun 11am–5pm

£🚌✳️👜P♿P🦽🍽☞➜🗂️⇒
⦿🦽♿♿wc⦿🍴🦽♿⦿🍵♿

The Bate Collection of Historical Instruments

Faculty of Music
St Aldate's
Oxford, Oxon. OX1 1DB
☎ 0865 276139

Oxford

≋🚍 Oxford

Most comprehensive collection in England.
European woodwind, brass and percussion
instruments. Keyboard instruments, Betford
collection, tools and bow making
equipment.

Jan–Dec Mon–Fri: 2pm–5pm

F©🚌✳️P🦽🗂️🏛️♿wc🦽♿

Venn Mill

Garford
Abingdon, Oxon. OX13 5PA
☎ 0367 718888

4 miles W of Abingdon on A338 Oxford–
Wantage road

🚍 Oxford & Abingdon

The only working water–powered corn mill
in the Vale of White Horse. Built about 1800
on an ancient site. Waterwheel house is
unlevel. ¼ of an acre with grass paths.

Apr–Oct: 2nd Sun in month
Other times by arrangement

OXFORDSHIRE

Stonor Park

Stonor
Henley–on–Thames
Oxon. RG9 6HF
☎ 049 163 587

Henley–on–Thames (A423 Oxford to B480)

Historic house of Lord & Lady Camoys and Stonor family for over 800 years. Site of prehistoric stone circle with Catholic chapel nearby. 10 acres with various paths.

Apr–Sep: Sun 2pm–5.30pm
May–Sep: Wed 2pm–5.30pm
Jul–Aug: Thu 2pm–5.30pm
Aug: Sat 2pm–5.30pm
BH Mon: 11am–5.30pm (Easter to Aug)

£©☺🚐🚂 P 🅿 ◢◣🚜🏰➤🛈 WC ‖ 🍴 🌲🏕 ♿ ✋

Tom Browns School

Broad St
Uffington, Oxon.
☎ 036 782 675

Wantage A417

Old school built in 1617 – endowed by Thomas Saunders; original school from Tom Brown's school days. Associated with author Thomas Hughes. Difficult stone steps in grass bank up to main entrance.

Easter–Oct: Sat–Sun 2pm–5pm

£🚐🚂 🚶 P 🛈 WC 🎏 ♿ ✋ ♿

Cogges Manor Farm

Church Lane
Witney, Oxon.
☎ 0993 772602

Witney A40

≋ Witney–Oxford

Secluded site: manor farmhouse, walled garden, riverside walks, nature/historical trails, working farm. Steps throughout the site but help given by staff. 6 acres with gravel paths.

Easter–31 Oct: Tue–Sun

£©☺🚐🚂 🚶 🌊 P🅿 P 🚶 ♿ ➤ ⌐ 🛈 🅠ᵂᶜ
WC 🏕 ✕ 🌲🏕 ♿ ✋ ©

Vale and Downland Museum Centre

The Old Surgery
Church St
Wantage, Oxon. OX12 8BL
☎ 02357 66838

Close to town centre, well signposted

≋ Didcot 🚌 Oxford

C16/17th house, modern extension, reconstructed barn. Permanent displays – geology, archaeology, local history of Wantage and the Vale of the White Horse. Temporary exhibitions.

Jan–Dec: Tue–Sat 10.30am–4.30pm
Sun 2.30pm–5pm

F🚐🚂 🚶 P 🅿 ♿ 🚂🏰 🅠ᵂᶜ WC 🎏 🍴 🌲
♿ ✋ ©

Waterperry Gardens

Waterperry
Nr Wheatley, Oxon. OX1 9JZ
☎ 0844 339226/339254

Wheatley, M40 junction 8

≋ Oxford

Peaceful ornamental gardens and magnificent trees, in 83 acres of grounds. Fine displays of indoor plants. Saxon church, river walk.

Apr–Sep: Mon–Sun 10am–5.30pm
Oct–Mar: Mon–Sun 10am–4.30pm

£©🚐🚂 🚶 P ♿ ➤ ⌐ WC 🍴 🌲🏕
♿ © ♿ᴸ

SHROPSHIRE

Ironbridge Gorge Museum

Ironbridge
Telford, Shrops., TF8 7AW
☎ 0953 43 3522

Telford A442

≋ Telford

One of the first world heritage sites in Britain, where the modern world began over 250 years ago. This was the birthplace of the Industrial Revolution. 42 acres of museums & open air sites (some closed during winter). Symbols below cover limited aspects of Ironbridge.

Jan–Dec: Mon–Sun 10am–5pm

£©🚐🚂 🚶 P🅿 P ♿ 🚂🏰 🅠ᵂᶜ WC 🎏 🍴
🌲 ♿ ✋ © ♿ᴸ

Hodnet Hall

Hodnet
Nr Market Drayton
Shrops., TF9 3NN
☎ 0630 84 202

A442 Shrewsbury to Market Drayton road

≋ 🚐 Shrewsbury

60 acres of brilliantly coloured flowers, magnificent forest trees, sweeping lawns and a chain of ornamental pools. Winner of 'Garden of the Year' 1985.

Apr–Sep: Mon–Fri 2pm–5pm
Sun & BH Mon 12noon–5.30pm

Aerospace Museum

Cosford
Shifnal, Shrops., TF11 8UP
☎ 0902 374872/374112

Between Wolverhampton & Telford; just off A41 & M54 (J3)

≋ Cosford

Largest aviation collection in Europe. 70 aircraft on display with missiles, engines, uniforms and aviation memorabilia. 30 acre open site exhibiting in three hangers.

Apr–Oct: Mon–Sun 10am–5pm
Nov–Mar: Mon–Sun 10am–4pm

Long Mynd & Carding Mill Valley NT

Nr Long Mynd
Shrops.,

Access to viewpoints on the Long Mynd and to the shop and restaurant at Carding Mill Valley. Thick–handled cutlery available. Adapted WC.

Wenlock Edge NT

Presthope
Shrops.,

A circular pathway, starting and finishing at the car park is suitable for less able and accompanied visually impaired walkers, and wheelchair users with strong pushers as some gradients are short but steep. It has a wood chipping surface, and leads past a viewpoint.

SOMERSET

Wells Museum

8 Cathedral Green
Wells, Somerset, BA5 2UE
☎ 0749 673477

Wells A39
🚌 Castle Cary/Bath/Bristol

Archaeological relics in the Museum found in the Caves at Wookey Hole. Visitors can also see the Victorian handmade paper mill, the 'Fairground by Night', Madame Tussaud's Travelling Show and the ever popular Penny Pier Arcade.

Summer: Mon–Sun 10am–5.30pm
Winter: Wed–Sun 11am–4pm

Hornsbury Mill

Nr Chard
Somerset, TA20 3AQ
☎ 0460 63317

A358 on Taunton Rd out of Chard

A historic working watermill set in 5 acres of landscaped, level gardens. It was used as a mill until World War 2 and then lay empty until renovated in 1962. Refurbished in 1991.

Jan–Dec: Mon–Sun 10am–6pm

Animal Farm Country Park & The Land of Legends

Red Road
Berrow, Burnham–on–Sea,
Somerset, TA8 2RW
☎ 0278 751628

Burnham–on–Sea

≋ 🚌 Highbridge

Variety of animals, many of which can be hand fed. Land of Legends has static scenes of local folk tales including King Arthur, Smugglers, Highwaymen and battling knights. 30 acres with gravel paths.

Easter–Oct 31: Mon–Sun 10am–5pm

Norwood Rare Breeds Farm

Bath Rd
Norton St Philip
Nr Bath, Somerset, BA3 6LP
☎ 0373 834356

6 miles from Bath & Frome, on B3110

🚌 Bath–Frome

Organic mixed farm in beautiful Mendip countryside, on Roman Road from Bath to Poole, breeding rare breeds of farm livestock. 16 acres with grass, rolled stone and concrete paths.

SOMERSET

Easter–3rd week in Sept: Mon–Sun
11am–5pm

£ © 🚍 🐾 P 🅿 🦯 ➔ ⊣ ┼ ♿ 🧗
🍴 🧴 🎪 🐾 ✆

Rosies Cider

Rose Farm
Lattiford
Wincanton, Somerset, BA9 8AF
☎ 0963 33680

Wincanton A371/A357 towards
Templecombe

�) 🚌 Templecombe

Thatched cottage in the style of a Somerset
Long House. Small museum housing a
unique private collection of loving cups and
mugs. ½ acre with mainly tarmaced paths.

Jan–Dec: Mon–Sat 8.30am–6.30pm
Sun 12 noon–3pm

 F 🚍 🐾 P ⅃ ➔ ♿ WC 🧴 🎪

West Somerset Railway

The Railway Station
Minehead
Somerset, TA24 5BG
☎ 0643 704996

A358 5 miles Taunton & M5

�), 🚌 Taunton

Britain's longest private railway. The trains
steam through 20 miles of glorious scenery
to the seaside and gateway to Exmoor at
Minehead. Wheelchair facilities in most
trains, telephone to check.

Mid–Mar–31 Oct: Sat–Sun
May–Oct: Mon & Fri
Jun–Sep: Mon–Sun

£ © 🚍 🐾 🥄 P 🅿 ⅃ ➔ ⊣ 🚗 ♿
WC 🧴 🎪 ⅃

Fleet Air Arm Museum

RNAS Yeovilton
Somerset, BA22 8AF
☎ 0935 840565

Yeovil A303/A37

�) 🚌 Yeovil

Home of one of the world's largest
collections of historic aircraft.

Mar–Oct: 10am–5.30pm
Nov–Feb: 10am–4.30pm
Closed: 24–26 Dec

£ © 🚍 ⅃ P 🦯 🛒 ➔ ⊣ ⇒ ┼ ♿
WC 🧗 🍴 🧴 🎪 ⅃ 🐾 ✆ ⅃

The Tropical Bird Gardens

Rode
Nr Bath, Somerset, BA3 4QW
☎ 0373 830326

Bath A36

�) 🚌 Bath

Brilliant exotic birds in lovely natural
surroundings. 1000 rare birds, 230 different
species. Woodland steam railway. 17 acres
of grounds with ornamental trees and
shrubs.

Summer: 10am–6.30pm
Winter: 10am–dusk

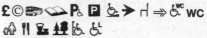 £ © 🚍 🥄 ⅃ P ⅃ ➔ ⊣ ⇒ ♿ WC

🧗 🍴 🧴 🎪 ⅃ ⅃

Haynes Sparkford Motor Museum

Sparkford
Nr Yeovil, Somerset, BA22 7LH
☎ 0963 40804

Wincanton A303

�) 🚌 Castle Cary

Over 200 classic, veteran and vintage motor
cars and motorcycles. 70 seat video
cinema. Paved paths.

Jan– Dec: Mon–Sun 9.30am–5.30pm

£ © 🚍 🐾 ⅃ P ⅃ ➔ ⊣ ♿ WC 🍴

🧴 🎪 🐾 ✆

Westonzoyland Pumping Station

Laitewall
Westonzoyland, Bridgwater,
Somerset
☎ 0823 412713

Bridgwater A372

�) 🚌 Bridgwater

Oldest pumping station on Somerset levels.
Engine dates from 1861: the only one in
country run on steam. 4 acres with gravel
paths.

1st Sun in Apr–Oct: 2pm–5pm
Sun & Mon of BH weekends

£ © 🚍 🐾 ⅃ P ⅃ ➔ ⊣ WC 🍴 🧴

🎪 🐾

Wells Cathedral

West Cloister Offices
Wells, Somerset, BA5 2PA
☎ 0749 674483

Wells, A37, A371

�) 🚌 Wells

Fine medieval cathedral with many points of

interest: including the West Front, Lady Chapel and Quire. 2 acres with paved paths.

Winter: Mon–Sun 7.15am–6.30pm
Summer: Mon–Sun 7.15am–8.30pm or dusk

F🚐☀️🖊️P🅿️♿🐕🏛️🚻♿🚻

🚻🏠🍴📷🌳🛶🎁♿

Somerset Rural Life Museum

Abbey Farm
Chilkwell St
Glastonbury, Somerset, BA6 8DB
☎ 0458 31197

Glastonbury A361 to Shepton Mallet

Medieval Abbey Barn and Victorian Farmhouse. Permanent displays on Somerset's rural history. Craft and farming demonstrations. 3½ acres with gravel and paved paths.

Easter–31 Oct: Mon–Fri 10am–5pm
Sat–Sun 2pm–6pm
1 Nov–Easter: Mon–Fri 10am–5pm
Sat: 11am–4pm

£©🚐☀️🖊️🅿️♿🐕🏛️🚻🚻

🚻🍴📷🌳🛶🎁♿

New Road Farm

East Huntspill
Nr Highbridge
Somerset, TA9
☎ 0278 783250

Highbridge

New Road Farm is one of the oldest farms in the area. Demonstrates both modern and traditional methods of farming. Over 60 different breeds of animals.

Easter–Oct: Mon–Fri 10am–6pm
Winter: Ring for details

£©🚐☀️🅿️♿🚻🚻🍴📷

🌳♿🛶

Brympton House & Gardens

Yeovil
Somerset, BA22 8TD
☎ 0935 862528

Yeovil off A3088 or A30

≋ Yeovil Penn Mill or Yeovil Junction

Set in prize winning gardens and vineyard. Own museum and distillery with exhibitions. 12 acres with paved and gravel paths.

1 May–30 Sep: Sat–Wed 2pm–6pm

£©🚐☀️🅿️♿🚻🚻♿🛶🐕🌳

🍴🛶♿🎁🛶

Hestercombe House Gardens

Cheddon Fitzpaine
Taunton, Somerset, TA2 8LQ
☎ 0823 337222

Taunton

≋ Taunton

The gardens are the unique work of Edwin Lutyens and Gertrude Jekyll. A typical Edwardian garden; lots of scent and pastel shades. Terraced garden with gravel and paved paths. Stonework uneven.

Jan–Dec: Mon–Fri 9am–5pm
May–Sep: Sat–Sun 2pm–5pm

£🚐☀️🚻🚻🚻🌳🛶♿

Brean Down Tropical Bird Garden

Brean Down
Burnham–on–Sea
Somerset, TA8 2RS
☎ 0278 751209

Coast Road Berrow – Brean Down

Small family run tropical bird garden a few yards from beach, under National Trust hill. Lovely views and walks close by. One acre with paved paths.

Easter–Oct: Mon–Sun 9.30am–dusk

£©🚐☀️🅿️♿🚻🚻🚻🍴

🌳🛶🎁©

Wookey Hole Caves & Papermill

Wookey Hole
Nr Wells, Somerset, BA5 1BB
☎ 0749 672243

Wells, 2 miles on the A371

🚐 Wells

From the spectacular caves, with their ancient history and legends, to the traditional papermaking. Offers visitors an entertaining and educational day out. 8 acres with paved paths. Steps in caves. Caves not accessible to wheelchair users.

Summer: Mon–Sun 9.30am–5.30pm
Winter: Mon–Sun 10.30am–4.30pm

£©🚐☀️🖊️🅿️♿🚻🚻🚻

🍴🌳🛶🛶🎁♿♿

SOMERSET

Glastonbury Abbey

Abbey Gatehouse
Glastonbury
Somerset, BA6 9EL
☎ 0458 832267

Glastonbury

⇌ 🚌 Glastonbury

First Christian sanctuary in British Isles. Legendary burial place of King Arthur. Extensive ruins in park. 36 acres with gravel paths.

Jan–Dec: Mon–Sun 9.30am–6pm

£©🚌✕P&P🅿&▬🏚➤ ⊣ ⊹ ⅙wc
wc 🎋👪👬🚶 🎧

Museum of South Somerset

Henford
Yeovil
Somerset, BA20 1UN
☎ 0935 24774

Yeovil

Located in the former coach house of Henford Manor. Hamstone and brick elevations housing collections of social history, archaeology, costume and firearms.

Jan–Dec: Tue–Sat 10am–4pm
Sun: 2pm–4pm
Open: BH Mons

F🚌✕P&🅿&🏚➤⇒⊹wc🎋
🚶🦢©

Minehead Shoe Factory & Shop

1 North Rd
Minehead, Somerset, TA24 5QW
☎ 0643 705591

Minehead – near sea front and station

⇌ 🚌 Minehead

Former stables which have been converted into a factory for production of footwear and factory shop for public. Formed in 1982 as a Worker's co–operative with 15 employees. Paved paths.

Jan–Dec Mon–Fri 9am–5pm
Sat 9am–12noon

F🚌✕🦢P&▬🖋➤ ⊣⇒👁
⊹wc🎋👪🦢

Dunster Castle NT

Dunster
Minehead, Somerset, TA24 6SL
☎ 0643 821314

Minehead A39 (3 miles SE)

🚌 & West Somerset Railway to Dunster

Castle dates from Norman times with Medieval features. C17th house remodelled during late C19th. 20 acres with a variety of paths.

Castle
1 Apr–30 Sep: Sat–Wed 11am–5pm
1 Oct–2 Nov: Sat–Wed 11am–4pm
Gardens & Shop
1 Feb–31 Mar: Mon–Sun 11am–4pm
1 Apr–30 Sep: Mon–Sun 11am–5pm
1 Oct–Dec: Mon–Sun 11am–4pm

Taunton Cider Mill

The Taunton Cider Co Ltd
Norton Fitzwarren
Taunton, Somerset, TA2 6RD
☎ 0823 332211

B3227 out of Taunton 3 miles

⇌ 🚌 Taunton

Working cider mill with exhibition showing the history of cider. Paved paths.

Shop: Jan–Dec: Mon–Fri 9am–12.30pm
1.30pm–5pm
Tours: Jan–Dec: Thurs only 3pm

£©🚌✕🅿🖋&➤⅙wc wc ¶¶🎋
&©

West Sedgemoor RSPB

Nr Taunton
Somerset, TA10 0PH
☎ 0458 252805

Signposted off A378 Taunton–Langport road; one mile east of Fivehead.

Hide for viewing large heronry in Swell Wood from March–June and other wildlife throughout the year. Easy access for wheelchair users; 60 yards from car park. Toilets at Langport with car parking. Meadow tracks are uneven and often wet.

Jan–Dec: Mon–Sun

The Willows English Basket & Hurdle Centre

Curload
Stoke St Gregory, Somerset, TA7 0RX
☎ 0823 69418

Taunton A361

⇌ 🚌 Taunton

Manufacturer of baskets and hurdles. 3 acres with gravel and tarmac paths.

Jan–Dec: Mon–Fri 9am–5pm
Sat 9am–1pm

F🚌🐕 P⛵➤🍴wc🖼🏕🤝©

Barrington Court Garden NT

Nr Ilminster, Somerset
☎ 0985 847777
Ilminster
🚌 to Barrington Village

Garden constructed in 1920's. Influence by
Gertrude Jekyll. Kitchen garden. 3 walled
flower gardens. Horse chestnut avenues
and apple orchards. Gravel, tarmac and
grass paths. Facilities being improved.

1 Apr–31 Oct: Sun–Thu 12 noon–5pm

£©🚌🐕 P♿ P➤ wc🖼 🍴
🖼🏕

Ebbor Gorge NT

Nr Wells
Somerset

Has a special nature trail for wheelchair
users with strong pushers from the car park
at the entrance.

Wellington Monument NT

Blackdown Hills
Somerset

A level track leads through the woods to the
car park by the Monument. Splendid views.
Open May–Oct, depending on ground
condition.

STAFFORDSHIRE

Shugborough Estate NT

Milford
Nr Stafford, Staffs., ST17 0XB
☎ 0889 881388

6 miles E of Stafford, A513 Stafford Rugeley
Rd

≋ 🚌 Stafford

C18th mansion house, home of Lord
Lichfield. County museum housed in
servants quarters. Park farm and rare
breeds centre. 900 acres with gravel and
cobbled paths.

Easter–Oct: Mon–Sun 11am–5pm
Jan–Dec: Booked parties

£©🚌🐕🐎♿ P♿⛵🖼➤ 🍴
🍴♿wc🖼🍴🖼🏕🐟🤝©

Brown End Quarry

Waterhouses
Staffs.,
☎ 08897 534

A523 Leek – Ashbourne Rd

Quarry showing geology of carboniferous
limestone; 350 million years old. Interpretive
displays. 4 acres with limestone paths.

Jan–Dec: Mon–Sun

F🚌🐕♿ P➤wc🏕♿

Gladstone Pottery Museum

Uttoxeter Rd
Longton
Stoke–on–Trent
Staffs.,
☎ 0782 319232

Stoke–on–Trent A50

≋ 🚌 Stoke–on–Trent

Typical C19th pottery factory with
traditional bottle kilns, yard and workshops.
Demonstrations of techniques, tile and
sanitary galleries. ¼ of an acre with cobbled
yard.

Mar–Oct: Mon–Sat 10am–5pm
Sun 2pm–5pm
Nov–Feb: Tue–Sat 10am–5pm

£©🚌🐕 P P♿🔨🖼➤🍴👁
🍴♿wc🍴🖼🏕♿🐟🤝©♿

Amerton Working Farm

Stowe–by–Chartley
Stafford
Staffs., ST18 0LA
☎ 0889 270294

A518 Stafford–Uttoxeter Rd; 1 mile E of
Weston

A real 'working farm' not a museum. 200
acre dairy farm making own ice–cream.
Farm animals, bakery, garden centre and
wild–life sanctuary. 2 acres with concrete
and paved brick paths.

Apr–Sep: Mon–Sun 9am–6pm
Oct–Mar: Mon–Sun 9am–5pm

F🚌🐕♿ P♿➤🍴♿wc🍴🖼
🏕♿

STAFFORDSHIRE

Trentham Gardens

Stone Road
Trentham
Staffs., ST9 0BN
☎ 0782 657341

A34–A500 Harley/Stoke

≋ 🚌 Stoke

Primarily set up as corporate hospitality venue, but is now also major leisure park with a number of attractions for all age groups, from wildlife reserve to action sports. 1000 acres with tarmac paths.

Apr–Oct: 11am–dusk

£🚐🎎 P ♿➤ ⌐⇒ ⊣ ⚷ WC ⊘
⛱ ♨⊘

Moseley Old Hall NT

Ford Houses
Wolverhampton
Staffs., WV10 7HY
☎ 0902 782808

4m N of Wolverhampton S of M54 between junction 1 and 2

≋ Wolverhampton

Retains much of the character of the C17th house the King would have seen. Half-timbered rooms, oak panelling, period furniture and ingenious hiding places give Moseley a fascinating character. Recreated C17th garden with knot garden and nut walk.

Apr–Oct: Wed/Sat/Sun 2pm–5.30pm
Jul–Aug: Tue–Wed/Sat–Sun 2pm–5.30pm
BH Mons: 11am–5pm

£©🚐🎎 P ♿🎡🏰➤ ⊣ ⊣
⚷ WC ⊘ ⛱🍴⊘

Stoke–on–Trent City Museum & Art Gallery

Bethesda St
Hanley, Staffs., ST1 3DW
☎ 0782 202173

Stoke–on–Trent A500/M6

≋ 🚌 Stoke–on–Trent

An award–winning purpose built museum all about 'The Potteries'. Includes one of the world's finest ceramics collections.

Jan–Dec: Mon–Sat 10am–5pm
Sun 2pm–5pm
Closed: Good Fri/24 Dec–2 Jan

F🚐🎎🔱♿P♿🔩📷➤⊣⚷WC
🎨🍴⛱🎧🍴⊘♿

Valley Heritage Centre

Valley Rd
Hednesford
Cannock, Staffs., WS12 5QX
☎ 0543 877666

Cannock – A460

≋ 🚌 Hednesford

The museum, through its exhibitions and its beautiful setting combines the social and natural history of Cannock and its surrounds.

May–Sep: Wed–Sun Ring for times
Oct–Apr: Thu–Sun

F🚐🎎 P P♿➤⊣⚷WC🍴⛱
♿⊘

Byrkley Park Centre

Rangemore
Burton–on–Trent
Staffs., DE13 9RN
☎ 0283 716467

5m W of Burton–on–Trent nr B5234

≋ Stoke–on–Trent

A new garden centre with a difference. Farm animals, display, gardens & carvery. 5 acres with gravel and paved paths.

Sep–Mar: Mon–Sun 9am–5pm
Apr–Aug: Mon–Sun 9am–6pm
Thu–Sat 9am–9pm

F🚐🎎 P♿ P ♿➤⊣⚷WC🐾🍴
⛱♨⊘♿

Wolesley Garden Park

Wolseley Bridge
Staffs., ST17 0YT
☎ 0889 574888

Rugeley (junction off A51 and A513)

≋ 🚌 Stafford

45 acres of theme gardens. 2 acre rose garden, scented garden, walks, wild flowers, wildlife habitat, medieval archaeological excavation.

Apr–Oct: Mon–Sun 10am–6pm
Nov–Mar: Mon–Sun 10am–dusk

£©🚐🎎 P♿ P ♿➤⊣⚷WC🍴
⛱♨🎧⊘

Bass Museum & Stables

Horninglow St
Burton–on–Trent
Staffs., DE14 0XT
☎ 0283 511000

A50

⇌ 🚌 Burton–on–Trent

Museum of brewing and transporting of beer. Exhibits include experimental brewhouse, historic vehicle fleet, visual and hands on displays, and the Bass shire horse stables.

Jan–Dec: Mon–Sat 10am–5pm
Sun 10.30am–5pm

£©🚌🐾 P♿️ ♿️🏛️➤⊣ ⊹ ♿️wc wc ⁇ 🍴 ♿️🛗

Ash End House Childrens' Farm

Middleton Lane
Middleton
Nr Tamworth, Staffs., B78 2BL
☎ 021 329 3240

Tamworth A4091

Family owned small holding. Open for schools, playgroups etc. Rare breeds, picnic barns, play areas.

Jan–Dec: Mon–Sun 10am–6pm

£©🚌🐾 P ♿️➤⊹♿️wc wc ⁇ 🛗 ♿️🤝

Ford Green Hall

Ford Green Road
Smallthorne
Stoke on Trent, Staffs., ST6 1NG
☎ 0782 534771

2½m NE of Hanley on the B5051

🚌 Hanley, Newcastle–under–Lyme and Burslem

A timber–framed Yeoman's farm house of 1624, with C18th brick additions, furnished as a family home with a collection of mainly oak furniture dating 1500–1800.

Jan–Dec: Mon–Sun 1pm–5pm
Closed: Gd Fri & Xmas week

F🚌🐾 P ♿️🍴🏛️➤♿️wc wc ⁇ 🛗🤝

SUFFOLK

West Stow Country Park & Anglo Saxon Village

West Stow
Bury St Edmunds
Suffolk, IP28 6HG
☎ 0284 728718

Between Bury St Edmunds and Mildenhall, off A1101

Country park is 125 acres of heath, woods, river and lake, linked by paths. Nature trail and unique reconstruction of Anglo–Saxon village on the site where it was excavated.

Jan–Dec: Mon–Sun 10am–5pm

£©🚌🐾 P P♿️➤⊣⊹♿️wc wc ⁇ 🛗♿️🎧🐟◆©

Ickworth NT

Horringer
Bury St Edmunds
Suffolk, IP29 5QE
☎ 0284 735270

3m SW of Bury St Edmunds on A143

⇌ Bury St Edmunds

Built between 1794 & 1830 the elliptical rotunda of Ickworth makes this fine mansion one of the most extraordinary in England. The unusual architecture features curved corridors and sumptuous state rooms with opulent late Regency and C18th French furniture. Italian garden and deer park.

Ring for times for 1992

£🐾🌱 P ♿️⊹♿️wc wc 🍴🛗♿️🎧◆🤝♿️

Gainsborough's House

46 Gainsborough St
Sudbury, Suffolk, CO10 6EU
☎ 0787 72958

Town centre

⇌ 🚌 Sudbury

Birth place of Thomas Gainsborough. Large collection of his work in C18th setting. Temporary exhibitions of historic and comtemporary art and craft. Garden and print workshop.

Jan–Dec: Tue–Sat 10am–5pm
Sun & BH 2pm–5pm
Nov–Easter: Tue–Sat 10am–4pm
Sun & BH 2pm–4pm

£©🚌🐾 P P♿️⊣🏛️⊣⊹♿️wc wc 🛗🤝

SUFFOLK

National Horseracing Museum

99 High St
Newmarket, Suffolk, CB8 8JL
☎ 0638 667333

Newmarket High St

⇌ Newmarket 🚌 Cambridge

Opened in 1983 in former Regency subscription rooms. The story of British horseracing in paintings, bronzes, memorabilia and personal effects in 6 galleries plus two galleries of sporting art. No guide dogs inside museum

Apr–Dec: Tue–Sat 10am–5pm
Sun 2pm–5pm
Jul–Aug: Mon–Sat 10am–5pm
Sun 12noon–5pm

The Clare Ancient House Museum

High St
Clare
Suffolk, CO10 8NY
☎ 0787 277865

Between Harefield & Sudbury

⇌ Sudbury/Marks Tey

House dates from 1473. Museum of local history opened 1978. Contains very old fragments but is mostly Victorian to mid–C20th. Agricultural equipment, costume display and toys.

Easter–30 Sep: Wed–Sun 2.30pm–4.30pm

£©🚐✖P🦽WC🅿🦽◐♿

Moyses Hall Museum

Cornhill
Bury St Edmunds
Suffolk, IP
☎ 0284 757072

A45

⇌ 🚌 Bury St Edmunds

The oldest secular building in East Anglia dating from 1180. The largest Bronze Age metal hoard in Europe, unique evidence from West Stow Anglo–Saxon Village, and gruesome relics of the famous Victorian 'Red Barn Murder'.

Jan–Dec: Mon–Sat 10am–5pm
Sun 2pm–5pm

F🚐✖P🦽🅿🛒📷WC🤝

The Clock Museum

Angel Corner
8 Angel Hill
Bury St Edmunds
Suffolk, IP33 1UZ
☎ 0284 757072

A45

⇌ 🚌 Bury St Edmunds

The elegant C18th setting of Angel Corner is filled with a glorious combination of art and technology, sight and sound, that draws visitors from across Britain.

Jan–Dec: Mon–Sat 10am–5pm
Sun 2pm–5pm

F🚐✖P🅿⛰🛒➤WC🅿♿🤝

Melford Hall NT

Long Melford
Sudbury, Suffolk
☎ 0787 880286

A134 Sudbury

⇌ 🚌 Sudbury

A turreted brick Tudor mansion dating mostly from the mid C16th. Inside are fine pictures, furniture and porcelain displayed in rooms of varying styles. Traditional garden with trees and clipped box hedges. 4 acres with gravel paths.

Mar–Apr: Sat/Sun/BH Mon: 2pm–5.30pm
May–Sep: Wed/Thu/Sat–Sun/BH Mon: 2pm–5.30pm
Oct: Sat–Sun: 2pm–5.30pm

£©🚐✖P🅿🦽🖼🍴➕♿♿
◐♿

Pleasurewood Hills American Theme Park

Corton
Lowestoft, Suffolk, NR32 5DZ
☎ 0502 513626

A12 from Lowestoft/Gt Yarmouth

⇌ 🚌 Lowestoft/Gt Yarmouth

Over 50 rides, shows and attractions. Pay once at the gate and then its free. 50 acres with concrete paths.

May–Sep: Mon–Sun

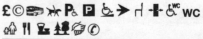

Horringer Crafts

Community Centre
Horringer, Suffolk
☎ 0284 766326

Bury St Edmunds

Artists and craftspeople demonstrate their skills.

Easter–30 Nov: Sun & BH Mon 2pm–6pm

Christchurch Mansion

Christchurch Park
Soare St
Ipswich, Suffolk
☎ 0473 253246

Ipswich

≽ Ipswich

House built 1550 on site of Augustinian Priory. Superb furniture collections. Lively programme of temporary exhibitions. Paved paths.

Jan–Dec Tue–Sat: 10am–5pm dusk in winter
Sun: 2.30pm–4.30pm dusk in winter

Ipswich Museum

High St
Ipswich
Suffolk, IP1 3QH
☎ 0473 213761

Ipswich

≽ Ipswich

Archaeology, ethnography and natural science displays. Victorian natural history gallery and Roman Suffolk gallery.

Jan–Dec: Tue–Sat 10am–5pm

Snape Maltings Riverside Centre

Nr Saxmundham, Suffolk, IP17 1SR
☎ 0728 88 303

3m from A12, via A1094

A remarkable old riverside maltings with shops galleries and the world famous concert hall. River trips in the summer.

Jan–Dec: Mon–Sun 10am–5pm

Haughley Park

Stowmarket
Suffolk, IP14 3JY
☎ 0359 40205

4m NW of Stowmarket on A45

≽ Stowmarket 🚌 Wetherdon

Jacobethan manor house 1620AD; lived in atmosphere, good furniture and pictures; beautiful gardens with woods and good paths.

May–Sep: Tue 3pm–6pm

Felixstowe Museum & Landguard Fort

8 Manor Terrace
Felixstowe, Suffolk, IP11 8EN
☎ 0394 286403

Felixstowe A45

≽ Felixstowe 🚌 to Fort

Military site since C16th. C18th building with 7 room museum adjacent to fort. Guided tours available.

Museum:
May–Sep: Wed/Thu/Sun 2.30pm–5pm
Fort:
May–Sep: Wed/Sun 2.45pm–4pm

Museum of East Anglian Life

Stowmarket, Suffolk, IP14 1DL
☎ 0449 612 229

Centre of Stowmarket

≽ 🚌 Stowmarket

70 acre open air site with historic buildings containing collections of agricultural, social, industrial and craft history; animals and steam engines.

22 Mar–1 Nov: Mon–Sun 10am–5pm

SUFFOLK

Ixworth Thorpe Farm Nature Trail & Bird Reserve

Manor Farm
Ixworth Thorpe
Bury St Edmunds, Suffolk, IP31 1QH
☎ 0359 269444/269386

On A1088 road between Ixworth and Honington

Opened in 1988. 2½m walk through woods, round fields and gravel pits and alongside river. Bird reserve with 4 hides, 2 with ramps and disabled facilities around water and wetlands.

All year by appointment only

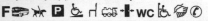

Suffolk Broads Nature Reserve & Visitor Centre

Burnt Hill Lane
Carlton Colville
Lowestoft, Suffolk
☎ 0502 564250

Lowestoft off A146 to Beccles

≋ ⛟ Oulton Broad

150 acre Nature Reserve, owned by the Suffolk Wildlife Trust. Variety of wetland habitats, broads, reedbeds, grazing marsh, and woodland.

Jan–Dec: Mon–Sat 9.30am–5pm
Suns 11am–5pm

Minsmere Nature Reserve RSPB

Westleton
Suffolk
☎ 072 873 281

Signposted off B1125 from Westleton to Dunwich

Resonably firm paths lead to three accessible hides, with adjustable viewing slots, overlooking famous Scrape with avocets and many other waders and wildfowl.

Jan–Dec: Wed–Mon 9am–9pm

Bruisyard Vineyard & Herb Garden

Church Rd
Bruisyard
Saxmundham, Suffolk, IP17 2EF
☎ 072 875 281
Saxmundham B1119

Vineyard and winery producing the estate–bottled Bruisyard St Peter wine. 10 acres with grass paths.

Easter–30 Nov: Mon–Sun 10.30am–5pm

Mechanical Music Museum

Blacksmith Rd
Cotton
Nr Stowmarket, Suffolk, IP14 4QN
☎ 0449 781988/613876

Stowmarket, B1113

≋ ⛟ Stowmarket

A veritable Aladdin's Cave, full of musical treasures. The roof is adorned with hundreds of old gramophone records and horn gramophones which earlier this century brought music to many homes.

Jun–Sep: Sun 2.30pm–5.30pm

James White Apple Juices

The Cider House
Friday St
Brandeston, Suffolk, IP13 7BP
☎ 0278 685537

A1120 Yoxford/Stowmarket

The Cider House is a farm with open countryside and narrow lanes. We make cider & apple juice on site from Sep/Jan and bottle on certain days throughout the year. JW has made juice for 12 years.

Jan–Dec: Mon–Fri 10am–1pm & 2pm–4.30pm
Evening: by appointment
Closed: BH

Dunwich Heath NT

Saxmundham, Suffolk
☎ 072 873 505

215 acres of sandy cliffs with a mile of beach, nature walk and access of public hides at the adjacent RSPB Minsmere reserve.Easy access to the Heath with level paths, but difficult path to shore for wheelchair users (possible access if Warden contacted). Guided walks for visually impaired people. Self–drive battery power car available.

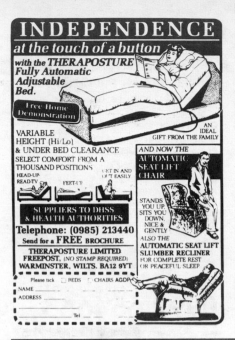

SURREY

Public Record Office (PRO)

Ruskin Avenue, Kew,
Richmond, Surrey, TW9 4DU
☎ 081 876 3444

Kew – off the S.Circular Rd A205

≋ Kew Gardens & Underground

The PRO at Kew houses central government
and court records of England and Wales
mostly dated from late C18th onwards.

Jan–Dec: Mon–Fri 9.30am–5pm

F 🚐 ⚡ P♿ P ♿ ▦ ▦ ♿wc wc ⫪ ⫫
⫪ ◈ ◷

Polesden Lacey NT

Dorking, Surrey, RH5 6BD
☎ 0372 458203

Between Guildford and Leatherhead A246

≋ Bookham

Originally an 1820's Regency villa,
remodelled after 1906 by the Hon. Mrs
Ronald Greville, well known Edwardian
hostess. Fine paintings, furniture, porcelain
and silver. Extensive grounds.

Mar & Nov: Sat/Sun 1.30pm–4.30pm
Apr–Oct: Wed–Sun 1.30pm–5.30pm
Jan–Dec: Grounds 11am–6pm
Open BH Mon & preceding Sun
11am–5.30pm

£ 🚐 ⚡ ◌ P♿ P ♿ ◢ ➤ ⊓ ⇒ ◉
⊹ ♿wc wc ⩍ ⫫ ⫪ ◈ ♿

Farnham Museum

38 West St
Farnham
Surrey, GU9 7DX
☎ 0252 715094

Off A31 Guildford to Acton Section

≋ 🚌 Farnham

Local history collection housed in Grade I
listed townhouse, built 1718. Walled garden
at rear. Regularly changing exhibtions.

Jan–Dec: Tue–Sat 10am–5pm

Closed 1992 for refurbishment. Facilities for
disabled people to be considerably
improved.

Thorpe Park Leisure

Staines Rd
Chertsey
Surrey, KT16 8PN
☎ 0932 562633

Staines A320

≋ Staines

One of Europe's leading leisure parks with
over 70 rides, attractions and shows – fun
for all ages. Waterbus. Train is not suitable
for wheelchair users.

Easter–Oct: Mon–Sun 10am–5pm

£ © 🚐 ⚡ P♿ P ♿ ☞ ▦ ⊓ ⇒ ⊹
♿wc wc ⩍ ⫫ ⫪ ⫪ ♿ ◈ ◷ ♿

Brooklands Museum

The Clubhouse
Brooklands Rd
Weybridge, Surrey, KT13 0QN
☎ 0932 857381

Weybridge B374

≋ Weybridge

The first banked concrete racing track in the
world and the birthplace of British aviation.
Display of cars, aeroplanes and
motorcycles.

Jan–Dec: Sat/Sun 10am–4pm

£ © 🚐 ⚡ P ♿ ➤ ♿wc wc ⫫ ⫪ ⫪
♿ ◈ ◷ ◷

Chessington World of Adventures

Theme Park & Zoo
Chessington
Surrey, KT2 9NE
☎ 0372 729560

A243 or A3

≋ 🚌 Chessington

Theme park and zoo for all the family. Lots
of things to do and see. Wheelchair users
are able to enjoy some of the rides.

Zoo: Jan–Dec: Mon–Sun 10am–5pm
Theme Park: Mar–Nov: Mon–Sun
10am–5pm

£ © 🚐 ⚡ ◌ P♿ P ♿ ➤ ⊓ ⊹ ♿wc
wc ⩍ ⫫ ⫪ ⫪ ♿ ◈

SURREY

Birdworld

Holt Pound
Farnham
Surrey, GU10 4LD
☎ 0420 221140

3m S of Farnham on A325

≈ 🚌 Aldershot

Plant enthusiasts will love the extensive gardens. Bird lovers should discover all kind of rare and unusual species. Children will find the park interesting and informative.

Summer: Mon–Sun 9.30am–6pm
Winter: Mon–Sun 9.30am–4pm

£ © 🚐 ✕ P🚫 P ₪ 🚹 ₪ ♿ WC ☕ ¶

🏖 👪 © 🚶

The Windmill

Outwood Common
Surrey, RH1 3HQ
☎ 0342 843458

Redhill A25

≈ 🚌 Redhill

England's oldest working windmill. Built in 1665, surrounded by common land and woods. Many friendly animals and small museum with collection of carriages.

Easter–31 Oct: Sun & BH Mon 2pm–6pm

£ © 🚐 ✕ 🌊 P 🚫 🏛 ♿ 🚹 ♿

WC 🏖 👪 🐟 🐾 ©

The Walled Garden

Sunbury Park
Thames St
Sunbury, Surrey
☎ 0784 446307

Sunbury on Thames riverside

≈ 🚌 Sunbury on Thames

Gardens set in 2 acres of level ground with very firm gravel. Includes various styles of gardens from past centuries, including knot gardens, parterres and a Victorian Rose garden.

Jan–Dec: Mon–Sun 8am–8pm

F ✕ P P ♿ 🚹 WC 🐟 🐾

Lightwater Country Park

The Avenue
Lightwater, Surrey, GU12 5SN
☎ 0276 51605

Bagshot/Junction 3, M3 or A322

≈ 🚌 Bagshot

This 149 acre heathland is a special habitat created by man dating back to Saxon times.

The Heathland Visitor Centre, provides an exciting interpretive display with talking models to illustrate this.

Apr–Sep: Tue–Fri 12noon–5pm
Sat–Sun/BH 10am–6pm
Oct–Mar: Sat–Sun/BH 10am–4pm

£ © 🚐 ✕ P P ♿ ✈ 🚹 ♿ ♿ WC

🏖 👪 ©

Bourne Hall Museum

Spring St
Ewell, Surrey, KT17 1UF
☎ 081 394 1734

Epsom A24

≈ 🚌 Ewell West

Founded in 1969, collections of local history, tools, cameras, radios, toys and old machinery in working order.

Jan–Dec: Mon–Sat 10am–5pm

F 🚐 ✕ 🌊 P ♿ 🏛 ✈ 🚹 ♿ WC ¶

👪 🐾 ©

Gatwick Zoo

Charlwood
Surrey, TH6 0EG
☎ 0293 862312

Gatwick airport A217/A23

≈ Gatwick

Landscaped grounds: monkeys, macaws, penguins, flamingoes and so much more, including walkthrough tropical birds and butterflies.

Mar–Oct: Mon–Sun 10.30am–6pm
Nov–Feb: Sat–Sun 2pm–4pm

£ 🚐 ✕ 🌊 P ♿ ✈ 🚹 ⇒ ♿ WC ¶

🏖 👪 🐾

Guildford Cathedral

Stag Hill
Guildford, Surrey, GU2 5UP

Guildford A3 (Guildford by–pass)

≈ 🚌 Guildford

The only entirely new Anglican Cathedral, built on a new site in the southern province, since the middle ages.

Jan–Dec: Mon–Sun 9.30am–5.30pm
(between services)

F 🚐 ✕ 🐾 🌊 P ♿ 🌿 🏛 ✈ 🚹 ♿

♿ WC ¶ 🏖 👪 🐾 © 🚶

Loseley Park Farms

Guildford
Surrey, GU3 1HS
☎ 0483 304440

Guildford A3 and A3100

⇌ Guildford

Elizabethan Manor House, still in the ownership of the original family. Famous Jersey Dairy Herd producing milk and cream for the delicious Loseley Dairy Products.

Jun–Sep: Wed–Sat 2pm–5pm

£©🚌✳ P ⚲ ⚒🏠➜ ⊣ ♿wc ‖ 🎒🌳✆

Royal Botanic Gardens

Kew
Richmond, Surrey, TW9 3AB
☎ 081 940 1171

Richmond

⇌ Kew Bridge ⊖ Kew Gardens Bus

300 acre garden with 4 acres of glasshouses, 2 art galleries and audio–visual exhibition.

Jan–Dec: Mon–Sun 9.30am

£©🚌✳🚐 P♿ P ⚲☛➜ ⊣ ⫯ ♿wc ‖ 🎒🌳♿

Painshill Park Landscape Garden

Portsmouth Rd
Cobham, Surrey, KT11 1JE
☎ 0932 868113

Cobham, A245/A3

Amazing vistas, exquisite buildings & large lake. Created in the C18th, it is emerging through restoration to it's former splendour.

Mid Apr–Mid Oct: Sun 11am–6pm
Other days by appointment for groups

£©🚌✳ P♿ P ⚲➜�♿wc ‖ 🎒🌳♿👓♿

Surrey Heath Museum

Knoll Rd
Camberley, Surrey, RG21 2PT
☎ 0276 686252 x 284

Camberley, A30 or M3 runs close

⇌🚐 Camberley

Small, but attractively designed museum with a permanent display on the history of the Borough of Surrey Heath, emphasising heathland habit and changing exhibitions of local and regional interest.

Jan–Dec: Tue–Sat 11am–5pm

F🚐✳ P♿P ⚲🦯☛ ♿wc ‖ ♿
🦆☕✆

Horton Park Rare Breed Farm

Horton Lane
Epsom, Surrey
☎ 0372 743984

Epsom

⇌🚐 Epsom

Rare breed farm on part of what was a 200 acre farm providing milk, beef and pork to 'Epsom Cluster' of mental hospitals. 32 acres with rolled hoggin and concrete paths.

Summer: Mon–Sun 10am–6pm
Winter: Mon–Sun 10am–5pm

£©🚌✳ P♿ P ⚲➜ ⊣ ♿wc ‖ 🎒🌳

Box Hill NT

Nr Leatherhead, Surrey
☎ 0306 885502

2½m S of Leatherhead

There are 3 car parks at the top of the Hill. Surfaces are uneven, but a tarmaced area by the restaurant. Access to the slopes is by the viewpoint and Donkey Green area. A special ½m wheelchair path is planned.

P♿ P ♿wc ‖ 🎒

Leith Hill Rhododendron Wood NT

Leith Hill
Surrey

A new route has been created to allow access to the upper part of the garden.

Reigate Hill NT

Reigate Rd
Surrey

Although much has been cleared, access may still be limited in some areas, after the storms of 1987 and 1990. Reigate Hill should be accessible from the Margery Lane car park via a path leading over the footbridge across the Reigate Road.

Runnymede NT

Nr River Thames
Surrey

These lovely meadows by the Thames are accessible and some riverboats admit

SURREY

disabled people. Riverside car parking April to end of September only; limited car parking in Tea Room car park (coach park); NT tea–room closed in winter. Adapted WC by tea–rooms.

Please contact Warden (0784 432891) for advice and information; details of tea–room access and opening times from Tea Room Manageress (0784 435797).

TYNE & WEAR

The Bede Monastery Museum

Jarrow Hall
Church Bank
Jarrow, Tyne & Wear, NE32 3DY
☎ 091 489 2106

Jarrow – just off A185 to South Shields

🚌 Bede/Jarrow or Metro

Georgian house with display telling story of St Paul's Anglo Saxon and medieval monastery, home of the Venerable Bede, church nearby. 3 acres with gravel, paved and tarmac paths.

Apr–Oct: Tue–Sat & BH Mon 10am–5.30pm
Sun 2.30pm–5.30pm
Nov–Mar: Tue–Sat 11am–4.30pm
Sun 2.30pm–5.30pm

Museum & Art Gallery

Borough Rd
Sunderland
Tyne & Wear, SR1 1PP
☎ 091 514 1235

Sunderland

🚋 🚌 Sunderland

Wildlife and geology of the North East, history of Sunderland and its industries, glass, pottery and shipbuilding. Also period rooms, silver and paintings.

Jan–Dec: Tue–Fri & BH Mon 10am–5.30pm
Sat 10am–4pm
Sun 2pm–5pm

Monkwearmouth Station Museum

North Bridge St
Sunderland
Tyne & Wear, SR5 1AP
☎ 091 567 7075

Sunderland

🚋 🚌 Sunderland

Land transport museum housed in original station of 1848. Restored Edwardian Booking Office, platform area, footbridge and siding area with rolling stock display.

Jan–Dec: Tue–Fri & BH Mon 10am–5.30pm
Sat 10am–4.30pm
Sun 2pm–5pm

Museum of Antiquities

The University
Newcastle upon Tyne
Tyne & Wear, NE1 7RU
☎ 091 222 7844

Newcastle upon Tyne

🚋 🚌 Newcastle or Metro

World famous prehistoric, Roman, Anglo Saxon collections, reconstruction of C3rd AD Temple to Mithras. Models of Hadrian's Wall, Roman Soldiers.

Jan–Dec: Mon–Sat 10am–5pm
Closed Good Fri

Tynemouth Priory & Castle EH

East St
Tynemouth
North Shields, Tyne & Wear, NE30 4BZ
☎ 091 257 1090

North Shields/Newcastle–upon–Tyne

🚋 🚌 Tynemouth

The castle walls and gatehouse enclose the substantial remains of a Benedictine priory founded 1090 on a Saxon monastic site. Their strategic importance has made the castle and priory the target of attack for many centuries. Tarmac and grass paths.

Jan–Dec: Mon–Sun

Tanfield Railway

Stanley–Sunniside Rd
Tyne & Wear, NG16 5ET
☎ 091 274 2002

Gateshead, A692 Consett Rd

⇌ 🚌 Newcastle

Oldest existing railway in world, opened 1725. Working steam–hauled passenger railway, using locos with local connection and Victorian carriages. Trains suitable for manual wheelchairs only.

Jan–Dec: Mon–Sun 10am–5pm for viewing
Summer: Sun & BH Mon Trains working
Mid Summer: Thurs & Sat also

£F©🚌⚡🐕 P ♿⚡➔ ⊣ ⊹ WC
🏊🎪♿🖐

WARWICKSHIRE

Warwickshire Museum

St John's House
Warwick
☎ 0926 412021

East side of Warwick on A445

⇌ Warwick

Displays are based on the social history of the county. Galleries have basic themes such as costume, domestic life, school life and general social history, but are changed fairly frequently.

Jan–Dec: Tue–Sat 10am–12.30 & 1.30pm–5.30pm
May–Sep: Sun & BH Mon 2.30pm–5pm

F🚌🐕 P ♿ 🍴🏛⊣ WC 🏊🎪
🖐♿

Warwick Doll Museum

Oken's House
Castle St
Warwick, CV34 4BP
☎ 0926 495546

Central Warwick

⇌ 🚌 Warwick

Includes the Joy Robinson Doll & Toy Collection. There are also dolls, toys and games from the Warwickshire Museum's own collection.

Easter–Sep: Mon–Sat 10am–5pm
Sun 2pm–5pm

£©🚌🐕 P ♿ 🍴🏛 WC 🏊🎪
🖐♿

Warwickshire Museum

Market Hall
Market Place
Warwick, CV34 4SA
☎ 0926 412501

Central Warwick

⇌ Warwick

Noted for the famous tapestry map of Warwickshire, habitat displays and a giant fossil plesiosaur. A temporary exhibition gallery has displays which change every 4–6 weeks.

Jan–Dec: Mon–Sat 10am–5.30pm
May–Sep: Sun 2.30pm–5pm

F🚌🐕 P♿ 🏛 WC 🏊♿🍷♿

Ryton Gardens

Ryton on Dunsmore
Coventry, Warks., CV8 3LG
☎ 0203 303517

Coventry or Rugby A45

⇌ Coventry

The 10 acre Ryton Gardens are at the National Centre for Organic Gardening, headquarters of The Henry Doubleday Research Association. Best known for its 'Muck and Magic' TV series on Ch4.

Apr–Sep: Mon–Sun 10am–6pm
Oct–Mar: Mon–Sun 10am–4pm

£© P ♿➔⊣⇒👁♿WC 🏠🍴
🏊🎪♿🍷♿

Museum of Science & Industry

146 Newhall St
Birmingham, Warks., B3 1RZ
☎ 021 235 1661

Birmingham

⇌ New Street

Locomotive hall, engineering hall, cycles and arms, communication equipment, aircraft, science and transport. Created in 1950.

Jan–Dec: Mon–Sat 9.30am–5pm
Sun 2pm–5pm

F🚌🐕 P♿ P 🐟 ♿🍴♿WC 🏠🍴
🏊♿🐟🍷♿

Baddesley Clinton NT

Knowle, Warks., B93 0DR
☎ 0564 783294

Knowle, A4141

⇌ Lapworth

Moated manor house dating back to 1350 and little changed since 1633. Armorial

WARWICKSHIRE

glass and priests hides.
Mar–Sep: Wed–Sun 2pm–6pm
Oct: Wed–Sun 12.30pm–4.30pm

£ © 🚌 🐕 🦯 P♿ P ♿ 🏠 → ✈ ⊢ ♿WC
WC ‖ 🎪 👥 ♿ 👐 ⊘ ♿

Lord Leycester Hospital

High St
Warwick, CV34 4BH
☎ 0926 492797
At the Westgate in High St, A429
🚂 🚌 Warwick

Grade 1 historic building built about 1400
AD by Guilds of Warwick. Home of Rest for
ex–servicemen and their wives.
Regimental museum.

Jan–Dec: Mon–Sat 10am–5.30pm
Closed: Good Fri

£ © 🚌 🐕 P P ♿ 👐 🏠 WC ‖ 🎪
♿ 👐 👐 ⊘

Twycross Zoo

Atherstone
Warks., CV9 3PX
☎ 0827 880250

On A444 Burton to Nuneaton Rd off M42
exit 11

Charitable trust – set in 50 acres of parkland
with large variety of animals, childrens
adventure playground plus many summer
attractions.

Summer: Mon–Sun 10am–6pm
Winter: Mon–Sun 10am–4pm

£ © 🚌 🐕 P♿ P ♿ → ⊢ ♿WC WC ‖
🎪 👥 ♿ ⊘ ♿

Jephson Gardens

The Parade
Leamington Spa
Warks., CV32 4AT
☎ 0926 450000

Leamington Spa
🚂 🚌 Leamington Spa

13 acres of beautifully laid out gardens &
bordered walks. Tropical birds and wild
ducks.

Jan–Dec: Mon–Sun 8am–sunset

F 🚌 P♿ P ♿ 👐 → ⊢ ♿WC WC ‖ 🎪
👥 ⊘ ♿

Leamington Spa Art Gallery & Museum

Avenue Rd
Leamington Spa
Warks., CV1 3PP
☎ 0926 426559

Leamington Spa
🚂 🚌 Leamington Spa

Permanent exhibitions of paintings,
ceramics and glass. Varied programme of
temporary exhibitions. Local history Gallery
opens Jan 1992.

Jan–Dec: Mon–Sat 10am–1pm & 2pm–5pm
Thurs 10am–1pm & 2pm–5pm & 6pm–8pm
Closed Good Fri

F 🚌 🐕 🖼 P♿ P ♿ ♿ → WC 🎪
♿ 🎧 ♥ 👐

Upton House NT

Nr Banbury, Oxon. OX15 6HT
☎ 0295 87266

A422 from Banbury, 7m (House is in
Warks.,)
🚂 Banbury

Late C17th house, remodelled 1920's.
Contains Bearsted collections of paintings.
Fine garden with lawns, terraced
herbaceous border, lakes and bog garden in
deep valley. 30 acres with gravel, paved and
grassed paths.

Apr & Oct: Sat–Sun & BH Mon 2pm–6pm
May–Sep: Sat–Wed 2pm–6pm

£ © 🚌 🐕 🦯 P♿ P ▲ 👐 🏠 ⊢ 🚐
🍴 ♿WC WC 🐕 ‖ 🎪 👥 🌲 ♿

Stratford Brass Rubbing Centre

RST Summerhouse
Avon Bank
Stratford, Warks.,
☎ 0789 297671

Stratford–upon–Avon
🚂 🚌 Stratford

England's unique heritage of medieval and
tudor brasses available to rub in bright,
metallic waxes to create a beautiful wall
hanging.

Easter–Sep: Mon–Sun 10am–6pm
Oct: Mon–Sun 11am–4pm

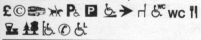

£ F © 🚌 🐕 P ♿ ♿ WC 🎪 👥

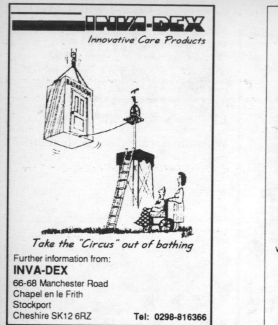
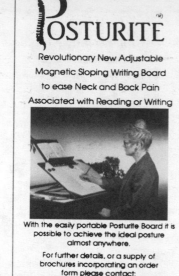

WEST MIDLANDS

Sandwell Valley Nature Reserve RSPB

Nr Birmingham
W. Mids., B43 5AG
☎ 021 358 3013

On Tanhouse Avenue, which is reached via Hamstead Rd in Great Barr; exit 7 on M6.

Nature centre with exhibition and observation room. Surfaced path leads 600 yards down a rather steep hill (assistance available) to four hides specially adapted for wheelchair users. Overlooks the lake and marsh.

⌐ㅓ &ʷᶜ wc ¶¶

Museum of British Road Transport

St Agnes Lane
Hales St
Coventry, W. Mids., CV1 1PN
☎ 0203 832425

Coventry city centre
⇌ 🚐 Coventry

Largest display of British road transport with over 150 cars, 200 cycles and 70 motorcycles.

Jan–Dec: Mon–Sun 10am–5pm

£©🚐⊁ P& P P &Ħ&ʷᶜ wc ⚘
¶¶ 🖼⚓🐟🧺ⓒ

Birmingham Botanical Gardens

Westbourne Rd
Edgbaston
Birmingham, W. Mids., B15 3TR
☎ 021 454 1860

Birmingham
🚐

15 acre 'Oasis of Delight'. Tropical House, Palm House, Orangery, Cactus House and beautiful gardens with paved, tarmac and gravel paths.

Jan–Dec: Mon–Sat 9am
Sun 10am

£©🚐⊁ P& P &🏛➤⌐ㅓ&ʷᶜ wc
⚘¶¶🖼⚓&ⓒ&ᴸ

Himley Hall Country Park

Himley Park
Dudley, W. Mids., DY3 4DF
☎ 0902 324093

5m S of Wolverhampton on A449
⇌ 🚐 Wolverhampton

Old ancestral home of Earls of Dudley – close ties with Royal family. Hall opened by special arrangement. Model village and miniature railway.

Jan–Dec: Mon–Sun 6am–½hr before dusk

£F©🚐⊁ P &Ħ⌐ㅓ🧑‍🤝‍🧑&🎧

Walsall Leather Centre Museum

56–57 Wisemore
Walsall, W.Mids, WS2 8EQ
☎ 0922 721153

Walsall
⇌ 🚐 Walsall

An 1891 leather factory. The building has always housed leather goods manufacturers and was opened as a museum in 1988.

Nov–Mar: Tue–Sat 9am–4pm
Sun 12noon–5pm
Apr–Oct: Tue–Sat 10am–5pm
Sun 12noon–5pm
Open BH Mon

F🚐⊁ P&⚓➤Ħ➤⌐ㅓ&ʷᶜ wc ¶¶
🖼🧑‍🤝‍🧑&🎧🐟🧺

Coombe Abbey Country Park

Coventry, W. Mids.,
☎ 0203 453720

3m E of city
🚐 Brinklow Rd

400 acres of formal garden, woodlands and nature trails. Heronry, paddle–boating for children. Bird hide accessible.

F⊁ P& P ➤⌐ㅓ⇒⁀ wc ¶¶ 🖼🧑‍🤝‍🧑

Herbert Art Gallery and Museum

Jordan Well
Coventry, W. Mids., CV1 5RW
☎ 0203 832381

Central Coventry
⇌ 🚐 Coventry

Coventry's local museum with exhibitions of social history, natural history, archaeology and the visual arts on permanent and temporary display.

Jan–Dec: Mon–Sat 10am–5.30pm
Sun 2pm–5pm

F🚐⊁ P ⚑ &Ħ⌐ㅓ⇒&ʷᶜ wc
&🧺

WEST SUSSEX

Mechanical Music & Doll Collection

Church Rd
Portfield
Chichester, W. Sussex., PO19 4HN
☎ 0243 785421

1m E of Chichester, off A27

≈ Chichester

The mechanical instruments are described and demonstrated. Musical boxes, barrel–pianos, street–pianos, fair organs, etc.

Easter–Sept: Mon–Sun 10am–5pm
Oct – Easter: Sat–Sun 10am–5pm

£ © 🚌 ✕ P 🅰 ⇒ WC 🎏 ♿ ◈ 🖐 ⊘

Corps of Military Police Museum

Broyle Rd
Chichester, W. Sussex., PO19 4BN
☎ 0243 786311 x 237

A286 Chichester–Midhurst Rd

🚌 Chichester/Midhurst/Bognor

The 'Redcap Museum' traces history of Military Police from Tudor to current times. Latest displays include new Medal Room and Gulf War.

Apr–Sep: Tue–Fri 10.30am–12.30pm & 1.30pm–4.30pm
Sat–Sun 2pm–6pm
Oct–Mar: Tue–Fri 10.30am–12.30pm & 1.30pm–4.30pm
Closed January

F 🚌 ✕ P ♿ WC 🎏 ♿ 🖐

Chichester District Museum

29 Little London
Chichester, W. Sussex., PO19 1PB
☎ 0243 784683

Chichester

≈ Southgate 🚌 Chichester

Museum of the Chichester area – fossils, archaeology and local history. Changing exhibitions first floor.

Jan–Dec: Tue–Sat 10am–5.30pm

F 🚌 ✕ 🅿 P 🅿 🖐 🏛 WC 🎏 ♿ ◈ 🖐

Littlehampton Museum

Manor House
Church St
Littlehampton
W. Sussex., BN17
☎ 0903 715149

Littlehampton

≈ 🚌 Littlehampton

Local maritime history museum with changing exhibitions – bygones, photographs, archaeology and paintings of the Arun district.

Jan–Dec: Tue–Sat 10.30am–4.30pm

F 🚌 ✕ P 🅿 🅰 ◈ ➤ WC 🎏 🌲 ⊘

Coombes Farm Tours

Church Farm
Coombes
Lancing, W. Sussex., BN15 0RS
☎ 0273 452028

Lancing & Shoreham–by–Sea, off A27

Tractor and trailer ride over 1000 acres of the South Downs, through cows and calves, ewes and lambs, cornfields and conservation areas. Scenic views out to sea and over the Weald. Trailer adapted to take wheelchairs. No walking involved. Very personal and organised by the owner.

Mar–Oct: by arrangement (daylight hours)

£ © 🚌 ✕ P ♿ 🍴 WC 🍴 🎏 🌲 ♿ 🖐

Buchan Country Park

Horsham Rd
Crawley, W. Sussex., RH11 9HQ
☎ 0293 542088

Crawley, A264

≈ 🚌 Crawley

160 acres of mixed woodlands and ponds. Information Centre. Motorised wheelchairs to view nature trail.

Jan–Dec: Mon–Sun 8am–8pm

F 🚌 ✕ P ♿ ➤ 🔄 📷 🍴 ♿ WC 🎏 🌲 ♿ 🖐 ⊘

Pagham Harbour Local Nature Reserve

Selsey Rd
Sidlesham, W. Sussex.,
☎ 0243 641508

On B1245 7m S of Chichester

≋ Chichester 🚌 Chichester to Selsey

Coastal nature reserve, nationally and internationally important for its birdlife, particularly wintering wildfowl and waders. Interesting local history.

Winter: Sat–Sun 10.30am–4.30pm
Summer: Mon–Fri 11am–5pm
Sat Sun & BH 10.30am–4pm

F🚌 ✳ P ⅙ ➤ ㅓ ⇒ ➕ ⅜ᵂᶜ WC ⅘
⛺🏕 🌼 🕐 ㅕ

Chichester Cathedral

Chichester, W. Sussex., PO19 1PX
☎ 0243 782595

Centre of Chichester

≋ 🚌 Chichester

Building started in 1091. Site of shrine of St Richard, Romanesque stone carvings, modern paintings, sculptures and tapestries, stained glass window by Chagall.

Easter–Oct: Mon–Sat 7.40am–7pm
Nov–Mar: Mon–Sat 7.40am–5pm
Sunday's between services

F🚌 ✳ P ⅃ ➥ ➤ ㅓ ⅜ᵂᶜ WC ‖ ◆ 🌼

Wildfowl & Wetlands Trust

Mill Rd
Arundel, W. Sussex., BN18 9PB
☎ 0908 883355

Arundel, off A27

≋ Arundel

Ducks, geese and swans set within a delightful 60 acre wetland scene – many of them will feed from your hand. Tar with chipping topped paths.

Summer: Mon–Sun 9.30am–6.30pm
Winter: Mon–Sun 9.30am–5pm

£© ✳ 🏞 P⅙ P ⅙🏛 ➤ ㅓ ➕ ⅜ᵂᶜ
WC ‖ ⅘ ⛺🏕 ㅕ 🌼 🕐 ㅕ

Worthing Museum & Art Gallery

Chapel Rd
Worthing, W. Sussex., BN11 1HD
☎ 0903 39999 x 121 Sat: 204229

A24 Worthing Northwards

≋ Worthing

Extensive collections of archaeology, local history, costume, toys and dolls. Art collections include English paintings, pottery and glass. Exhibition programme. Disabled toilets to be available shortly.

Apr–Sep: Mon–Sat 10am–6pm
Oct–Mar: Mon–Sat 10am–5pm

Denmans Garden

Denmans
Fontwell
Nr Arundel, W. Sussex, BN18 0SU
☎ 0243 542808

Midway Arundel and Chichester on A27

≋ Barnham

Walled, gravel and water gardens; Natural layout of trees. All year interest. Glass area for tender species. School of garden design.

Jan–Dec: Mon–Sun 9am–5pm

£© 🚌 P ⅙ ➥ ➤ ㅓ WC ⚘ ‖ ⅘
⛺🏕 ㅕ ◆

Bignor Roman Villa

Bignor
Pulborough, W. Sussex., RH20 1PH
☎ 07987 259

A27/Pulborough–Arundel A29

🚌 Wed only

Fine mosaic floors of Venus, Medusa, Gladiators etc. Able to walk on some, in a superb country setting.

Mar–May & Oct: Tue–Sun & BH Mon 10am–5pm
Jun–Sep: Mon–Sun 10am–6pm

£© 🚌 ✳ P⅙ P ⅙ ⅃ ㅓ ➕ WC ‖
⅘ ⛺🏕 ㅕ ◆

Borde Hill Garden

Haywards Heath
W. Sussex., RH16 1XP
☎ 0444 450326

1½m N of Haywards Heath on Balcombe Rd

≋ Haywards Heath

Award winning informal country garden with unique collection of rhododendrons, magnolias, camellias and azaleas. Outstanding views, woodland walks. Woodland difficult – North Park grass only.

Mar–Oct: Mon–Sun 10am–6pm

£© 🚌 ✳ P⅙ P ⅙ ➤ ㅓ ➕ ⅜ᵂᶜ WC
‖ ⛺🏕 ㅕ 🌼 🕐 ㅕ

WEST SUSSEX

Rainbows End Adventure Park

Haltham Park
Bognor Regis
W. Sussex., PO21 1DB
☎ 0243 825255

Bognor Regis

≋ 🚌 Bognor Regis

Children's adventure park featuring Old MacDonalds mini farm, aviaries, caves, big top show and much more.

Mar–Oct: Mon–Sun 10am–6pm

£©🚐⚡🌳 P🦽 ▰ ⬩⬩ ⚹ᵂᶜ WC ‖ 🛥
🏕🦽🎁ℂ

Hammerwood Park

Nr East Grinstead
W. Sussex., RH19 3QE
☎ 0342 850594

A264 between East Grinstead and Tunbridge Wells

The house built in 1792 by Latroke (architect of the White House and Capital in Washington USA), is on the edge of the Ashdown Forest.

By appointment only

£©🚐⚡🌳🛶 P🦽 P 🦽🏛➤ ┤ᵂᶜ
WC ‖ 🛥 🦽 ◆🎁ℂ

Highdown Gardens

Goring-by-Sea
W. Sussex
☎ 0903 48067

≋ 🚌 Goring-by-Sea

Chalk garden created by Sir F Stern in 1910, wide selection of spring bulbs, shrubs, trees and climbing roses.

Jan–Dec: Mon–Fri 10 am–4.30pm
Apr–Oct: Sat/Sun & BH 10am–8pm

F🚐⚡🌳 P 🦽 ┤ᵂᶜ WC🏕🦽

Amberley Chalk Pits Museum

Amberley
Arundel, W. Sussex, BN18 9LT

B2139 between Arundel and Storrington

≋ Amberley

Working museum with craftsmen, railway buses, workshops and many others in a 36 acre open air site.

1 Apr–1 Nov: Wed–Sun & BH Mon 10am–5pm
Summer: Mon–Sun

£©🚐⚡🌳🐾🛶 P🦽 P 🦽➤ ┤⟹

🦼🦽ᵂᶜ WC🤸 ‖ 🛥🏕🦽🧁🎁ℂ🦺

Ditchling Museum Trust

Church Lane
Ditchling
Nr Hassocks, W. Sussex., BN6 8TB
☎ 0273 844744

A23 Hurstpierpoint

🚌 Hassocks

History of area, dioramas and rooms with models in period dress, model trains and cars. Special exhibitions.

Apr–Oct: Mon–Sun 10.30am–5pm
Nov–Mar: Sat–Sun & BH 2pm–5pm

£©🚐⚡🛶P🦽P🦽➤ ┤⟹ᵂᶜ
WC ‖ 🛥🦽◆🎁ℂ🦺

Fishbourne Roman Palace & Museum

Salthill Rd
Fishbourne
Chichester, W. Sussex., PO19 3QR
☎ 0243 785859

1½m W of Chichester off A27

≋ Fishbourne

Remains of large Roman palace with many excellent mosaic floors protected by a modern cover building. Items of everyday Roman life displayed in site museum. Re–planted Roman formal garden.

Mar/Apr/Oct: Mon–Sun 10am–5pm
May–Sep: Mon–Sun 10am–6pm
Nov: Mon–Sun 10am–4pm
Dec–Feb: Sun 10am–4pm

£©🚐⚡ P 🦽➤ ┤ᵂᶜWC ‖ 🛥
🏕🎧◆🎁ℂ🦺

Tilgate Park & Nature Centre

Tilgate Park
Crawley, W. Sussex., RH10 5PQ
☎ 0293 521168

Near A23/M23, Crawley

≋ Crawley 🚌 Tilgate

450 acres of forest and parkland, including ornamental gardens, 3 lakes, play areas. Nature centre with small collection of British wildlife and domestic livestock.

Summer: Mon–Sun 10am–6pm
Winter: Mon–Sun 10am–4pm

F🚐⚡🐾P🦽 P 🦽🦽➤ ┤ᵂᶜ WC ‖
🏕🦽ℂ

Tangmere Military Aviation Museum Trust

Tangmere Airfield
Tangmere
Chichester, W. Sussex., PO20 6ES
☎ 0243 775223

Chichester, main A27 to Arundel, well signposted

≷ 🚌 Chichester

Famous Battle of Britain Fighter Station. Unique collection of aviation exhibits, photographs, documents, working displays. 70 years of military aviation.

Feb–Nov: Mon–Sun 10am–5.30pm

£ⓒ🚌⚡ ⭐ P ☂ ➤ ⊣ ♿ WC ‖ 🌲
🌳 ⚓ 🐾 ⓒ ♿

Petworth House NT

Petworth, W. Sussex., GU28 0AE
☎ 0798 43929/42207

Petworth

≷ 🚌 Pilborough

Late C17th house overlooking deer park. Landscaped by Capability Brown. Fine collection of paintings, sculpture and carvings.

1 Apr–31 Oct: Tue–Thu/Sat–Sun
Open Gd Fri & BH Mon. Closed the following Thurs.

£ⓒ🚌⚡ 🛒 P☂ P ⚡ ☂ 🏛 ➤ ☂WC
WC 🏠 ‖ 🌲 🌳 ⚓ 🐾 ♿

Holly Gate Cactus Nursery

Billinghurst Rd
Ashington, W. Sussex., RH20 3BA
☎ 0903 892930

A24 between Worthing and Horsham

≷ Horsham 🚌 Ashington

Nursery established 30 years, sells plants world–wide. Garden contains 30,000 exotic plants, many rare, mature specimens, some with spectacular flowers.

Jan–Dec: Mon–Sun 9am–5pm

£ⓒ🚌⚡ P 🛒 ➤ ⊣ WC ‖ 🌲 🌳
🐾 ⓒ

Heale Gardens & Plant Centre

Middle Woodford
Nr Salisbury, Wilts., SP4 6NT
☎ 072 273 504

A360 or A345

≷ 🚌 Salisbury

8 acres of beautiful gardens beside River Avon. Varied collection of plants, shrubs, musk and other roses in formal setting of clipped hedges and mellow stonework. Best June/July. Magnificent magnolia and acers surrounding authentic Japanese Tea House and Nikko Bridge.

Jan–Dec: Mon–Sun 10am–5pm

£ⓒ🚌⚡ P ➤ ⊣ ☂WC 🌲 🌳ⓒ

Stourton House Garden

Stourton
Warminster, Wilts., BA12 6QF
☎ 0747 840417

3m NW of Mere (A303); Next to Stourhead (Nat.Trust)

4 acres of informal flower garden; level grass paths lead through a vista of colourful shrubs, trees and many unusual plants.

Apr–Nov: Wed,Thu,Sun & BH Mon
11am–6pm

£ⓒ🚌⚡ P ➤ ⊣ ☂WC ‖ 🌲 🌳♿

Great Barn Museum

Avebury, Wilts., SN8 1RF
☎ 06723 555

5m W of Marlborough on A4

≷ Pewsey

A C17th thatched barn housing a museum of Wiltshire rural life. Regular craft demonstrations take place throughout the season.

Mid Mar–Mid Nov: Mon–Sun 10am–5.30pm

£ⓒ🚌⚡ ⭐ P P☂ ➤ ⊣ ‖
🌲 🌳

Atwell–Wilson Motor Museum

Downside
Stockley Lane
Calne, Wilts., SN11 0NF
☎ 0249 813119

Calne: A4 to Marlborough

🚌 Calne

Range of vintage cars, classic cars and

WILTSHIRE

motor bikes.
Apr–Oct: Mon–Thu 10am–5pm
Sun 11am–5pm
Nov–Mar: Mon–Thu 10am–4pm
Sun 11am–4pm

£©🚌🏇🛶P♿P♿&→⌐🚾wc
🎎♿©

The Trowbridge Museum

The Shires
Court St
Trowbridge, Wilts., BA14 8AT
☎ 0225 751339

Bradford–on–Avon, A363
🚆 Trowbridge

Opened July 1990, telling the story of a west
country woollen town with working textile
machinery and local history displays.
Jan–Dec: Tue–Fri 2pm–5pm
Sat 10am–5pm

F🚌🏇P♿P&🍴→⌐🚾wc🍴
♿🖐

Salisbury & South Wiltshire Museum

The King's House
65 The Close
Salisbury, Wilts., SP1 2EN
☎ 0722 332151

Salisbury A30
🚆🚌 Salisbury

Award–winning museum in Grade I building.
Displays of Stonehenge, Early Man, Pitt
Rivers collection, ceramics, Wedgwood,
pictures, costume, lace and embroidery.
Jan–Dec: Mon–Sat 10am–5pm
Jul & Aug: Sun & Salisbury Festival
2pm–5pm

£©🚌🏇P♿&🏠→⌐-♿-🚾
wc🍴🍴◆

Cholderton Rare Breeds Farm

Amesbury Road
Cholderton
Salisbury, Wilts., SP4 0BW
☎ 0980 64438

Amesbury A303, Andover
🚌 Cholderton

Endangered farm animal breeds. 15 acre
parkland setting with beautiful views.
Animals close enough for disabled people
to touch and feed. Pets–park, ponds and
gardens.

Easter–Oct: Mon–Sun 10am–5pm

£©🚌🏇P♿👋🛶→⌐-🚾wc
🍴🎎♿

Bowood House & Gardens

Estate Office
Calne, Wilts., SN8 1TS
☎ 0249 812102

Calne A4
🚌🚍 Chippenham

Home of Earl of Shelburne. House built in
1754 surrounded by 100 acre park and lake
created by 'Capability' Brown. Many
beautiful pictures and family treasures.
Apr–Nov: Mon–Sun 11am–6pm

£©🚌🏇P♿&👋🏠→⌐-🚾
🚾wc🍴🍴🎎🖐©

Farmer Giles Farmstead

Teffont
Salisbury, Wilts., SP3 5QY
☎ 0722 716338

Just off A303 London–Exeter Rd at Teffont
🚌🚍 Salisbury

Opened in 1989 with extensive area under
cover. Large selection of farm animals and
birds. Watch the 150 cows milked.
Mar–Nov: Mon–Sun 10.30am–6pm
Winter months by booking

£©🚌🏇P&→⌐⇒👁🚾wc
🍴🎎◆🖐©🔔

Swindon & Cricklade Railway

Tadpole Lane
Blunsdon
Swindon, Wilts.,
☎ 0793 771615/721252

Swindon A419

Standard gauge railway – steam and diesel.
Special charges for parties. Old MSWJ
Railway.
Open weekends–please tel for train
operating times

£©🚌🏇P&→⌐-🚾wc🎎
🍴🎎🖐©

Great Western Railway Museum

Faringdon Rd
Swindon, Wilts., SN1 5BJ
☎ 0793 493189

Swindon M4 (A420/A419)

≋ Swindon

A collection devoted to history of the Great Westerm Railway. 5 locomotives, nameplates, posters and other railwayana.
Jan–Dec: Mon–Sat 10am–5pm
Sun 2pm–5pm

Longleat House & Safari Park

Warminster
Wilts., BA12 7NT
☎ 0985 844551/844328

A362 Warminster/Frome

≋ 🚌 Warminster, Frome & Westbury

A magnificent C16th house set in rolling parkland. Priceless family heirlooms spanning 4 centuries. A safari park with lions, white tigers, monkeys, rhinos, wolves, zebras, giraffes, camels, buffalo and elephants. Facinating exhibtions. Rides, amusements and the world's largest Maze.

Longleat House: Jan–Dec: Mon–Sun 10am–4pm
Safari Park: 9th Mar–3rd Nov: Mon–Sun 11am–5.30pm
& other attractions

£©🚌🐾 P 🐾 ♿🏛→ ⊓ ⊣⊢ ♿
wc 🏠 ⁙ ⚏🎪

Sheldon Manor

Chippenham, Wilts., SN14 0RG
☎ 0249 653120

Chippenham 1½m, A420

≋ 🚌 Chippenham

Early manor–house, sole survivor of a deserted medieval village, with a beautiful garden, and distinguished catering.
Easter–4 Oct: Sun/Thu/BH's 12.30pm–6pm
House opens 2pm

£©🚌🐾🍽 P♿ P ♿🏛⊓ ⇒
WC ⁙ ⚏🎪🐾♥🤝ⓒ ♿

YORKSHIRE

Bempton Cliffs Reserve RSPB

Cliff Lane
Bempton
Bridlington, E. Yorks., YO15
☎ 0262 851179

Bridlington B1229

≋ 🚌 Bempton

England's largest sea–bird colony with over 200,000 breeding birds. Close–up views of Gannet, Puffins and other sea birds. ¾ mile with level compacted stone paths.

Reserve: open all times
Centre: Easter–Sep Mon–Sun 10am–4pm

£©🚌🐾 P♿ P ♿→ ⊓ ⊣⊢♿wc
⁙ ⚏🎪♿🤝ⓒ♿

South Farm Craft Gallery

Blacktoft
via Gilberdyke
Goole, E. Yorks., DN14 7XT
☎ 0430 441082

Howden B1230 to Gilberdyke

Renovated old farm buildings creating an award winning gallery, studio and restuarant complex which still retains the spirit of the original. 2 acres with gravel and paved paths.
Jan–Dec: Wed–Sat 10am–5pm
Sun & BH Mon 11am–5pm

Bolton Abbey

Nr Skipton, N. Yorks., BD23 6EX
☎ 075 671 533

Skipton, on A59 to Harrogate

≋ 🚌 Skipton

Traditional country estate with ruined priory by the River Wharfe. 30,000 acres with nature trails and heather moors. 30 miles of footpaths; 5 miles are sultable for wheelchair users.
Jan–Dec: Mon–Sun 9am–dusk

£©🚌🐾🍽 P♿ P ♿🤝→⊓ ⇒
⊣⊢♿wc ⁙ ⚏🎪🤝 ♿

Jorvik Viking Centre Museum

Coppergate
York, N. Yorks., YO1 1NT
☎ 0904 643211

Centre of York

Step aboard a time car and be whisked back through the centuries on a journey to real–life Viking Britain.

1 Apr–31 Oct: Mon–Sun 9am–7pm
1 Nov–31 Mar: Mon–Sun 9am–5.30pm

£🚐✕🔍P♿🏠📷♿WC🧸
🐟🖐

Fountains Abbey & Studley Royal NT

Fountains,
Ripon, N. Yorks., HG4 3DZ
☎ 0765 620333

Ripon – B6265 Ripon–Pateley Bridge

Founded by Cistercian Monks in 1132.
Largest Monastic ruin in Britain, C18th
water garden and deer park. 700 acres with
gravel & paved paths.

Jan–Dec: Mon–Sun From 10am
Closed Jan/Nov/Dec on Fridays.

£🚐✕🔍P♿P♿➜🚽⇒📷🍴
♿WC🔥🍴🧸🎪🖐🎡♿

Kilnsey Park Country Park

Kilnsey
Nr Skipton, N. Yorks., BD23 5PS
☎ 0756 752150

B6160 between Threshfield and Kettlewell
🚐

'Daleslife' Visitors Centre – trout farm,
aquarium, flora and fauna, traditions of
Yorkshire Dales with aid of many displays,
video films and activities. Trout feeding
areas and Vietnamese Pigs. 3 acres with
gravel paths.

Jan–Dec: Mon–Sun

£©🚐✕P♿🏠➜🚽🍴WC🍴
🧸🎪♿🏃

Parcevall Hall Gardens

Skyreholme
Skipton, N. Yorks., BD23 6DE
☎ 0756 72311/72269

Skipton or Pateley Bridge

Historic garden dating from 1926 (Hall not
open). 23 acres with rough paths.

Easter–31 Oct: Mon–Sun 10am–6pm
Winter: By appointment

£🚐✕P🏭🚽WC🍴🎪♿🏃

York City Art Gallery

Exhibition Square
York, N. Yorks., YO1 2EW
☎ 0904 623839

York
🚉🚐 York

Treasure house of European and British
paintings spanning 7 centuries. Exciting
programme of temporary exhibitions,
events and workshops.

Jan–Dec Mon–Sat 10am–5pm
Sun 2.30pm–5pm
Closed Good Fri

F🚐✕🔍P♿🏠➜🚽♿WC
🧸🖐

Harlow Carr Botanical Gardens

Crag Lane
Harrogate, N. Yorks., HG3 1QB
☎ 0423 565418

Harrogate/B6162 to Otley
🚉🚐 Harrogate

Plant trials to discover suitablity for
Northern conditions. 68 acres of
landscaped gardens with gravel paths.
Woodlands, arboretum, wildlife area and
bird hide.

Jan–Dec: Mon–Sun 9.30am–7.30pm or
dusk

£©🚐✕🔍P♿P➜🚽♿WC
🍴🧸🎪♿🎧🐟🖐♿

Lightwater Valley Theme Park

Northstanley
Ripon, N. Yorks., HG4 3HT
☎ 0765 635368

3 miles N of Ripon on A6108, signed from
A1
🚉 Thirsk & Harrogate (9 miles)

125 acres of country park featuring the
world's biggest rollercoaster. Leisurely, skill
testing activities with undercover
entertainment.

Easter–Oct: ring for times

£©🚐✕P♿P🚽➜🚽📷♿WC
🔥🍴🧸🎪♿🖐🐟

Castle Howard

York, N. Yorks., YO6 7DA
☎ 065 384 333

York, A64
🚐 York

Collections of furniture, paintings, statuary
& historic costumes. Plant centre and
gardens. 1000 acres with gravel, grass and
tarmac paths. Chapel, woodland garden
and lakeside not accessible.

22 Mar–31 Oct: Mon–Sun Centre : from
10am

House & Galleries : from 11am

£ © 🚌 ⚡ P& P 🔋 ⬅ ⬛ 📷 ➤ ⌐
⇒ 🥤 🍴 &ᵂᶜ WC 🍴 🍸 👥

National Railway Museum

Leeman Road
York, N. Yorks., YO2 4XJ
☎ 0904 621261

York – central
≋ York

The Great Railway Show celebrates the railway age – from the 1820's to the present day. 16 acres with gravel and paved paths.

Jan–Dec Mon–Sat: 10am–6pm
Sun: 11am–6pm Last admissions 5pm

£ © 🚌 ⚡ P& P 📷 👤 ➤ ⌐ ⇒ 🍴
&ᵂᶜ WC 🔥 🍴 🍸 🎯 © &ᴸ

Pickering Castle EH

Pickering, N. Yorks., YO18 7AX
☎ 0751 74989

Pickering A170
🚌 Pickering

Splendid castle of motte and bailey design, founded by William the Conqueror in the C11th. 4½ acres with gravel and paved paths. No access to motte for wheelchair users.

Good Fri/1 Apr–30 Sep: Mon–Sun
10am–6pm
1 Oct–Maundy Thu: Tue–Sun 10am–4pm

£ © 🚌 ⚡ P 📷 🔋 🏛 🍴 &ᵂᶜ WC 🍸
👥 &ᴸ 🎯

Ryedale Folk Museum

Hutton le Hole
York, N. Yorks., YO6 6UA
☎ 0751 5367

A170 Kirbymoorside
≋ Malton

Yorkshire's leading open air museum, containing rescued buildings including manor house, cruck house and barns. Large collection of tools and crafts. 2½ acres with grass, tarmac and concrete paths.

Mar–Oct: Mon–Sun 10.30am–5.30pm

£ © 🚌 ⚡ P& P 👤 ⌐ 🍴 &ᵂᶜ WC 🍸
👥 &ᴸ 🎯

North Riding Forest Park FC

Nr. Pickering, N. Yorks., YO18 7DU
☎ 0751 72771

Pickering

Visitors centre and two forest drives. Walks, picnic places & viewpoints.

Forest: Jan–Dec Mon–Sun
Centre: Easter–Nov Mon–Sun

£ 🚌 ⚡ P& P 👤 &ᵂᶜ WC 🍴 🍸 👥
&ᴸ 🎯

Sheriff Hutton Park

Sheriff Hutton
York, N. Yorks., YO6 1RH
☎ 034 77 442

5 miles to W of A64 travelling York to Malton
≋ York

Grade 1 mansion built by Sir Arthur Ingram in 1614. Original Jacobean plaster ceilings and oak screen passage. Theatrical events in rehersal or production. Beautiful peaceful grounds with woodlands & lakes. 170 acres with gravel and grass paths. Ramps to house by appointment.

20 Jan–19 Dec: Mon–Fri 10am–4.30pm

£ © 🚌 ⚡ P& P ⬛ ⬅ 📷 ⌐ 🍴 &ᵂᶜ
WC 👥 &ᴸ 🎯 © &ᴸ

Embasy Steam Railway

The Station
Embasy
Nr Skipton, N. Yorks., BD23 6AX
☎ 0756 794727

Skipton
≋ 🚌 Skipton

Steam railway running 2½ miles to Holywell Halt and beyond. Interesting station with lots of events for children. 2 acres with gravel and paved paths. Trains not suitable for wheelchair users.

Jan–Dec: Sun & BH (exc.Xmas & Box.Day)
Jul: Tue/Sat/Sun
Aug: Tue/Wed/Thu/Sat/Sun

£ © 🚌 ⚡ P& P 👤 ➤ ⌐ 🍴 WC 🍸
🍸 👥 🎯 ©

NORTH YORKSHIRE

Whitby Museum & Pannett Art Gallery

Pannett Park
Whitby, N. Yorks., YO21 1RE
☎ 0947 602908

Whitby

≋ 🚌 Whitby

Situated in the centre of the town in an open park. Extensive collection of local history with special exhibitions periodically. 5 acres with paved paths.

1 May–30 Sep: Mon–Sat 9.30am–5.30pm
Sun: 2pm–5pm
1 Oct–30 Apr: Mon–Tue 10.30am–1pm
Wed–Sat: 10.30am–4pm
Sun: 2pm–4pm
and all public holidays exc. Xmas & New Year.

£©🚐✕ 🅟 ﻬ🔥☞ ⊣ wc ✕ 🍴
🏔🏞©

Theaksons Brewery

The Brewery
Masham
Ripon, N. Yorks., HG4 4DX
☎ 0765 689057

Ripon A6108 or A1 exit to B6267

🚌 Ripon

Discover how Theaksons Traditional Ales are brewed. See the Coopers raising wooden casts. Brewery not accessible to wheelchair users.

Good Fri–31 Oct: Wed–Sun 10.30am–4pm
Nov–Dec: Wed/Sat/Sun 10.30am–1pm & 2pm–4pm

£🚐✕P✕ 🔥▪️🏚➤ ⊣ ▪️▪️🌡wc
wc 🔥🏞✕

Dales Countryside Museum

Station Yard
Hawes
Wensleydale, N. Yorks.,
☎ 0969 667450

Hawes A684

Collections relating to life in upland Britain, specifically the Yorkshire Dales, with displays on coal mining, butter/cheese making and farming. Paved paths.

Apr–Oct: Mon–Sun 10am–5pm

£©🚐✕P🔥☞⇒wc🍴🏔
🔥🏞

Eden Farm Museum

Old Malton
N. Yorks., YO17 0RT
☎ 0653 692093

Malton A169

≋ Malton

A working farm of 260 acres open to visitors since 1988. A large museum of hand tools and horse equipment. Farm walks with many animals. Paved and grass walks.

1 Apr–31 Oct: Mon–Sun 10am–4.30pm

£🚐✕🅟🔥🔥☞➤⊣▪️wc🍴🍴
🏔©

The Yorkshire Museum of Farming

Murton Park
Murton
York, N. Yorks., YO1 3UF
☎ 0904 489966

Murton, York, A1079 then A166

Museum of Yorkshire social and agricultural history. Displays of implements, machinery and livestock. 8 acres with gravel paths. Mezzanine floor cannot be reached.

Mar–Oct: Tue–Fri 10.30am–5.30pm
Sat–Sun 12noon–5.30pm

£©🚐✕ 🅟 🔥☞🏚⇒▪️🌡wc
🍴🍴🏔🔥©

Sion Hill Hall

Kirby Wiske
Thirsk, N. Yorks.,
YO7 4EU
☎ 0845 587206

Thirsk, A167

≋ Thirsk

Neo–Georgian country house holding the Mawer collection of fine period furniture, paintings, porcelain, clocks and other antiques.

May–Oct: First Sun in each month
2pm–5pm
Groups by appointment

£©🚐✕ 🅟 🔥🏚wc🍴🏔🔥©

Duncombe Park

Helmsley
N. Yorks., YO6 5EB
☎ 0439 70213

A170: 2 minutes Helmsley Market Square

Baroque style house, family home of Lord and Lady Feversham. Unique C18th landscape garden & visitor centre. 300

acres with gravel paths.
5/12/26 Apr: 11am–6pm
Good Fri to following Tues: 11am–6pm
2 May–25 Oct: Sun–Thu 11am–6pm
BH Sat and tel for events.

£©🚌✕ P ⬛ ♨ ⌐ ♿ WC ⛲ ❢ ⛄
⛹ ♿ ✋

Kirkham Priory EH

Whitwell–on–the–Hill
York, N. Yorks., YO6 7JS
☎ 065381 768

York A64 to Malton
≋ 🚌 Malton

Founded in 1121 and set in idyllic
surrroundings beside River Derwent,
including magnificent Gatehouse carved
with sculptures and Heraldic shields. 5½
acres with grass paths.

1 Apr–30 Sep: Mon–Sun 10am–6pm
1 Oct–31 Mar: Mon–Sun 10am–4pm

£©🚌 ✕ P 🐾 ♿ ➤ ⌐ ⛄ ♿ ✋

Mount Grace Priory

Staddlesbridge
Northallerton, N.Yorks DL6 3JG
☎ 0609 83494

7m NE of Northallerton, on A19 near Ingleby
Arncliffe
≋ 🚌 Northallerton

Extensive remains of Carthusian monastery.
Founded in 1398. Restored and furnished
monk's cell. Special exhibition on Priory's
history in restored Manor House built in
1654. 5 acres with grass paths.

Easter–30 Sep: Mon–Sun 10am–6pm
1 Oct–Easter: Tue–Sun 10am–1pm &
2pm–4pm

£©🚌 ✕ P 🐾 ♨ ⚓ 🏠 ➤ ⌐ ❢

WC ⛄ ⛄ ♿

Richmond Castle EH

Richmond, N. Yorks., DL10 4QW
☎ 0748 822493

Richmond town centre
≋ 🚌 Northallerton/Darlington

Castle built in 1071 and keep 100 years
later. Originally built for Alan the Red, who
was one of William the Conquerors trusted
servants. No dogs/guide dogs.

Summer: Mon–Sun 10am–6pm
Winter: Tue–Sun 10am–4pm

£©🚌 P ⬛ ♨ ⌐ ❢ ♿ WC ⛄ ⛹ ♿

Byland Abbey EH

Coxwold, N. Yorks., YO6 4BD
☎ 03476 614

2m S of the A170, between Thirsk and
Helmsley, near Coxwold
≋ 🚌 Thirsk

A hauntingly beautiful ruin, set in peaceful
meadows in the shadow of the Hambleton
Hills. Contains superb samples of medieval
glazed floor tiles and the remains of a great
circular window.

1 Apr–30 Sep: Mon–Sun 10am–6pm
1 Oct–31 Mar: Tue–Sun 10am–4pm

£©🚌 ✕ P ♿ ➤ ⌐ ⇒ ♿ WC
⛄ ♿

Abbeydale Industrial Hamlet

Abbeydale Road South
Sheffield, S. Yorks., S7 2QW
☎ 0742 367731

Sheffield located on A621
≋ Dore & Totley 🚌 Sheffield

C18th restored water–powered agricultural
tool works. Four working waterwheels,
crucible furnace and working craftsmen.
Victorian cottages. 7 acres with paved,
grass & earth paths.

Jan–Dec: Wed–Sat: 10am–5pm
Sun: 11am–5pm
Closed: 24–26 Dec/1 Jan

£©🚌 ✕ 🐾 P ♿ ⚓ ⬛ 🏠 ⌐ ❢

WC ❢ ⛄ ⛹ ♿ ✒

Doncaster Museum & Art Gallery

Chequer Rd
Doncaster, S. Yorks., DN1 2AG
☎ 0302 734287

Doncaster
≋ 🚌 Doncaster

A purpose built museum with outstanding
collections of fine art, decorative art,
archaeology, history and natural science.
Kings Own Yorkshire Light Infantry Gallery.

Jan–Dec Mon–Sun
Closed: Good Fri and 25 Dec

F🚌 ✕ 🐾 P ♿ 📠 ➤ ⌐ ♿ WC ⛄
✒ ✒

WEST YORKSHIRE

Roche Abbey EH

Abbey House
Maltby
Rotherham, S. Yorks., S66 8NW
☎ 0709 812739

1½m S of Maltby, off the A634

≋ Coinsbrough (7m) 🚌 Rotherham–
Maltby

The standing ruins, dominated by the
church which date from 1170, rank in
importance with the finest early Gothic
architecture in the North. 31 acres with
gravel paths.

1 Apr–30 Sep: Mon–Sun 10am–6pm
1 Oct–31 Mar: Sat–Sun 10am–4pm

£©🚐✳🐕P♿☞➤◁WC🛒👪
♿©

East Riddlesden Hall NT

Bradford Road
Keighley, W. Yorks., BD20 5EL
☎ 0535 607075

Keighley

≋ 🚌 Keighley

C17th West Yorkshire manor house.
Panelled rooms, fine plasterwork and
mullioned windows. Provides an ideal
setting for pewter, domestic utensils and
Yorkshire oak furniture. Walled garden.
120ft Great barn and a collection of
traditional agricultural machinery.

Apr–30 Oct: Sat–Wed 12noon–5pm

£🚐✳🐕🏛P♿🏛➤◁🔸WC
🍴🛒👪🔶🎁©

Nostell Priory NT

Wakefield
W. Yorks., WF1 1QE
☎ 0924 863892

Wakefield, A638

≋ 🚌 Wakefield

One of England's greatest collections of
Chippendale furniture designed specially for
the house by the famous cabinet maker.
Gravel paths.

30 Mar–27 Oct: Sat: 12noon–5pm
Sun: 11am–5pm
Jul–Aug: Sat–Thu 12noon–5pm
Open all BH

£©🚐✳🐕🏛P🅿♿🛗🎋➤
♿wc🏠🍴🛒👪♿🔶🎁©♿

The Yorkshire Mining Museum

Caphouse Colliery
New Rd
Overton
Wakefield, W. Yorks., WF4 4RH
☎ 0924 848806

Wakefield A642 Huddersfield

≋ 🚌 Wakefield

Shaft first shown on a map in 1791. Many
listed buildings on site including 1876 steam
winder house with working engine. 17 acres
with gravel and paved paths.

Jan–Dec: Mon–Sun 10am–5pm

£©🚐✳🐕P♿🅿♿🎋➤◁
♿wc🏠🍴🛒👪♿🔶🎁©♿

The Leeds Industrial Museum

Armley Mills
Canal Rd
Leeds, W. Yorks., LS12 2QF
☎ 0532 63781

2 miles W of Leeds, off A65

≋ 🚌 Leeds

Built in 1806, and once the world's largest
woollen mill. Working waterwheel, textiles,
clothing, optics, heavy engineering
galleries, reconstructed 1920's cinema. 8
acres with cobbled stone paths.

1 Apr–31 Oct: Tue–Sat 10am–5pm
Sun 2pm–5pm
1 Nov–31 Mar: Tue–Sat 10am–4pm
Sun 2pm–4pm

£©🚐✳🅿🅿♿🛗⇒🔸♿wc
🛒👪🔶🎁©

Calderdale Industrial Museum

Square Rd
Halifax, W. Yorks., HX1 0QG
☎ 0422 358087

Halifax town centre, A646, A58

≋ 🚌 Halifax

Located in former engineering works
adjacent to the Piece Hall. Collections
illustrate wide variety of industries located in
Halifax and Calderdale. Award winning
museum with 4 floors of working machinery.

Tue–Sat: 10am–5pm
Sun: 2pm–5pm
BH Mon: Open

£©🚐✳P♿🔲🛗♿wc🛒🔶

Keighley & Worth Valley Railway

The Railway Station
Haworth, W. Yorks., BD22 8NJ
☎ 0535 645214

Keighley

≥ 🚌 Keighley

Preserved 1950's railway with 6 superbly restored stations, featured on 'The Railway Children', 'Poirot' etc. Paved paths. Steam train services. Wheelchairs can be accommodated on most trains.

Summer: Mon–Sun 9.20am–5.30pm
Winter: Sat–Sun 9.20am–5.30pm

£©🚌 P P◀🛒▶ ⌐🚂♿ wc ❚❚ 🖤

Fairburnings RSPB

Nr Castleford
W. Yorks.,
☎ 0977 673257

Off A1 one mile west of Fairburn or off A656 north of Castleford and 1½ miles east of Allerton Bywater.

Boardwalk for disabled visitors encircles a small marsh with pond and leads to a hide adapted for wheelchair access.

Jan–Dec: Sat–Sun 10am–5pm
Other times by arrangement with warden.

🚌♿ wc

Tolson Museum

Ravensknowle Park
Wakefield Rd
Huddersfield, W. Yorks., HD5 8DJ
☎ 0484 530591

Huddersfield Wakefield and Sheffield Rd
A629

≥ 🚌 Huddersfield

Victorian mansion housing natural and local history, transport, archaeology etc. Exhibitions and events. Tarmac paths.

pls.tel.for opening dates and times.

£🚌🐾P🅿️◀🛒▶🏰→⌐♿

The Colour Museum

Perkin House
82 Grattan Rd
Bradford, W. Yorks., BD1 2JB
☎ 0274 390955

Centre of Bradford, off Westgate B6144

≥ 🚌 Bradford

This unique, award winning museum has two galleries with visitor operated displays which look at light, colour, dyeing and textile printing. No dogs.

Jan–Dec: Tue–Fri 2pm–5pm
Sat 10am–4pm

£©🚌🐾P🐾◀🛒▶🏰⌐♿wc
🖤🐾

Shibden Hall

Lister's Road
Halifax, W. Yorks., HX3 6XG
☎ 0422 352246

Halifax, off A58 Leeds road

≥ 🚌 Halifax

An early C15th timber framed house displayed with furniture and domestic items of later centuries. Rural crafts and horse drawn vehicles. 90 acres with gravel paths.

Mar–Nov: Mon–Sat 10am–5pm
Sun 12noon–5pm
Feb: Sun 2pm–5pm
Dec–Jan: Closed

£©🚌🐾🦌P🐾🏰⌐
wc❚❚🖤🐾◆🐾©

Cliffe Castle Museum

Spring Gardens Lane
Keighley, W. Yorks., BD20 6LH
☎ 0535 618230

Keighley, off A629 Skipton Rd

≥ 🚌 Keighley

Formerly a mill owner's mansion, set in parkland. The museum displays include crystals, geology, natural history, bygones and furnished rooms. 24 acres with tarmac paths.

Apr–Sep: Tue–Sun 10am–6pm
Oct–Mar: Tue–Sun 10am–5pm
Closed: Mon/Good Fri/25–26 Dec

F🚌🦌P🐾♿🏰→⌐♿
wc🐾❚❚🖤🐾

Bagshaw Museum

Wilton Park
Batley, W. Yorks., WF17 0AS
☎ 0924 472514

Batley: A62; M62; A652

≥ Batley

Beautiful Victorian mansion set in delightful park. Displays of local and natural history. Oriental pottery and objects from all over the world. 35 acres with tarmac and woodchip paths.

Nov–Feb: Mon–Sun 12noon–5pm

WEST YORKSHIRE

Mar–Oct: Mon–Fri 10am–5pm
Sat–Sun 12noon–5pm

F 🚌 P♿ 🅿 ♿ ➤ ⊣ ⊣⊦ WC ♨ ⛟ ♿
🐟 👁 ©

Dewsbury Museum

Crow Nest Park
Heckmondwike Rd
Dewsbury, W. Yorks., WF13 2SA
☎ 0924 468171

Dewsbury, A644

≼ 🚌 Dewsbury

Kirklees oldest museum re–opened as a
museum of childhood in 1985. Displays tell
the story of children at work, school and
play. 30 acres with tarmacadam paths. Not
suitable for wheelchair users.

Nov–Feb: Mon–Sun 12noon–5pm
Mar–Oct: Mon–Fri 10am–5pm
Sat–Sun 12noon–5pm

F 🚌 ✳ P♿ 🅿 ♿ 🏛 ➤ ⊣ ⊣⊦ WC ♿
🐟 👁 © ⛏

Tunnel End Canal & Countryside Centre

Waters Rd
Marsden, W. Yorks., HD7 6NQ
☎ 0484 846062

Huddersfield/Oldham A62

≼ 🚌 Marsden

Situated at mouth of the longest & highest
canal tunnel in Britain. Exhibitions on
countryside, canal and transport
development in Colne Valley.

Summer: Tue 2pm–4pm
Wed–Fri 10am–1pm and 2pm–4pm
Sat–Sun 10am–5pm
Winter: Tue 2pm–4pm
Wed–Thu 11am–1pm and 2pm–4pm
Sat–Sun 10.30am–4.30pm

F 🚌 ✳ P♿ 🅿 ⚑ ♿ ⬛ 🏛 ⊣ ⇒ 👁
⊣⊦ WC ⁑ ⛟ ♿ 🐟 ©

Bradford Industrial Museum

Moorside Rd
Bradford, W. Yorks., BD3 3HP
☎ 0274 631756

Bradford A658

≼ 🚌 Bradford

Bradford's outstanding textiles and
industrial heritage in authentic mill setting.
With working Shire horses and restored
Back–to–Backs. Paved paths.

Jan–Dec Tue–Sun & BH Mon 10am–5pm

F 🚌 ✳ P♿ 🅿 ♿ 🏛 ⊟ ➤ ⊣ ©wc WC ♨
⁑ ⛟ ♿ ♦ 👁 © ⛏

Oakwell Hall Country Park

Nutter Lane
Birstall
Batley, W. Yorks., WF17 9LG
☎ 0924 474926

Birstall A643 to Cleckheaton

🚌 Bradford

87 acres of country park with formal
gardens, visitor and information centres. No
dogs allowed in hall or cafe. Gravel and
crushed stone paths surround. Portable
ramps (Telephone for more information).

Mar–Oct: Mon–Fri 10am–5pm
Sat–Sun 12noon–5pm
Nov–Feb: Mon–Sun 12noon–5pm

£ © 🚌 ✳ P♿ 🅿 ♿ 🏛 ⊣ ⊣⊦ ©wc WC ♨
⁑ ⛟ ♿ © 👁 ©

Manor House Art Gallery & Museum

Castle Yard
Ilkley
W. Yorks., LS29 9DT

Leeds/Bradford

≼ 🚌 Bradford

A picturesque Elizabethan building on the
site of a Roman Fort. The ground floor
houses a display on Ilkley as a Spa resort,
plus some Roman and prehistoric artefacts.
Paved paths.

Apr–Sep: Tue–Sun & BH 10am–6pm
Oct–Mar: Tue–Sun & BH 10am–6pm

F 🚌 ✳ P♿ ⚑ ⚑ ☞ ⬛ 🏛 ➤ ⊣ ©wc
WC ⛟ ⁑ ♿

National Museum of Photography, Film and Television

Prince's View
Bradford, W. Yorks., BD5 0TR
☎ 0274 727488
Bradford city centre
⇌ Bradford Interchange

Explores the past, present and future of the media using interactive displays and dramatic reconstructions. Also houses IMAX, UK's largest cinema screen, over 5 storeys high.

Jan–Dec: Tue–Sun 10.30am–6pm

£©🚐⋇ P 𝆏 ⅊ ▄ 🖼 ♿ WC ⚶
🍴 🛒 🛗 🕮 👐 ⅄

Sooty's World

Windhill Manor
Leeds Rd
Shipley, W. Yorks., BD18 1BP
☎ 0274 531122
Bradford
⇌ 🚌 Bradford

Permanent exhibition of those unique items many of which are brought to life by detailed animation. Humorous memories of childhood long forgotten along with the appeal of a modern television character.

Jan–Dec: Mon–Thu 10.30am–4.30pm

£©🚐⋇ P₆ 🅿 ⅊ ☞ 🏠 WC 🍴 🛒
🛗 👐 ⅅ

Hardcastle Craggs NT

Hebden Water
Nr Halifax, W. Yorks.,

Reached via a track that is accessible to wheelchair users but can be rough in places. The Crags, however, are nearly 2m from the car park, and the full journey should only be attempted by those with a strong companion. The area is recommended to accompanied visually impaired visitors; birdsong and water sounds.

NOTES

Action for Disabled Customers

For your free copy of BT's Guide to Equipment and Services for Disabled Customers 1991 contact your local BT Sales Office: the address and telephone number is in the Phone Book or dial 150 for further information.

BT

SCOTLAND

SYMBOL DESCRIPTIONS

£   Admission charge

F   No admission charge but donation in some places

©   Special concession charge for disabled people, elderly people, carers and children

    Groups must book in advance – special rates may apply

    Guide dogs accepted except in certain areas

    Sympathetic Hearing Scheme participated in or Loop System

    Special information available for disabled people

PARKING

    Designated disabled parking space

    Own car park with a dropping off point within 50 yards

P   Public car park nearby and/or street parking within 200 yards

    Dropping off point or disabled parking place by telephone appointment

MAIN ENTRANCE

    Entrance level or ramped and over 30″ wide

    Steps into building 1–5 or bumpy

    Steps into building 6 or more

    More suitable entrance freely available, telephone for details or help. Temporary ramps to be made available.

    Steps within the buildings that cannot be overcome by ramps

    More than one floor level and no lift

    More than one floor level and suitable lift/stairclimber/stairlift for wheelchair users

OUTSIDE

    Routes around the site are free of steps or steps can be avoided

    Seats available around the site

    Routes indicated for wheelchair users

    Routes indicated for visually handicapped people

    Transport around the site suitable for disabled people and wheelchair users – telephone in advance

    Transport around the site not suitable for disabled people or elderly people

    There are limited areas that cannot be reached due to steps or doorways less than 30″

170

TOILETS

&ᵂᶜ Unisex toilets designed or adapted for disabled people or public toilets within 50 yards. Radar key required in some

WC Ordinary toilets with level access

WC No toilets on site but public ones nearby

👪 Baby changing/parents room available

GENERAL

🍴 Restaurant/tea room/cafe/ not accessible due to steps/narrow doorway/first floor with no lift

🍴 Restaurant/tea room/cafe/vending accessible by ramp or level or lift with 30" doors

🛒 Shop not accessible due to stairs but may be accessible with help

🛒 Shop/sales area accessible by ramp or level and 30" doorway

⛹ Picnic area only, or nearby

♿ Wheelchair users are advised to come accompanied

🎧 Taped guides available/or person

👁 Facilities for visually handicapped/braille or by request

✋ People available to help (telephone beforehand if you require help)

✆ Telephone accessible for wheelchair users

🚶 This site is suitable for elderly people but unsuitable for wheelchair users

♿ᴸ Wheelchairs/batricars for loan or hire – telephone for advance booking

NT The National Trust

EH English Heritage

NTS National Trust for Scotland

RSPB Royal Society For the Protection of Birds

FC Forestry Commission

🚆 British Rail

🚌 Bus

☎ Telephone

⊖ Underground

NOTES

SCOTLAND

BORDERS

Magnum Leisure Centre

Harbourside
Irvine
Ayrshire, Borders, KA12 8PP
☎ 0294 78381

Irvine

⇌ Irvine

Leisure pools, ice rink, bowls hall, sports hall, squash courts, theatre/cinema, kiddies play areas, and much more. 1500 acres with gravel and tarmac paths.

Jan–Dec: Mon–Sun 9am–11pm

£© P P wc

Traquair House

Innerleithen
Peebles, Borders, EA44 6PW
☎ 0896 830323

Innerleithen A72 to Peebles

Secret stairs, spooky cellars, books, embroideries and letters of former times. Art gallery & C18th brewhouse still producing 50,000 bottles per annum. 50 acres with gravel and paved paths.

Apr/May/Jun/Sep: Mon–Sun 1.30pm–5.30pm
Jul–Aug: Mon–Sun 10.30am–5.30pm

£© P P

Tweeddale Museum

Chambers Institute
High St
Peebles, Borders, EH45 8AP
☎ 0721 20123

A72 Peebles

⇌ Edinburgh Waverley

Showing varied exhibitions on local history. Gallery exhibiting contemporary art & ornamental plasterwork. Paved paths.

Easter–Oct: Mon–Fri 10am–1pm & 2pm–5pm
Sat–Sun 2pm–5pm
Nov–Mar: Mon–Fri 10am–1pm & 2pm–5pm

F P wc

BORDERS

Neidpath Castle

Peebles, Borders, EH45 8NW
☎ 0721 20333

Peebles A72; castle 1m W

⇌ 🚌 Peebles

C14th tower house, splendid views and locations. Home of Frasers, Hays and Douglas. Stone, grass and gravel paths.

Thu before Easter–30 Sep: Mon–Sat 11am–5pm
Sun 1pm–5pm

£ © 🚐 🐕 🅿 🏔 🏛 ⊣ wc 🌲 ♿ Ⓒ 👤

Abbotsford House

Melrose, Borders, TD6 9BQ
☎ 0896 2043

Melrose

🚌 Melrose & Galashiels

Historic house built and lived in by Sir Walter Scott overlooking the Tweed. Contains his library, collection of armour and historic relics.

Apr–Nov: Mon–Sat 10am–5pm
Sun 2pm–5pm

£ © 🚐 🐕 🅿 🅿 ♿ 🍽 ⊣ wc ♿ 🤝 Ⓒ

The Hirsel Country Park & Craft Centre

Coldstream
Berwick, Borders, TD12 4LP
☎ 0890 2834

Coldstream A697

⇌ Berwick–upon–Tweed 🚌 Coldstream

Beautiful quiet parkland with walks round gardens, lake and valley. Old trees and many flowers and birds. Museum of old tools, archaeology. 100 acres with cobbled paths.

Jan–Dec: Mon–Sun All daylight hours

£ © 🚐 🐕 🅿 ♿ 🏔 🏛 ⊣ ⇒ ⊣ 🚻 wc 🍴 🌲 👥 ♿

Jedforest Deer & Farm Park

Mervinslaw Estate
Camptown, Jedburgh
Roxburgh, Borders, TD8 6PL
☎ 08354 364266

A68 SE of Jedburgh

Working farm with a large conservation collection of rare breeds of farm animals & species of red deer. 60 acres with grass and soft wooded paths.

1 May–31 Oct: Mon–Sun 10am–5.30pm

£ © 🚐 🐕 🅿 ♿ ➤ ⊣ ⊣ 🚻 wc 🍴 🌲 👥 ♿ 🎧 Ⓒ

John Buchan Centre

Broughton
Peebles, Borders
☎ 0899 21050

Biggar 5 miles

🚌 Biggar

Centre tells story of life and work of John Buchan, well–known novelist, author of 'The Thirty–Nine Steps.' Display of family belongings and other memorabilia.

May–Sep: Mon–Sat 2pm–5pm

£ © 🚐 🐕 🅿 🔦 wc 🍽 👥 ♿

Thirlestane Castle

Lauder
Berwick, Borders, TD2 6RU
☎ 05782 430

Lauder

One of the oldest and finest castles in Scotland, set in the magnificent Border hills at Lauder. 30 acres with gravel paths.

Easter: 2pm–5pm
Jul–Aug: Mon/Fri 2pm–5pm
May–Sep: Wed/Thu/Sun 2pm–5pm

£ 🚐 🐕 🅿 🏔 🔦 🏛 ⊣ ⊣ ♿ wc 🍴 👥 ♿ 🚫

Priorwood Garden NTS

Melrose
Borders
☎ 089 682 2555

Unique to Priorwood is a special garden (where the majority of flowers grown are suitable for drying) and an associated dried–flower shop.

Tel. for opening times

🅿 P ⊣ 🚫

St Abb's Head NTS

Berwickshire
Borders
☎ 089 07 71443

Off A1107, 2m N of Coldingham

National Nature Reserve, managed jointly with the Scottish Wildlife Trust. A spectacular headland of 192 acres, with 300ft cliffs. The most important location for cliff–nesting seabirds in SE Scotland, with

colonies of guillemots, kittiwakes, razorbills, shags, fulmars, puffins and herring gulls.
Jan–Dec: Mon–Sun

Dawyck Botanic Garden

Stobo
Peebles, Borders, EH45 9JU
☎ 07216 254
Peebles
🚌 Peebles

Outstation of the Royal Botanic Garden, Edinburgh. Contains a fine collection of mature specimen trees, particularly conifers, many of them over 100 years old. The Royal Botanic Garden is adding to this impressive arboretum by planting trees and shrubs, mostly of known wild origin, from throughout the world.

15 Mar–22 Oct: Mon–Sun

£ⓒ🚐⋇ 🅿 ➤ ⊣ ♣ ₵ᵂᶜ wc 🎋

Manderston Stately Home

Duns
Berwickshire, Borders, TD11 3TA
☎ 0361 83450
2m from Duns, on A6105 Duns/Berwick
⇌ 🚌 Berwick–upon–Tweed

Manderston, its buildings, park and gardens, form an ensemble which is unique in Britain, Georgian in taste, but with all the elaborate planning for Edwardian convenience and comfort. 56 acres with gravel paths.

Mid May–30 Sep: Thu & Sun 2pm–5.30pm
May & Aug: BH Mon's 2pm–5.30pm

£ⓒ🚐⋇ 🅿₵ 🅿 🔔🏰➤ ⊣ ♣ wc
🏃 🎋 🎋 🦽

Bowhill House & Country Park

Bowhill
Selkirk, Borders, TD7 5ET
☎ 0750 20732
Selkirk A7 to Edinburgh
⇌ 🚌 Selkirk

Internationally renowned art and French furniture collections. Queen Victoria, Sir Walter Scott and Monmouth relics. Extensive country park.

House:
1–31 Jul: Mon–Sat 1pm–4.30pm
Sun 2pm–6pm

Park:
28 Apr–28 Aug: Mon–Sat 12 noon–5pm
Closed Fri except July
Sun 2pm–6pm

£ⓒ🚐⋇ 🐚 🅿₵ 🅿 🔔🏰➤ ⊣ ⇒
👁 ₵ᵂᶜ wc 🍴 🎋 🎋 🔹 🍽 ⓒ 🦽

Blair Drummond Safari & Leisure Park

Blair Drummond
Nr Stirling, Central, FK9 4UR
☎ 0786 841456/841396
Stirling A84, take exit 10 off M9
⇌ 🚌 Stirling

120 acres of parkland with wild animals from all over the world. Lions, tigers, elephants, bison & hundreds more. Pets farm, chimp island, sealion shows and adventure playground. Gravel and paved paths.

4 Apr–5 Oct: Mon–Sun 10am–5.30pm

£ⓒ🚐⋇ 🅿 🦽➤ ⊣ ⇒ 🚙 🔹 ₵ᵂᶜ
wc 🏠 🍴 🎋 🎋 🦽 🔹 🍽 ⓒ

Stirling Castle Visitor Centre NTS

Upper Castle Hill
Stirling, Central
☎ 0786 62517

Access for wheelchairs to Centre with ramp to audio–visual area.

🔍 🅿 🦽 wc 🎋 🎧

Bannockburn Heritage Centre NTS

Stirling
Central, FK7 0LJ
☎ 0786 812664
Off M80/M9 at junction 9, 2m S of Stirling

Situated at one of the most important historic sites in Scotland. A few yards from the centre is the famous Borestone site which by tradition was Bruce's command post before the battle.

🅿 🦽 ₵ᵂᶜ 🍴 🎋 🦽

DUMFRIES & GALLOWAY

Crichton Royal Museum

Easterbrook Hall
Bankend Rd
Dumfries, DG1 4TG
☎ 0387 55301 x 2360
Dumfries
≉ Dumfries

150 year old pioneering psychiatric hospital. Beautiful gardens with rock garden, arboretum & greenhouses. Church organ music, museum, art gallery and operating theatre. 140 acres with tarmacadam paths.

Jan–Dec: Thu & Fri 1.30pm–4.30pm
Easter–Oct: Also Sat & other times by appointment

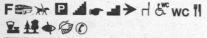

Castle Kennedy Gardens

Stair Estates
Rephad, Stranraer,
Dumfries & Galloway, DG9 8BX
☎ 0776 2024
Stranraer, 5m
≉ 🚌 Stranraer

Large peaceful wooded and formal gardens, in beautiful surroundings, between two lochs. Contains many rare plants, rhododendrons & many exotic species of conifer. 75 acres with grass paths.

Easter–30 Sep: Mon–Sun 10am–5pm

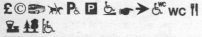

Glenwhan Garden

Dunragit by Stranraer
Dumfries & Galloway, DG9 8PH
☎ 05814 222
Stranraer A75
≉ 🚌 Stranraer

Started in 1979, this unique garden has been hacked out of a hillside covered in bracken and gorse, set in an area of outstanding beauty. The garden is round two small lochans with a wide variety of plants, overlooking Luce Bay. 12 acres with bark paths.

Apr–30 Sep: Mon–Sun 10am–5pm

Cally Gardens

Gatehouse of Fleet
Castle Douglas
Dumfries & Galloway, DG7 2DJ
30m W of Dumfries
🚌 Dumfries

Victorian walled garden, now converted into a rare plant nursery; over 3000 varieties grown, mainly herbaceous perennials. 2.7 acres with gravel paths.

Easter–Mid Oct: Sat–Sun

Threave Gardens

Castle Douglas
Dumfries & Galloway, DG7 1RA
☎ 0556 2575
Castle Douglas
≉ 🚌 Dumfries

60 acre garden with a wide variety of plants and glasshouses. National Trust for Scotland's School of Horticulture.

Jan–Dec: Mon–Sun 9am–sunset

Glenluce Abbey

Glenluce
Newton Stewart
Dumfries & Galloway, DG8 0AF
☎ 058 13 541
Glenluce, A75 Dumfries–Stranraer road
🚌 Glenluce

Cistercian Abbey founded in 1190. The C15th Chapter House is still intact. 1½ acres with gravel paths.

Apr–Sep: Mon–Sat 9.30am–6pm
Sun 2pm–6pm
Oct–Mar: Sat 9.30am–4pm
Sun 2pm–4pm

'Little Wheels' Toys & Models

6 Hill St
Portpatrick
Dumfries & Galloway, DG9 8JX
☎ 0776 81 536
Off A77 Stranraer–Portpatrick

See rare and original items by the great toy and model makers. Collectors items interspersed with memorabilia of early days of transport.

Pls. tel. for dates and times

£©🚌☀️🐕‍🦺🔭P♿🚾WC🏛♿👋

The Newton Stewart Museum

York Rd
Newton Stewart
Wigtown, Galloway, DG8 6HH
☎ 0671 2472

Newton–Stewart

Contains a wealth of historical treasures from before the early Victorian era. Also exciting and interesting displays of the natural and social history of Galloway. ½ an acre with paved paths.

Easter–Oct: Mon–Sun 2pm–5pm
Jul/Aug/Sep: Mon–Sun 10am–12.30pm

£©🚌☀️🐕‍🦺P🔭♿🏰⊣-🍴WC
🏛👋

Robert Burns Centre

Mill Rd
Dumfries
☎ 0387 64808

A74 to Lockerbie, then A709 to Dumfries
🚉🚌 Dumfries

Situated in the town's converted C18th watermill, on the west bank of the River Nith. The centre tells the story of Robert Burns and his life in Dumfries. Audio visual theatre. 1 acre with paved paths.

Apr–Sep: Mon–Sat 10am–8pm
Sun 2pm–5pm
Oct–Mar: Tue–Sat 10am–1pm & 2pm–5pm

£F©🚌☀️🐕‍🦺🔭🚈P♿☞→
⊣🚾WC🍴🏛👋©

Dumfries Museum & Camera Obscura

Dumfries, DG2 7SW
☎ 0387 53374

A74 to Lockerbie, then A709 to Dumfries
🚉🚌 Dumfries

The largest museum in SW Scotland. Situated in and around an C18th windmill tower. Exhibitions trace the history of the people and landscape of Dumfries and Galloway. Camera obscura not accessible to wheelchair users. 1 acre with paved paths.

Apr–Sep: Mon–Sat 10am–1pm & 2pm–5pm
Sun 2pm–5pm
Oct–Mar: Tue–Sat 10am–1pm & 2pm–5pm

F©🚌☀️🐕‍🦺🔭🚈P♿🚈🏛⊣⇒
-🍴🚾WC🏛👫♿👋©

Stranraer Museum

55 George St
Stranraer
Dumfries & Galloway, DG9 7JP
☎ 0776 5088

Stranraer

🚉🚌 Stranraer

Museum with permanent displays on farming, archaeology, polar explorers. Temporary exhibition programme, childrens activities and worksheets.

Jan–Dec: Mon–Sat 10am–5pm
Closed: BH

F🚌☀️P🔭♿🏛🚾WC🏛👋©

Castle of St John

Castle St
Stranraer
Dumfries & Galloway
☎ 0776 5544/5088

Stranraer

🚉🚌 Stranraer

Towerhouse with castle displays on law and order medieval covenanters and town jail. Spiral staircase.

Apr–30 Sep: Mon–Sat 10am–1pm & 2pm–5pm

£©🚌☀️🐕‍🦺P🔭♿🚈🏰🏛👋©⚓

Savings Bank Museum

Ruthwell, Dumfries, DG1 5NN
☎ 038787 640

Annan on A75 to Ruthwell on B724

Building in which Savings Banks began in 1810, examples of early work leading to worldwide movement.

Jan–Dec: Mon–Sun 10am–1pm & 2pm–5pm

F☀️🚈P♿→⊣⇒-🚾WC🏛
◀👋©

Carlyle's Birthplace NTS

Ecclefechan
Dumfries & Galloway
☎ 057 63 666

The arched house in which Thomas Carlyle was born (4 December 1795) contains a collection of his belongings and manuscript

DUMFRIES & GALLOWAY

letters.

29 Mar–27 Oct: Mon–Sun 12noon–5pm

P ⌂ ➤ WC ⚿

Threave Garden NTS

Castle Douglas
Stewarty
Dumfries & Galloway
☎ 0556 2575

The extensive garden provides interest thoughout the year with colour always in evidence. The garden's special spectacle is the magnificent springtime display of nearly 200 varieties of daffodil.

Jan–Dec: Mon–Sun 9am–dusk

 P ⚿ WC ✗ ⚿

Hill of Tarvit NTS

Nr Cupar
Dumfries & Galloway
☎ 0334 53127

Off A916, 2½m S of Cupar

The present mansionhouse was virtually rebuilt in 1906 by Sir Robert Lorimer for Mr F B Sharp to form a suitable setting for his notable collection which includes French, Chippendale and vernacular furniture, Dutch paintings and pictures by Raeburn and Ramsay. Gardens also by Lorimer, as a setting for his house. Scented Braille Garden.

Tel. for opening times

P ⚿ ▄ ⚿ ❙❙

FIFE

Kellie Castle & Gardens

Pittenweem
Fife, KY10 2RF
☎ 033 38 271

3m NW of Pittenweem on B9171

C16th castle with fine plaster ceilings & panelling. Seat of Earls of Kellie to 1828. Victorian nursery and walled garden.

Easter/Good Fri/Easter Mon: 2pm–6pm
Apr: Sat–Sun 2pm–6pm
May–Oct: Mon–Sun 2pm–6pm

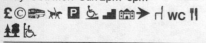

Cambo Country Park

Kingsbarns
St Andrews
Fife, KY16 8QE
☎ 0333 50810

St Andrews, A917

🚌 St Andrews

Fun park for all the family of all ages. Variety of animals. 150 acres with sand tracks and grass paths.

Easter–30 Sep: Mon–Sun 10am–6pm

£ © 🚐 ✗ P ⚿ ➤ ⌐ ⚿ WC ⚘ ❙❙ ▄ ⚿ ⚿

Scottish Fisheries Museum Trust

Harbourhead
Anstruther, Fife, KY10 3AB
☎ 0333 310 628

Anstruther

🚌 Anstruther

This award winning museum located in historic building provides a unique record of Scotland's fishing industry and fishing folk over the last 200 years. Fishing boats & gear, whaling exhibits and restored fisherman's cottage.

Easter–31 Oct: Mon–Sat 10am–5.30pm
Sun 11am–5pm
Nov–Easter: Mon–Sat 10am–4.30pm
Sun 2pm–4.30pm

£ © 🚐 ✗ P ⚿ ⚿ 🏠 ➤ ⌐ ⚿ WC ⚘ ❙❙ ▄ ⚿ ⚿ ⚿ ⚿ ⚿

Scottish Deer Centre

Bow–of–Fife
By Cupar, Fife, KY15 4NQ
☎ 0337 81 391

Cupar, A91 to St Andrews

⇌ 🚌 Cupar

Beautifully restored Georgian Courtyard with adjoining 50 acres in scenic mid–Fife. No dogs as deer become stressed. Gravel, grass and paved paths.

Mar–31 Oct: Mon–Sun 10am–5pm
Nov–Dec: Sat–Sun 10am–5pm

£ © 🚐 ⚿ P ⚿ ✏ ➤ ⌐ ✛ ⚿ WC ⚘ ❙❙ ▄ ⚿ ⚿ ⚿ ⚿

Kirkaldy Museum & Art Gallery

War Memorial Gardens
Kirkaldy, Fife, KY1 1YG
☎ 0592 260732

Nr Edinburgh, M90

≋ Kirkaldy

Building part of War Memorial Gardens built in 1925, comprising museum, art gallery, park and library. Tarmac paths.

Jan–Dec: Mon–Sat 11am–5pm
Sun 2pm–5pm

Crail Museum & Heritage Ctr

62/64 Marketgate
Crail, Fife, KY10 3TL
☎ 0333 50869

St Andrews

≋ 🚌 St Andrews

A small museum in an C18th house. A fishing village with picturesque harbour, an ancient parish church, and medieval market place.

Easter Week: 10am–12.30pm & 2.30pm–5pm
Easter–31 May: Weekends only
1 Jun–15 Sep: Mon–Sat 10am–12.30pm & 2.30pm–5pm
Sun 2.30pm–5pm

Fife Folk Museum

The Weigh House
High St
Ceres, Fife, KY15 5NF

Cupar 2m; St Andrews 8m

≋ 🚌 Cupar

Range of buildings including C17th court house and dungeon, weavers' cottages, modern annexe on site of old bothy. Open terraced areas and paved paths.

Easter–31 Oct: Wed–Mon 2.15pm–5pm

Balgonie Castle

By Markinch
Fife, KY7 6HQ
☎ 0592 750119

Markinch or Glenrothes, A911

≋ 🚌 Markinch

Historic castle as a home and a living museum. Banqueting in Great Hall. Weddings in C14th chapel. No dogs.

Jan–Dec: Mon–Sun

Balmerino Abbey NTS

Dundee
Fife

Off A914 in Balmerino, 5m W of Tay Bridge

Ruins of a Cistercian monastery, founded in 1229, presented by the Earl of Dundee in 1936. Visitors may not enter the buildings but can view them from the grounds. Restoration work is being carried out as funds allow.

Culross NTS

Fife
☎ 0383 880359

Off A985, 12m W of Forth Rd Bridge

The small Royal Burgh on the north shore of the Forth is a striking introduction to Scottish domestic life. Culross was a thriving community trading in coal and salt.

Falkland Palace NTS

Falkland
Fife
☎ 0337 57 397

On A912, 11m N of Kirkcaldy

The Royal Palace of Falkland was the country residence of the Stewart kings and queens when they hunted deer and wild boar in the Fife forest. The garden, with three herbaceous borders enclosing an attractive, wide lawn with many varieties of shrubs and trees, also contains the original Royal Tennis Court, the oldest in Britain, built in 1539. The palace still belongs to Her Majesty The Queen.

29 Mar–31 Oct: Mon–Sat 10am–6pm
Sun 2pm–6pm

GRAMPIAN

Aden Country Park

Mintlaw
By Peterhead, Grampian, AB42 8FQ
☎ 0771 22857
Mintlaw, 1m W, off A950
⇌ 🚌 Aberdeen

Woodland walks, nature trail, picnic areas, adventure playground, garden for blind people, wildlife centre with ranger service. 230 acres with gravel and paved paths.
Country Park:
Jan–Dec: Mon–Sun 7am–10pm
Wildlife Centre:
May–Sept Sat–Sun 2pm–5pm

F 🚌 🐾 P♿ P ♿ 🍴 👁 ✈ ♿ WC
🍴 🛒 🎪 ♿ 🐟 🎨 🎫 ♿

North East Scotland Agricultural Heritage Centre

Aden Country Park
Mintlaw
By Peterhead, Grampian, AB42 8GQ
☎ 0771 22857
Mintlaw, 1m W, off A950
⇌ 🚌 Aberdeen

Award winning museum presents this region's farming past and present in the unique semi–circular former Aden home farm. 230 acres with gravel and paved paths.
Apr & Oct: Sat–Sun 12noon–5pm
May–Sep: Mon–Sun 11am–5pm

£ © 🚌 🐾 P♿ ♿ 🛒 🏛 🍴 ✈ ♿ WC
🍴 🛒 🎪 ♿ 🎨 🎫 ♿

The Glenfiddich Distillery

Dufftown
Keith, Grampian, AB55 4DH
☎ 0340 20373
½m N of Dufftown, on A941
⇌ Elgin (20m)

The only distillery in the Highlands where malt whisky is made from barley to the bottle. Try a dram and discover the unique taste of the world's most celebrated malt whisky. Paved paths.
Easter–Mid Oct: Mon–Sat 9.30am–4.30pm
Sun 12noon–4.30pm
Mid Oct–Easter: Mon–Fri 9.30am–4.30pm

F 🚌 🐾 P♿ P ♿ 🏛 🍴 ✈ ♿ WC
🌲 🎨

Storybook Glen Theme Park

Maryculter
Aberdeen, Grampian, AB1 0AT
☎ 0224 732941
5 miles west of Aberdeen
⇌ 🚌 Aberdeen

22 acre park set in beautiful scenic gardens with over 100 models of nursery rhymes. Tarmacadam paths.
Mar–Oct: Mon–Sun 10am–6pm
Nov–Feb: Sat–Sun 11am–4pm

£ © 🚌 🐾 P♿ P ♿ 🛒 ✈ 🍴 ♿ WC
🍴 🛒 🎪 ♿ 🎫

N.E. Falconry Visitor Centre

Broadland
Cairnie
By Huntly, Grampian, AB54 4UU
☎ 0466 87 328
A920 Huntly to Dufftown – 3m from Huntly

Large collection of eagles, falcons and owls, flown free daily. Also highland cattle and red deer. No guide dogs/dogs. Tarmac paths.
Apr–Sep: Mon–Sun 10am–6pm

£ © 🚌 P♿ P ♿ ✈ 🍴 ⇒ ♿ WC 🍴
🛒 🎨 🎫

Music Hall

Union St
Aberdeen, Grampian, AB1 1QS
☎ 0224 632080
A94, Dundee
⇌ 🚌 Aberdeen

Opened in 1824 and refurbished in 1986. Now one of Scotland's finest concert complexes. 3 acres with paved paths.
Jan–Dec: Mon–Sat 8am–11.30pm
Sun by arrangement

£ F © 🚌 🐾 🐕 ✈ 🛋 P♿ ♿ 🍖 🛒 ✈
🍴 ⇒ ♿ WC 🍴 🛒 ♿ 🎨 🎫

Balmoral Castle

Ballater
Aberdeenshire, Grampian, AB35 5TB
☎ 03397 42334
Ballater
Royal family's Highland holiday home. Gardens, exhibitions in castle ballroom,

pony cart rides, country walks. Tarmac paths.

May–Jul: Mon–Sat 10am–5pm

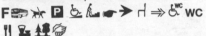

Cromie Visitor Ctr

Grandholm Mills
Woodside
Aberdeen, Grampian, AB9 2SA
☎ 0224 483201

Aberdeen, A96

≋ 🚌 Aberdeen

Home of the world famous Crombie Coat. Facilities include audio visual telling 'The Crombie Story', museum and mill shop. ½ an acre with paved paths.

Jan–Dec: Mon–Sat 9am–4.30pm
Sun 12noon–4.30pm

Fochabers Folk Museum

High St
Fochabers
Moray, Grampian
☎ 0343 820362

Fochaber 9m from Elgin on A96

≋ 🚌 Elgin/Keith

Converted church with horse drawn carts plus over 4000 items relating to village life through the ages including village shop and victorian parlour.

Jan–Dec: Mon–Sun 9.30am–1pm & 2pm–6pm Winter 5pm

Cruickshank Botanic Garden

University of Aberdeen
St Machar Drive
Aberdeen, Grampian, AB9 2ND
☎ 0224 272704

Old Aberdeen, off A92 Peterhead Rd

🚌 Aberdeen

Founded in 1898. Collection of trees, shrubs, herbaceous and alpine plants in an attractive setting.

Jan–Dec: Mon–Fri 9am–4.30pm
May–Sep: Mon–Fri 9am–4.30pm
Sat–Sun 2pm–5pm

Castle Fraser NTS

Grampian
☎ 033 03 463

Off A944 4m N of Dunecht

Belongs to the same period of native architectural achievement as Crathes Castle and Craigivar Castle and it is the most sophisticated example of this indigenous style owned by the Trust.

Castle: May,Jun,Sep: Mon–Sun 2pm–6pm
Jul,Aug: Mon–Sun 11am–6pm
Oct: Sat–Sun 2pm–5pm
Garden & Grounds: Jan–Dec Mon–Sun 2pm–5pm

Craigievar Castle NTS

Gordon
Grampian
☎ 033 983 635

On A980 6m S of Alford

Often described as a fairy tale castle, Craigievar exemplifies the best of Scottish baronial architecture. The great tower stands just as it was when completed by William Forbes in 1626.

Grounds: Jan–Dec: Mon–Sun 9.30am–dusk
Castle: May–Sep: Mon–Sun 2pm–6pm

Crathes Castle NTS

Kincardine & Deeside
Grampian
☎ 033 044 525

On A93 3m E of Banchory

Royal historic associations date from 1323, when the lands of Leys were granted to the Burnett family. The castle's features include remarkable, late C16th painted ceilings.

Castle: Apr–Oct: Mon–Sun 11am–6pm
Garden & Grounds: Jan–Dec: Mon–Sun 9.30am–dusk

Drum Castle NTS

Kincardine & Deeside
Grampian
☎ 033 08 204

Off A93 3m W of Peterculter

The great, square tower of Drum Castle is one of the three oldest tower houses in Scotland. Family memorabilia in the Irvine Room. The grounds contain the 100 acre Old Wood of Drum, a natural oakwood. Walled garden of Historic Roses.

Castle: May–Sep Mon–Sun 2pm–6pm

Closed 18 Jun
5–27 Oct Sat–Sun 2pm–5pm
Roses: Jul–Sep Mon–Sun 10am–6pm
5–27 Oct Sat–Sun 2pm–5pm
Grounds: Jan–Dec Mon–Sun 9.30am–dusk

Fyvie Castle NTS

Banff & Buchan
☎ 065 16 266

Off A947 8m SE of Turriff

The five towers of this castle enshrine five
centuries of Scottish history, each being
named after one of the 5 families who
owned the castle.

Castle: 29 Mar–31 May,Sep Mon–Sun
2pm–6pm
Jun–Aug Mon–Sun 11am–6pm
5–27 Oct Sat–Sun 2pm–5pm
Grounds: Jan–Dec Mon–Sun 9.30am–dusk

Haddo House NTS

Gordon
Grampian
☎ 065 15 440

Off B999 4m N of Pitmedden

Designed in 1731 by William Adam. Haddo
House replaced the old House of Kellie,
home of the Gordons of Methlick for
centuries.

House: Apr,May,Sep,Oct: Mon–Sun
2pm–6pm
Jun,Jul,Aug: Mon–Sun 11am–6pm
Grounds: Jan–Dec: Mon–Sun

Leith Hall NTS

Gordon
Grampian
☎ 046 43 216

Off B9002 1m W of Kennethmont

The mansion house of Leith Hall is at the
centre of a 286 acre estate which was the
home of the head of the Leith family from
1650. The house contains personal
possessions of successive lairds.

House: May–Sep Mon–Sun 2pm–6pm
5–27 Oct Sat–Sun 2pm–5pm
Garden & Grounds: Jan–Dec Mon–Sun
9.30am–dusk

Pitmedden Garden NTS

Gordon
Grampian
☎ 065 12 2352

On A920 1m W of Pitmedden village

The centrepiece of this property is the Great
Garden, originally laid out by Sir Alexander
Seton.

May–Sep: Mon–Sun 10am–6pm

Povost Ross's House NTS

Shiprow
Aberdeen
Grampian
☎ 0224 572215

Built in 1593 and the third oldest house in
Aberdeen. It now houses Aberdeen
Maritime Museum.

Museum: Jan–Dec: Mon–Sat 10am–5pm
Visitor Ctr & Shop: May–Sep: Mon–Sat
10am–4pm

The Glenlivet Distillery

Ballindallock
Banffshire, Grampian
☎ 08073 427

Tomintoul B9009

The Glenlivet Distillery is one of the first
licensed distilleries in the Highland's,
distilling the famous 'The Glenlivet' – 12
years old single malt whisky. Paved paths.

Easter–31 Oct: Mon–Sat 10am–4pm

Royal Lochnagar Distillery

Crathie
Ballater
Aberdeenshire, Grampian, AB35 5TB
☎ 03397 42273

Ballater, A93

Founded in 1845 by John Begg. Tours of
the distillery show ripe malted barley, pine
water and yeast transformed into one of the
finest single malt whiskys of the Highlands.

Easter–Oct: Mon–Sat 10am–5pm
Sun 11am–4pm
Nov–Easter: Mon–Fri 10am–5pm

Grampian Transport Museum

Alford
Aberdeenshire, Grampian, AB33 8AD
☎ 09755 62292

In village of Alford, 25m W of Aberdeen on
A944

🚌 Aberdeen

A museum housing a comprehensive
display of all forms of road transport from
horse drawn to state of the art vehicles.
Themed displays; many "hands-on"
exhibits. 15 acres with paved paths.

Ring for times for 1992

£©🚌 ⚡ 🐕 P♿ P ♿ ⛏ ➤ ⌐ ⊢ ♿ WC
🍴 ♿ ♿

HIGHLANDS

Clan Macpherson Museum

Main St
Newtonmore, Highlands, PH20 1DE
☎ 054 03 332

Newtonmore, junction of old A9 and A86,
45m S of Inverness

≋ Newtonmore

In the heart of Macpherson Clan country.
Displays Macpherson mementoes and
those of other famous Clansmen.

May–Sep: Mon–Fri 10am–5.30pm
Sun 2.30pm–5.30pm

F🚌 🐕 P ♿ WC

Highland Wildlife Park

Kincraig, Kingussie
Inverness–shire, Highlands, PH21 1NL
☎ 05404 270

Kingussie, A9

≋ Kingussie

Scottish wildlife, past and present, in 260
acres. Drive through reserve. Walkabout
area with disabled persons vehicle access.
Visitor centre, beautiful scenery. No dogs in
park.

Apr–Oct: Mon–Sun 10am–4pm
Jun–Aug: Mon–Sun 10am–5pm

£©🚌 P ♿ 🐾 🚂 ⌐ ⇒ 🚃 ⊢ ♿
WC 🍴 🔋 ♿ ♿ 🌿 ©

Loch Garten RSPB

Nr Aviemore, Highlands
☎ 047 983 694

Signposted off B970 road from Boat of
Garten–Nethybridge.

Osprey observation post usually open from
mid–April to end– Aug. Accessible to
wheelchair users via rather uneven but firm
450 yd track. Assistance is available or cars
may be driven closer on prior arrangement
with Warden.

Jan–Dec: Mon–Sun

£♿ ⌐ WC 🌿 ♿

The Scottish Tartans Museum

Drummond St
Comrie
Perthshire, Highlands, PH6 2DW
☎ 0764 70779

In centre of Comrie on A85 road

🚌 Perth

Follow the history of tartan and Highland
dress. At rear, see reconstructed weaver's
Bothy and Dye plant garden. Gravel paths.

Jan–Dec: Mon–Sun
Nov–Mar: Sundays by arrangement
Closed 25/26 Dec 1/2 Jan

£©🚌 🐕 P ♿ 🐾 ➤ ⌐ ⇒ WC
🔋 🌿

Thurso Heritage Museum

Town Hall, Thurso
Caithness, Highlands
☎ 0847 62692

Thurso

≋ 🚌 Caithness

Museum was rearranged in recent years by
the Council for Museums & Galleries,
Scotland. Paved paths.

Jun–Sep: Mon–Sun

£©🚌 🐕 P P ♿ 🐾 ➤ ⌐ ⇒ ♿
WC 🏠 ♿ ♿

Strathspey Railway

Aviemore Speyside Station
Dalfaber Rd, Aviemore
Inverness–shire, Highlands, PH22 1PY
☎ 0479 810725

Aviemore, A9

≋ 🚌 Aviemore

Scotland's Steam Railway in the Highlands.
Public steam train service between
Aviemore Speyside and Boat of Garten.
Guards van accessible for wheelchair users.
Gravel and paved paths.

Easter–Oct: ring for train times

HIGHLANDS

£ © ⊟ P ⅃ ➤ ⊣ ⋙ WC 🏛 🪑 🎋
♿ ✋

Kilravock Castle

Croy
Inverness, Highlands, IV1 2PJ
☎ 066 78 258

Nairn, A96

🚌 Nairn & Inverness

Bonnie Prince Charlie dined here on the eve
of the Battle of Culloden. Gardens are noted
for variety of trees unique in Scotland.
Gravel paths.

May–Sep: Mon–Sat Grounds
Wed Castle tours 11am/2pm/3pm/4pm

£ ⊟ ⋇ P ⅃ ⊿ 🏛 ⊣⊦ WC ¶
♿ ♪

Speyside Heather Garden Centre

Dulnain Bridge
Inverness–shire, Highlands, PH26 3PA
☎ 047 985 359

Aviemore 9m

Over 300 heathers, show garden and visitor
centre. 2 acres with quarry dust paths.

Apr–Oct: Mon–Sat 9am–5.30pm
Sun 10am–5pm
Nov–Mar: Mon–Sat 9am–5pm

£ ⊟ ⋇ P& P ⅃ ⊷ ⊣ ⇒ ♿ WC 🏛
¶ 🪑 🎋 🔯 ♿

Caithness Glass Visitor Centre

Airport Industrial Estate
Wick
Caithness, Highlands
☎ 0955 2286

Wick A9

🚄 🚌 Wick

See glassmaking at close quarters from raw
materials to finished product. Upper and
lower viewing gallery. New factory being
built. Details may be subject to alteration.
Paved paths.

Easter–30 Sep: Mon–Sat 9am–5pm
Sun 11am–5pm
Oct–Easter: Mon–Sat 9am–5pm

F ⊟ ⋇ P& P ⅃ 🏛 ➤ ⊣ ♿ WC 🏛
¶ 🪑 🔯 ♿

Claunie Deer Farm Park

By Beauly
Inverness–shire, Highlands, IV4 7AE
☎ 0463 782415

4m from Beauly on A831

Many rare breeds, wild and tame, of cattle,
sheep, ponies and deer with the facility of
mixing with them. Wheelchair users love the
venue and the Deer Farm welcomes them.
20 acres with grass paths.

Mid May–Mid Oct: Mon–Sun 10am–5pm

Visitor Centre NTS

Killiecrankie
Pitlochry
Perthshire, Highlands, PH16 5LG
☎ 0796 3233

Pitlochry, off A9

🚄 Pitlochry

First Battle of the Jacobite uprisings was
fought here in 1689. Visitor centre is at entry
to spectacular wooded gorge. 54 acres with
gravel paths of which some are unsuitable
for disabled people.

Site: Jan–Dec Mon–Sun 10am–5pm
Ctr.: Easter–May Mon–Sun 10am–5pm
Jun–Aug Mon–Sun 9.30am–6pm
Sep–Oct Mon–Sun 10am–5pm

£ © ⊟ ⋇ P& P ⅃ ⊣ ⊣⊦ ♿ WC 🏛
⋇ 🪑 🎋 ♿ ✋

Landmark Highland Heritage & Adventure Park

Carrbridge
Inverness, Highlands, PH23 3AJ
☎ 0479 84613

Between Inverness and Aviemore on old A9

🚄 Carrbridge ½m

One of Scotland's top attractions;
something for all ages. Highlander
multivisionshow, nature centre and trail, tree
top trail, giant forest tower, adventure play
area and much more. 33 acres with gravel,
paved, boardwalk and hardcore paths.

Apr–Jun/Sep–Oct: Mon–Sun 9.30am–6pm
Jul–Aug: Mon–Sun 9.30am–6pm
Nov–Mar: Mon–Sun 9.30am–5pm

£ © ⊟ ⋇ P& P ⅃ ➤ ⊣ ⇒ ⊣⊦ ♿
WC ¶ 🪑 🎋 ♿ ♿

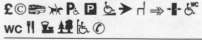

Aigas House & Field Centre

By Beauly
Inverness, Highlands, IV4 7AD
☎ 0463 782443

4m to Beauly; 15m to Inverness

Home of Sir John Lister–Kaye, used as a field centre. Nature trail and garden overlooking River Beauly. Nature trail unsuitable for wheelchair users, but accessible paths to loch. 80 acres with paths that are largely unsuitable to wheelchair users.

Apr–Oct: Mon–Sun 10.30am–5.30pm

Clan Donald Centre

Armadale
Sleat
Isle of Skye
Highland, IV45 8RS
☎ 047 14 305

A851 from Broadford or Armadale Ferry Terminal

≋ ☷ Mallaig; Ferry from Mallaig

Based around Armadale Castle, ancestral home of the MacDonalds. Now a visitor centre with 40 acres of exotic woodland gardens, museum and exhibition.

Apr–Oct: Mon–Sun 9.30am–5.30pm
Winter: open by arrangement

Inverewe Garden NTS

Poolewe
W.Ross, Highlands, IV22 2LQ
☎ 044 586 229

Poolewe

A remarkable garden started in 1862. Now opened by the National Trust for Scotland. 60 acres with gravel and paved paths.

Jan–Dec: Mon–Sun 9.30am–dusk

LOTHIAN

Royal Observatory Edinburgh

Blackford Hill
Edinburgh, Lothian, EH9 3HJ
☎ 031 668 8405

Edinburgh

≋ ☷ Edinburgh

Visitor centre housed in original 1894 building. Observatory surrounded by Blackford Hill Park.

Summer: Mon–Fri 10am–4pm
Sat–Sun & BH 12noon–5pm
Winter: Mon–Sun 1pm–5pm

Edinburgh Zoo

Corstorphine Rd
Edinburgh, Lothian, EH12 6TS
☎ 031 334 9171

2m from Edinburgh city centre on A8 (Glasgow Rd)

≋ ☷ Edinburgh

Scotland's largest animal collection located on hillside parkland, offering unrivalled views from the Pentlands to the Firth of Forth. 80 acres with tarmac paths.

Summer: Mon–Sun 9am–6pm
Winter: Mon–Sat 9am–5pm
Sun 9.30am

Almondell & Calderwood Country Park

By Broxburn
W.Lothian, EH52 5PE
☎ 0506 882254

Edinburgh

☷ Edinburgh

River valley, woodlands, meadows, visitor centre with displays on waterlife, woodlands and local history. 97 acres with dust and shale paths.

Park: Jan–Dec: Mon–Sun
Visitor Centre: Apr–Sep: Mon–Wed
9am–5pm
Thu 9am–4pm
Sun 10.30am–6pm
Oct–Mar: Mon–Thu 9am–5pm
Sun 10.30am–4.30pm

LOTHIAN

F🚌🐕♿🅿️♿🦽☕🍴🚻⚓♿🚻

🚻🍴🥾👥🎧

Bennie Museum

9–11 Mansefield St
Bathgate
W.Lothian
☎ 0506 634944

A8 mid way between Edinburgh and
Glasgow

🚃 Edinburgh

Birthplace of James Y Simpson of
Chloroform fame. First place in which
James (Paraffin) Young produced oil in the
history of oil. Place where recent universally
acclaimed fossils have been found. Paved
paths.

Apr–Oct: Mon–Sat 10am–4pm
Oct–Mar: Mon–Sat 11am–3.30pm

F🚌🐕P🦽♿☕♿🚻🚻🥾🎧

Haddington Garden Trust

St Mary's Pleasance
Haddington House
Sidegate, E.Lothian, EH41 4BZ
☎ 062 082 3738

In Haddington, just off A1

🚌 Haddington

The C17th gardens of Haddington House
features the old roses and medicinal herbs
used in ancient times and are of particular
pleasure to blind and disabled visitors.
Capture the atmosphere of Scotland's past
in this colourful, tranquil and most
interesting of gardens. Paved paths.

Jan–Dec: Dawn–Dusk

F🚌🐕🅿️P♿🦽➤🚻🚻👥

Royal Museum of Scotland

Chambers St
Edinburgh, Lothian, EH1 1JF
☎ 031 225 7534

Edinburgh

🚃 Edinburgh Waverley

This museum is the flagship of the National
Museum of Scotland. Displays include
decorative arts of the world, geology,
natural history, science and technology in a
splendid C19th building.

Jan–Dec: Mon–Sat 10am–5pm
Sun 2pm–5pm

Myreton Motor Museum

Aberlady, E.Lothian, EH32 0PZ
☎ 087 57 288

Aberlady

🚃 Drem 🚌 Edinburgh

Cars, commercials, motorcycles & bicycles
from 1896. World War II military vehicles
and period advertising. Gravel paths.

Oct–Easter: Mon–Sun 10am–5pm
Easter–Oct: Mon–Sun 10am–6pm

£©🚌🐕🥄🅿️♿🚻🥾
👥🎧

Almond Valley Heritage Centre

Millfield West
Livingston, W.Lothian, EH54 7AR
☎ 0506 414957

Livingston

🚌 Edinburgh

Discover the 'shale–mine' and explore the
oil worker's cottage in a new museum which
tells the secrets of Scotland's shale oil
industry. Meet the friendly farmyard animals
of Mill Farm. Visit the countryside museum
and see the working C18th watermill. 10
acres with gravel and paved paths.

Jan–Dec: Mon–Sun 10am–5pm

£©🚌🐕♿🅿️♿➤🚻♿🚻

🍴🥾👥🎧

Gorgie City Farm

Gorgie Rd
Edinburgh, Lothian, EH11 2LA
☎ 031 337 4202

Edinburgh

🚃🚌 Haymarket

Farm with livestock, organic garden, kitchen
and craft rooms. 2½ acres with paved paths.

Jan–Dec: Mon–Sun 9.30am–4.30pm

F🚌🐕🅿️♿☕🏛️➤♿🚻

🍴👥⚓👥

The Scottish Whisky Heritage Centre

354 Castlehill
The Royal Mile
Edinburgh, Lothian, EH1 2NE
☎ 031 220 0441

Edinburgh
≋ Edinburgh Waverley

A visit brings the story of Scotch Whisky vividly to life with a guided tour. Audio visual show & journey through whisky history. Paved paths.

Jan–Dec: Mon–Sun 10am–5pm

£©🚌🔭👜P🅿♿🏛🚻 wc🏕🍴🎣🐟🗪🅒

Scottish Agricultural Museum

Ingliston
By Edinburgh, Lothian
☎ 031 333 2674

Edinburgh on A8 near Edinburgh Airport
🚌 Edinburgh

Scotland's national museum of country life. Old farming skills and the economic and social life that went with it. Paved paths.

Apr–Sep: Mon–Fri
Jun–Aug: Sat

F🚌🔭P🅿♿🏛➤🚻 wc🏕🍴🗪🎣🐟🗪🅒

Museum of Flight

East Fortune
North Berwick, E.Lothian, EH39 5LE
☎ 0620 88308

On A1, 1m S of Haddington
≋ Drem

On a listed wartime airfield. A collection of 35 aircraft from Puss Moth to Vulcan Bomber & 50 engines from 1910 to Concorde. 45 acres with paved paths.

Apr–Sep: Mon–Sun 10.30am–4.30pm

F🚌🔭P♿➤🚻 wc🍴🗪🎣🐟🗪🅒🔡

The People's Story Museum

Canongate Tolbooth
163 Canongate
Edinburgh, Lothian, EH8 8BN
Edinburgh
≋🚌 Edinburgh

Deals with the lives, work and leisure of the People of Edinburgh from the late C18th to the present day. Paved paths.

Jun–Sep: Mon–Sat 10am–6pm
Sun 2pm–5pm(during Edinburgh Festival)
Oct–May: Mon–Sat 10am–5pm

F🚌🔭P🅿♿🏛🚻 wc🏕🗪🅒
🗪🅒

Museum of Childhood

42 High St
Edinburgh, Lothian, EH1 1TY
☎ 031 225 2424

Edinburgh
≋ Waverley

The first museum in the world to be devoted to the history of childhood.

May–Oct: Mon–Sat 10am–6pm
Oct–May: Mon–Sat 10am–5pm

F🚌🔭👜P♿🏛🚻 wc🏕🗪
🎧🗪🔡

City Art Centre

2 Market St
Edinburgh, Lothian, EH1 1DE
☎ 031 225 2424

Next to Waverley Station

A major venue on several floors with a constantly changing temporary exhibition programme, ranging from contemporary art to ancient artefacts.

Jun–Sep: Mon–Sat 10am–6pm
Oct–May: Mon–Sat 10am–5pm

Closed for Refurbishment: Re–opens August 1992

£F©🚌🔭👜P🅿♿🏛🚻 wc🍴
🗪🅒🔡

Inveresk Lodge Garden NTS

E.Lothian

On A6124, S of Musselburgh

This colourful garden of a C17th house in the attractive village of Inveresk displays a range of plants for the small garden. Good shrub–rose borders and selection of climbing roses.

P🏡➤wc

Malleny Garden NTS

Edinburgh, Lothian
Off A70 in Balerno

The garden has an outstanding collection of shrub roses and a woodland walk. The National Bonsai Collection for Scotland is housed here.

P➤�

LOTHIAN

Preston Mill NTS

Preston Rd
East Linton, Lothian
☎ 0620 860426

This mill, dating from the C16th, is the oldest mechanically working, water–driven meal mill in Scotland, and was last commercially in production in 1957.

The Georgian House NTS

7 Charlotte Sq
Edinburgh, Lothian
☎ 031 225 2160

Opened in 1975 as a focal point of interest for visitors to the New Town. The rooms are furnished as they might have been by the first owners, showing the domestic surroundings and reflecting the social conditions of that age.

Gladstone's Land NTS

477b Lawn Market
Edinburgh, Lothian
☎ 031 226 5856

Is a typical example of a C17th tenement building of the overcrowded Old Town which grew up along the ridge between Edinburgh Castle and the Palace of Holyroodhouse; the Royal Mile.

House of The Binns NTS

W. Lothian
☎ 050 683 4255

Off A904 15m W of Edinburgh

Historic home of the Dalyells, among them General Tam Dalyell who raised the Royal Scots Greys here in 1681. Parts of the present house date from the time of General Tam's father.

STRATHCLYDE

Street Level Photography Gallery & Workshop

279–281 High St
Glasgow, Strathclyde, G4 0QS
☎ 041 552 2151

Central Glasgow
⇌ Queen St or Central 🚌 Buchanan St

First photographic centre in Glasgow,

comprises two gallery spaces, a darkroom, workroom & a programme of temporary exhibitions including historical and contemporary photography.

Jan–Dec: Wed–Sat 11am–6pm
Sun 12noon–4pm

Peoples' Palace

Glasgow Green
Glasgow, Strathclyde, G40 1AT
☎ 041 554 0223

Glasgow
⇌ Queen St or Central

Glasgow's main social history museum, built as a multi–purpose cultural centre for the working classes of the overcrowded east end.

Jan–Dec: Mon–Sat 10am–5pm
Sun 12noon–6pm

Botanic Gardens

Glasgow
Strathclyde, G12 0UE
☎ 041 334 2422

Glasgow A82
🚌 Glasgow ⊖ Hillhead

Gardens on present site since 1841. Outstanding features including Kibble Palace, a large Victorian glasshouse. Herb garden and systematic garden. Special collections of orchids & begonias. 30 acres with tarmac paths.

Jan–Dec: Mon–Sun 7am–dusk

The Glasgow Dome of Discovery

South Rotunda
100 Govan Rd
Glasgow, Strathclyde, G51 1JS
☎ 041 427 1792

Glasgow South Side
⇌ Exhibition Centre ⊖ Kinning Park Bus

The Dome contains 60 exhibits in a lively 'hands–on' environment which allows each visitor to interact with a variety of phenomena.

Jan–Dec: Tue–Sun & BH 10am–5.30pm

Glasgow Cathedral

Castle St
Glasgow, Strathclyde, G4
☎ 041 552 6305

Glasgow

≋ Queen St. or Central

Cathedral first dedicated 1136 in full use
and with many architectural and historic
features.

Oct–Mar: Mon–Sat 9.30am–1pm &
2pm–4pm
Sun 2pm–4pm
Apr–Sep: Mon–Sat 9.30am–1pm &
2pm–6pm
Sun 1pm–4pm

Formakin Estate Country Park

Millhill Rd
Bishopston
Renfrew, Strathclyde, PA7 5NX
☎ 0505 863400

Paisley

≋ Bishopton

150 acre country park with woodlands,
SSSI, formal and oriental gardens. Farm and
adventure playground. Grass and gravel
paths.

Jan–Dec: Mon–Sun 11am–5pm

McLean Museum & Art Gallery

15 Kelly St
Greenock, Strathclyde, PA16 8JX
☎ 0475 23741

Greenock

≋ Greenock West 🚌 Kilblain St

Newly refurbished museum with displays on
James Watt, industrial and local history,
ship models, ethnography and natural
history. Paved paths.

Jan–Dec: Mon–Sat 10am–12noon &
1pm–5pm
Closed National & local PH

Glasgow Zoo

Calderpark
Uddingston
Glasgow, Strathclyde, G71 7RZ
☎ 041 771 1185

On the A74 where it joins M73 and M74, E of

Glasgow

🚌 Glasgow

Animal collection specialising in reptiles and
cats. Award–winning black bear enclosure.
Large enclosures in open parkland. No
guide dogs/dogs. 30 acres with paved
paths.

Jan–Dec: Mon–Sun 10am–5/6pm

Collins Gallery

The University of Strathclyde
22 Richmond St
Glasgow, Strathclyde, G1 1XQ
☎ 041 553 4145

Glasgow

≋ Queen St

An integral part of the University of
Strathclyde, the Collins Gallery shows 12
exhibitions per year ranging from
contemporary fine art to craft and
photography. Paved paths.

Jan–Dec: Mon–Fri 10am–5pm
Sat 12noon–4pm
Closed: BH/wks between exhibitions

Greenbank Garden NTS

Greenbank House
Clarkston
Glasgow, Strathclyde, E76 8RB
☎ 041 634 3281

Clarkston on south side of Glasgow

≋ Clarkston 🚌 Glasgow–Merarnskirk

Wide range of plants & regular
demonstrations on how to grow them,
including help for disabled people. 4 acres
with hard gravel,paved and reinforced grass
paths.

Jan–Dec: Mon–Sun 9.30am–sunset

Museum of Lead Mining

Wanlockhead
Goldscaur Row
Wanlockhead
By Biggar
Lanarkshire, Strathclyde, ML12 6UT
☎ 0659 74387

8m from A74 at Abington

2 period cottages, walk in lead–mine, visitor

STRATHCLYDE

centre with unique mineral displays, visitor trail and open air museum in 5 acres.
Easter–Oct: Mon–Sun 11am–4.30pm

£ © 🚌 ⚓ 🅿 ♿ ➜ ⊣ ⊣ ♿ WC ⊬
⚓ 🎋 ⊬ 🕮 ©

Kelburn Country Centre
South Offices
Fairlie
Ayrshire, Strathclyde, KA29 0BE
☎ 0475 568685

Largs, A78 to Ayr
⇌ 🚍 Largs

Historic home of the Earls of Glasgow. Spectacular views, waterfalls, woodland walks, lovely gardens and childrens activities. 500 acres with gravel and paved paths.
Easter–Mid Oct: Mon–Sun 10am–6pm
Mid Oct–Easter: Mon–Sun 11am–5pm
(grounds only)

£ © 🚌 ⚓ 🅿 ♿ 🔥 ⊣ ⊣ WC 🐴 ⊬
⚓ 🎋 ⊬ © ♿

Burns Cottage & Museum
Alloway
Ayr, Strathclyde, KA7 4PY
☎ 0292 41215

2m S of Ayr
🚍 Ayr

Birthplace of Robert Burns, Scotland's National poet with adjacent museum relating to his life. 3 acres with paved and gravel paths.
Nov–Mar: Mon–Sat 10am–4pm Closed Sun
Apr–May: Mon–Sat 10am–5pm Sun 2pm–5pm
Jun–Aug: Mon–Sat 9am–7pm Sun 10am–7pm
Sep–Oct: Mon–Sat 10am–5pm Sun 2pm–5pm

£ © 🚌 ⚓ 🅿 ⊬ ➜ ⊣ ♿ WC ⊬ ⚓
🎋 © ©

Airdrie Observatory
Airdrie Library
Wellwynd
Airdrie, Lanarkshire,
Strathclyde
☎ 041 339 2558

Airdrie town centre

One of 4 public observatories in Scotland. In Airdrie for 100 years. Six inch Cooke

refracting telescope donated 60 years ago.
Jan–Dec Fri: 7.30pm
Other times: by arrangement

F © 🚌 ⚓ 🅿 ♿ 🔥 🚩 🕮 WC ⊬
🕮 ♿

Weavers Cottages Museum
23/25 Wellwynd
Airdrie
Lanarkshire, Strathclyde, ML6 0BN
☎ 0236 747712

Airdrie
⇌ 🚍 Airdrie

Reconstruction of C19th master weaver's house and exhibition gallery for temporary displays.
Jan–Dec: Mon,Tue,Thu,Fri 10am–5pm
Sat 10am–1pm & 2pm–5pm
Other times by arrangement

F 🚌 ⚓ 🅿 ⊬ ➜ ⊣ WC ⊬ 🕮 ©

New Lanark Visitor Centre
New Lanark Mills
Lanark, Strathclyde, ML11 9DB
☎ 0555 65876/61345

Lanark
⇌ Lanark

200 year old cotton spinning village, made famous by social experiments of Robert Owen. Nominated world heritage site.
Jan–Dec: Mon–Sun 11am–5pm

£ © 🚌 ⚓ 🔥 🅿 ♿ ⊣ ⇒ ⊣ ♿
WC ⊬ ⚓ 🎋 ⊬ 🐟 🕮 © ♿

Bargany Gardens
Bargany Estate Office
Girvan
Ayr, Strathclyde, KA26 9GL
☎ 046 587 249

Girvan

Woodland garden and lake; azaleas, rhododendrons and fine trees. Best May and June. 40 acres with gravel paths.
Apr–Oct: Mon–Sun 10am–7pm

 F 🚌 ⚓ 🅿 ➜ WC 🎋 ⊬

Springburn Museum
Atlas Sq, Ayr St
Springburn
Lanark, Strathclyde, G21 4BW
☎ 041 557 1405

Glasgow, on A803 to Kirkintilloch

≋ 🚌 Springburn

Social and Industrial History Museum of the Year in 1989. Community museum in an area known worldwide for locomotive manufacture.

Jan–Dec: Mon–Fri 10.30am–5pm
Sat 10am–4pm
Sun 2pm–5pm
Most BH's 2pm–5pm

F🚌 ⚟ 🅿 ♿ ➤ ⊣ ⊣- wc 🖼 🛝
💨 🄫

Baron's Haugh RSPB

By Motherwell
Strathclyde, ML8 5TB
☎ 0555 70941

Entered from Motherwell.

Tarmac path leads from special entrance for 150 yds to 2 of the marsh hides with wheelchair access. Contact Warden to unlock gate.

Loch Gruinart RSPB

Islay
Strathclyde, PA44 7PS
☎ 049 685 363

In winter large flocks of barnacle and white–fronted geese can be watched closely from the quiet, level road. Good bird–watching from the car elsewhere on the island.

Lochwinnoch RSPB

Strathclyde
☎ 0505 842663

Off A760 ½m E of Lochwinnoch village.

Nature centre with exhibitions. Two slightly uneven but firm paths provide access to three bird–watching hides overlooking marsh and open water on the Bird Meadow.

Jan–Dec: Fri–Wed 10am–5pm

£ 🚾 wc 🖼 ♿

Summerlee Heritage Trust

West Canal St
Coatbridge
Lanark, Strathclyde, ML5 1QD
☎ 0236 31261

Coatbridge – A89 – Glasgow

≋ 🚌 Coatbridge Central and Coatbridge Sunnyside

Museum of social and industrial history. Working machinery, reconstructed interiors, working electric tramway, ironwork gallery.

Jan–Dec: Mon–Sun 10am–5pm

F🚌 ⚟ 🅿 ♿ ➤ ⊣ 🛝 ⊣- 🚾 wc
🏠 ¶¶ 🖼 🛝 ♿ 🄫 ♿

Transmission Art Gallery

28 King St
Trongate
Glasgow, Strathclyde, G1 5QP
☎ 041 552 4813

Glasgow city centre

≋ 🚌 Glasgow

Based in east end of city centre near central shopping area, beside Glasgow print studio, project ability and Tron Theatre. Paved paths.

Mon–Sat 11am–5.30pm

F🚌 ⚟ 🅿 ♿ 🚾 wc 🖼 💨

Hunterian Art Gallery

University of Glasgow
Glasgow, Strathclyde, G12 8QO
☎ 041 330 5431

Glasgow – West end

≋ 🚌 Glasgow

A purpose–built art gallery, housing the University of Glasgow's world famous art collection, comprising old masters and the estates of C.R.Mackintosh and J.M.Whistler. Paved paths.

Jan–Dec: Mon–Sat 9.30am–5pm

F🚌 ⚟ 🅿 ♿ 🚾 wc 🖼
💨 ♿

Balloch Castle Country Park

Balloch
Dunbartonshire, Strathclyde, G83 8LX
☎ 0389 58216

Balloch

≋ 🚌 Balloch

A park on the south end of Loch Lomond. Visitor centre, walled gardens and numerous paths and walks available. 250 acres with gravel and paved paths.

Park: Jan–Dec: Mon–Sun Dawn–Dusk
Visitor Centre: Easter–Sep w/end: Mon–Sun 10am–6pm

F🚌 ⚟ 🅿 🅿 ♿ ➤ ⊣ ⊣- 🚾 wc ¶¶
🖼 🛝 ♿ 💨

STRATHCLYDE

Scottish Maritime Museum

Denny Ship Model Experimental Tank
Castle St
Dumbarton, Strathclyde, G82 1QS
☎ 0389 63444

Dumbarton, A82 from Glasgow

 Dumbarton Central

The first existing commercial shipyard hull
test tank, built 1882–83 by W M Denny &
Bros, preserved as a working industrial
artefact.

Jan–Dec: Mon–Sat 10am–4pm

£©🚌🏃‍♂️P ⚡ 🏭🏛wc ♿ ✈🖐
©♿

Bachelors' Club NTS

Tarbotton, Strathclyde
☎ 0292 541940

7m NE of Ayr

In this C17th thatched house, Robert Burns
and friends formed a debating club in 1780.
Burns attended dancing lessons, and was
initiated into Freemasonry.

P ♿ ⚡wc

Brodick Castle, Garden & Country Park NTS

Isle of Arran, Strathclyde
☎ 0770 2202

This ancient seat of the Dukes of Hamilton,
was more recently the home of the late
Mary, Duchess of Montrose. The contents
include superb silver, porcelain, and
paintings. The woodland garden ranks as
one of Europe's finest rhododendron
gardens.

P♿ ⚡ ♿➤♿ 🍴 ♿

The Hill House NTS

Upper Colquhoun St
Helensburgh, Strathclyde
☎ 0436 3900

Off B832, between A82 and A14, 23m NW
of Glasgow.

Overlooking the estuary of the River Clyde,
is considered the finest example of the
domestic architecture of Charles Rennie
Mackintosh.

P ⚡🏛wc ♿

The Tennement House NTS

145 Buccleuch St
Garnethill, Strathclyde
☎ 041 333 0183

Built in 1892 when Garnethill was
established as a superior residential district
in Glasgow's west end.

P⚡ ⚡wc ♿

Weaver's Cottage NTS

Renfrew District, Strathclyde
☎ 050 57 5588

Off A737, in Shuttle St at The Cross,
Kilbarchan, 12m SW of Glasgow.

This typical cottage of an C18th handloom
weaver contains looms, weaving equipment
and domestic utensils.

P⚡ ⚡wc ♿♿

Souter Johnnie's Cottage NTS

Kirkoswald, Strathclyde
☎ 065 56 603

4m SW of Maybole

The home of John Davidson, village souter
(cobbler) and the original Souter Johnnie of
Robert Burns' Tam O Shanter. Life sized
stone figures of the Souter, Tam the
innkeeper and his wife.

P⚡ ⚡wc

Scottish Maritime Museum

Laird Forge
Gottries Rd
Irvine, Strathclyde, KA12 8QE
☎ 0294 78283

Irvine, A736 to Glasgow or A71/A77

 Irvine

Developing museum, founded 1983, Irvine
Harbour – wharf displays, exhibition hall,
tenement flat and historic vessels, some
accessible to public.

1 Apr–31 Oct: Mon–Sun 10am–5pm

£©🚌🏃‍♂️ P P♿⚡🚩🔨 ⬆wc ♿
✈🖐

TAYSIDE

Vane Farm RSPB

Nr Kinross
Tayside, KY13 7LX
☎ 0577 62355

2m E of M90 exit 5 on Glenrothes road.

Panoramic views of Loch Leven with
wintering pink footed geese and other
wildfowl.

£ P ➤⇒♿wc ♿

Scone Palace
Perth
Tayside, PH2 6BD
☎ 0738 52300
Perth A93 to Blairgowrie
≋ 🚌 Perth

One time crowning place of Scottish Kings upon the Store of Score. Now home of the Earls of Mansfield. 100 acres with grass and tarmac paths.

Good Fri–Mid Oct: Mon–Sat 9.30am–5pm
Sun 1.30pm–5pm

£©🚌🛥️Ⓟ🅿🔦🏰➜♿ wc ‖
🦪🎪♿♦🎨✆

Blair Castle
Blair Atholl
Pitlochry
Perth, Tayside, PH18 5TL
☎ 079 681 207
Pitlochry
≋ Blair Atholl

Scotland's leading historic house showing over 700 years of Scottish history in 32 fully furnished rooms. 20 acres with gravel paths.

Apr–Oct: Mon–Sun 10am–6pm

£©🚌🌸Ⓟ🅿🔨🎞️🏰➜🚻♿
wc ‖ 🦪🎪♿🎨©♿

Atholl Country Collection
Blair Atholl
Perth, Tayside, PH18 5SG
☎ 079 681 232
A9 Blair Atholl
≋ 🚌 Blair Atholl

An interesting and lively museum of life in the district of Atholl, portrayed in unique displays ranging from the Smiddy to the Schoolroom.

End May–Mid Oct: Mon–Sun
1.30pm–5.30pm

£©🚌🌸 🅿P♿🚻 wc 🦪🎪🎨
©♿

Hydro–Electric Visitor Ctr
Pitlochry Power Station
Perth, Tayside
☎ 0796 3152
Pitlochry
≋ 🚌 Pitlochry

Pitlochry Power Station is a fully operationed station, with Dam and Salmon ladder. Paved paths.

Apr–Oct: Mon–Sat 9.40am–5.30pm

£©🚌🌸🅿♿🔦🏰♿ wc 🦪🤚

Lower City Mills
West Mill St
Perth, Tayside, PH1 5QP
☎ 0738 30572
Perth city centre
≋ 🚌 Perth

Restored C18th town oatmeal mill with working C19th machinery. Part of Britains most complete complex of Georgian Grain Mills. Cobbled streets.

Easter–31st Oct: Mon–Sat 10am–5pm
July–Sept: Sun 12noon–5pm
Winter by arrangement

£©🚌🌸P🅿♿🏰➜♿ wc ‖
🦪🤚

Clan Donnachaidh Museum
Bruar Falls
Blair Atholl
Pitlochry
Perth, Tayside, PH18 5TW
☎ 079 683 264
Pitlochry 11m, A9
≋ 🚌 Blair Atholl

Items of Clan and Jacobite interest. Tartans, maps, glass, silver and weapons. The Clan Society at home and abroad. Paved entrance.

Apr–Oct: Mon–Sat 10am–1pm/2pm–5pm
Sun 2pm–5pm

F🚌🌸 🅿🔦⌐✝wc🆔 🦪🎪
♿©

McManus Galleries
Albert Sq
Dundee
Tayside, DD1 1DA
☎ 0382 23141 x 65136
Central Dundee
≋ Dundee 🚌 Seagate

Built in 1867, and designed by Sir George Gilbert Scott, house an art collection of national importance. Includes fine examples of paintings and sculpture.

Jan–Dec: Mon–Sat 10am–5pm

F🌸P♿P🅿♿🏥♿ wc 🦪©♿

TAYSIDE

Yarnspinners Workshop

65 Willoughby St
Muthill
Nr Crieff
Perth, Tayside, PH5 2AE
☎ 0764 81 326

3m S of Crieff on A822 to Stirling

🚌 Crieff/Stirling/Auchterarder

Handspinning workshop in conservation village with spinning tradition. Spinning demonstrations and tuition, equipment, fibres, fleeces, natural dyes, books and gifts.

Open most days. Please tel.

Angus Folk Museum NTS

Angus, Tayside
☎ 030 784 288

One of the finest in Scotland, was given into the care of the Trust in 1974.

Barrie's Birthplace NTS

Angus, Tayside
☎ 0575 72646

A926, in Kirriemuir, 6m NW of Forfar

In this two–storeyed house, where JM Barrie was born, the upper floors are furnished as they may have been when Barrie lived there.

Branklyn NTS

Dundee Rd
Perth, Tayside
☎ 0738 25535

A85

This attractive little garden in Perth has been described as the finest 2 acres of private garden in the country.

Dunkeld NTS

Perth & Kinross, Tayside
☎ 035 02 460

Off A9, 15m, N of Perth

The Trust owns 20 houses in Cathedral and High Streets; most date from the rebuilding of the town after the Battle of Dunkeld in 1689.

BEHIND EVERY DISABLED PERSON SHOULD BE AN ABLE BODY.

One that can only be realised with your support.

We want to be able to provide the level of care that will give disabled people this choice: either to live in the familiar surroundings of their own homes. Or, if they prefer, to move into the comfort of one of ours.

So please help us in any way you can. It is only through legacies, covenants and the generosity of our friends that our work can continue.

THE LEONARD CHESHIRE FOUNDATION

26-29 Maunsel Street, London SW1P 2QN.

WALES

SYMBOL DESCRIPTIONS

£   Admission charge

F   No admission charge but donation in some places

© Special concession charge for disabled people, elderly people, carers and children

Groups must book in advance – special rates may apply

Guide dogs accepted except in certain areas

Sympathetic Hearing Scheme participated in or Loop System

Special information available for disabled people

PARKING

P   Designated disabled parking space

P   Own car park with a dropping off point within 50 yards

P   Public car park nearby and/or street parking within 200 yards

P   Dropping off point or disabled parking place by telephone appointment

MAIN ENTRANCE

Entrance level or ramped and over 30″ wide

Steps into building 1–5 or bumpy

Steps into building 6 or more

More suitable entrance freely available, telephone for details or help. Temporary ramps to be made available.

Steps within the buildings that cannot be overcome by ramps

More than one floor level and no lift

More than one floor level and suitable lift/stairclimber/stairlift for wheelchair users

OUTSIDE

Routes around the site are free of steps or steps can be avoided

Seats available around the site

Routes indicated for wheelchair users

Routes indicated for visually handicapped people

Transport around the site suitable for disabled people and wheelchair users – telephone in advance

Transport around the site not suitable for disabled people or elderly people

There are limited areas that cannot be reached due to steps or doorways less than 30″

TOILETS

  ♿ wc   Unisex toilets designed or adapted for disabled people or public toilets within 50 yards. Radar key required in some

WC   Ordinary toilets with level access

WC   No toilets on site but public ones nearby

   Baby changing/parents room available

GENERAL

   Restaurant/tea room/cafe/ not accessible due to steps/narrow doorway/first floor with no lift

   Restaurant/tea room/cafe/vending accessible by ramp or level or lift with 30″ doors

   Shop not accessible due to stairs but may be accessible with help

   Shop/sales area accessible by ramp or level and 30″ doorway

   Picnic area only, or nearby

   Wheelchair users are advised to come accompanied

   Taped guides available/or person

   Facilities for visually handicapped/braille or by request

   People available to help (telephone beforehand if you require help)

   Telephone accessible for wheelchair users

   This site is suitable for elderly people but unsuitable for wheelchair users

   Wheelchairs/batricars for loan or hire – telephone for advance booking

NT   The National Trust

EH   English Heritage

NTS   National Trust for Scotland

RSPB   Royal Society For the Protection of Birds

FC   Forestry Commission

   British Rail

   Bus

   Telephone

   Underground

NOTES

WALES

CLWYD

Llangollen Railway Society

The Station
Abbey Road
Llangollen, Clwyd, LL20 8SN
☎ 0978 860979/860951

Junction of A5 & A539 by river bridge

≋ ⊞ Ruabon

The railway line from Ruabon to Llangollen was closed in 1965. Since 1981, passenger train services have operated from Llangollen towards Corwen. 2 weeks notice required for wheelchair users. Telephone for booking.

Jan–Dec: Mon–Sun Tel for timetable

£ 🚌 ✕ P P ♿ ▟ 🏠 ➤ ⊣ ⇒ ╬
WC 🏠 🍴 ✕ ♿ 🐟 ✗

Erddig Hall NT

Nr Wrexham
Clwyd, LL13 0YT
☎ 0978 355314

Wrexham A483, A585

≋ ⊞ Wrexham

Although a treasure house, Erddig is best known for its social history and has been described as the most evocative 'upstairs–downstairs' house in Britain. Wheelchair users telephone in advance.

Apr–mid Oct: Sat–Wed 11am–5.00pm

£ © 🚐 ✈ ✕ 📖 🗑 P 🏳 📛 🏠 ⊣ ╬
♿WC WC ✕ ✕ 🔥 ⚒ ♿ 🐟 🌀 ♿L

Bersham Industrial Heritage Centre

Bersham
Nr Wrexham, Clwyd, LL14 4HT
☎ 0978 261529

Wrexham, A525

≋ ⊞ Wrexham

Sited on one of the most important industrial sites in Europe.

Easter–Oct: Tue–Sat & BH 10am–12.30pm & 1.30pm–4pm
Sun 2pm–4pm

Nov–Easter: Tue–Fri 10am–12.30pm & 1.30pm–4pm
Sat 12.30pm–3.30pm

F P WC

King's Mill Visitor Centre

King's Mill Rd
Wrexham, Clwyd
☎ 0978 362967

On A525 from Wrexham

Wrexham

Restored mill building with waterwheel and display showing the life and work in an C18th mill–'The Miller's Tale'.

Easter–Sep: Tue–Sun 10am–5pm
Sep–Easter: Sat–Sun 10am–5pm

£ © WC

Wrexham Maelor Heritage Centre

47–49 King St
Wrexham, Clwyd, LL11 1HQ
☎ 0978 290048

In Wrexham town centre

Wrexham

Small heritage centre illustrating the history of Wrexham and District.

Jan–Dec: Mon–Sat 10am–5pm

F WC

Ty Mawr Country Park

Cae Gwilym Rd
Cefn Mawr
Wrexham, Clwyd, LL14 3PE
☎ 0978 822780

From Wrexham B5605 to Park

Wrexham or Llangollen

Located on the River Dee, Ty Mawr is a picturesque country park with riverside walks, picnic areas, abundant wildlife and farm animals.

Apr–Sep: Mon–Sun 10am–5pm
Oct–Mar: Sat–Sun 10am–5pm

F WC

Nant Mill Visitor Centre

Nant Rd
Coedpoeth
Wrexham, Clwyd, LL11 3BT
☎ 0978 752772

Wrexham, along A525 towards Ruthin

Wrexham to Coedpoeth

Site was formerly a corn mill and farm. Now part of Clywedog Valley with a focus on conservation.

Easter–Sep: Tue–Sun 10am–5pm
Oct–Good Fri: Sat–Sun 10am–4pm

£ © WC

Llangollen Motor Museum

Pentrefelin
Llangollen, Clwyd, LL20 8EE
☎ 0978 860324

1m from Llangollen towards Ruthin

Established since 1980, the museum displays the collection of British cars from the 1920's to 1960's. Spares and souvenirs shop.

Easter–Oct: Mon–Sun 10am–5pm
Nov–Mar: Mon–Fri 10am–5pm

£ © WC

Bodnant Garden

Tal Y Cafn
Colwyn Bay
Clwyd, LL28 5RE
☎ 0492 650460

Colwyn Bay and Llandudno

Llandudno

82 acres of beautiful garden in the Conwy Valley

Mid Mar–31 Oct: Mon–Sun 10am–5pm

© WC

DYFED

Teifi Valley Railway

Henllan Station Yard
Llandysul, Dyfed, SA44 5TD
☎ 0559 371077

A484 Carmarthen/Cardigan

Henllan

Unlimited travel on a narrow gauge railway,

DYFED

using steam and diesel locomotives.
Easter–Oct: Mon–Sun 10.30am–6pm

£ © 🚌 ✕ 🅿 ♿ ✋ ➜ ⌐ 🚂 -ᚂ- ♿
🍴 🎇 🏕 ♿ 👐

Oakwood Adventure & Leisure Park

Canaston Bridge
Narberth, Dyfed, SA67 8DE
☎ 0834 891373

Haverfordwest, A40

Wales' largest tourist attraction. 80 acres
packed full of things to do – Assault
courses, go–karts, boating lake, miniature
railway, mini golf and peaceful woodland
walks.

Easter–30 Sep: Mon–Sun 10am

£ © 🚌 ✕ 🅿♿ 🅿 ♿ ➜ ⌐ -ᚂ- ♿ WC
⛺ 🍴 🎇 🏕 ♿ 👐 © ♿

Kidwelly Industrial Museum

Kidwelly, Dyfed, SA17 4LW
☎ 0554 891078

Llanelli or Carmarthen, A484

≋ 🚌 Kidwelly

Remains of Tinworks 1737–1941. Coal
complex with steam & diesel locomotives.
Exhibitions on river–side site.

Easter–Mid–Sep: Mon–Fri 10am–5pm
Sat–Sun 2pm–5pm

£ © 🚌 ✕ 🅿 ✒ ♿ 🔥 ◢ ➜ -ᚂ- ♿
WC 🍴 🏕 ♿ ©

Stackpole Quarry NT

Stackpole
Pembroke, Dyfed, SA71 5DQ
☎ 0646 661359

4m S of Pembroke on B4319

The quarry gives countryside access to all.
Facilities for abseiling, rock climbing and
other outdoor activities. Cliff–top walk for
accompanied wheelchair users.

Jan–Dec: Mon–Sun

F 🚌 ✕ 🅿 ♿ ➜ ⌐ ⇒ -ᚂ- ♿ WC 🍴
🏕 ©

Ynys–Hir Nature Reserve RSPB

Nr Machynlleth
Dyfed, SY20 8TA
☎ 065 474 265

Entrance off A487 Aberystwyth–

Machynlleth road in Eglwyfach.

Cars may be driven by arrangement to Ynys
Eidol estuary hide, suitable for wheelchair
users. Hide is one mile from car park and
reception with seats en route. Marian Mawr
pools hide is 650 yards from reception and
accessible to ambulant disabled. Some
firmer woodland tracks are negotiable.

Tenby Museum & Picture Gallery

Castle Hill
Tenby, Dyfed, SA70 7BP
☎ 0834 2809

Tenby

≋ 🚌 Tenby

Collection of local art, natural & maritime
history, geology & archaeology displayed in
part of old castle.

Easter–31 Oct: Mon–Sun 10am–6pm
Nov–Easter: Mon–Fri 10am–12noon &
2pm–4pm

£ © 🚌 ✕ 🅿 ✒ ◢ ◢ 🏛 ⌐ -ᚂ- WC
⛺ 🎇 🏕 ♿ 👐 ♿

Silent World Aquarium & Wildlife Art Gallery

Slippery Back
Narberth Rd
Tenby, Dyfed
☎ 0834 4498

Tenby, A478

≋ 🚌 Tenby

Housed in an attractive C19th chapel in
interesting & unusual surroundings. Exotic
fish, amphibions, reptiles and invertebrates.

Easter–Sep: Mon–Sun 10am–6pm
Oct: Some odd days
Other times by appointment

£ © 🚌 ✕ 🅿♿ 🅿 ♿ 🏛 WC 🍴 🎇 🏕
♿ ©

Scotton Manor Museum

Spittal
Haverfordwest
Dyfed, SA62 ,5QL
☎ 0437 731378

Haverfordwest, 5m N on B4329

Museum about Pembrokeshire life &
industry in the past, set in country park.
Period rooms in Victorian manor house.
Rural crafts in stable block.

May–Sep: Tue–Sun 10am–4.30pm

£©📷🚌✕♿️🅿️♿️🏛️-📶-wc 🍴 🅿️
👥♿️🧺♿️

Llanarth Pottery

Llanarth, Dyfed, SA47 0PU
☎ 0545 580584

Between Newquay and Aberaeron

Watch the potter working. Fantastic range of handthrown stoneware pots for sale at prices all can afford.

Jan–Dec: Mon–Sun 9.30am–6pm
Occasionally closed in winter.

F🚌✕ 🅿️ ✏️♿️➤🅿️🧺

Cardigan Coast NT

Nr Cardigan
Pembroke
Dyfed

A concrete ramp gives access to the beach at Penbryn, near Cardigan. Adapted WC's at Penbryn and Mwnt and at Martin's Haven on the Pembroke coast near Marloes.

GWENT

Chepstow Museum

Gwy House
Bridge St
Chepstow, Gwent. NP6 5EZ
☎ 0291 625981

Chepstow
≥ 🚌 Chepstow

Attractive displays focus on the history of Chepstow, once an important port and market town.

Mar–Oct: Mon–Sat & BH 11am–1pm & 2pm–5pm
Sun: 2pm–5pm

£©📷🚌✕ 🅿️♿️🛒🏛️➤ 🅿️♿️wc
🅿️👥♿️

Bryan Bach Park

Merthyr Rd
Tredegar, Gwent. NP2 3AY
☎ 0495 711816

Between Tredegar and Rhymney A465
≥ Rhymney

New country park with 600 acres of reclaimed land with paved and gravel paths. Visitor centre and lake. Free fishing for

OAP'S. Vending machines.
Jan–Dec: Mon–Sun 9am–dusk

F🚌✕♿️🅿️♿️➤🅿️♿️wc 🍴👥
♿️🧺♿️

Newport Museum & Art Gallery

John Frost Square
Newport, Gwent.
☎ 0633 840064

Town centre
🚌 Newport

Collections of fine and applied art, archaeology, local and natural history with temporary exhibitions.

Jan–Dec: Mon–Thu 9.30am–5pm
Fri 9.30am–4.30pm
Sat 9.30am–4pm

F🚌✕ 🅿️♿️📊📊🗃️wc 🅿️♿️
🧺♿️

The Old Station Countryside Centre

Tintern
Chepstow, Gwent. NP6 7NX
☎ 0291 689566

Chepstow/Monmouth Rd, A466
≥ 🚌 Chepstow

Built as a Victorian country station on the picturesque Wye Valley Line, now a visitor centre.

Apr–Oct: Mon–Sun 10.30am–5.30pm

£🚌✕ 🅿️♿️➤🗑️⇒🅿️♿️wc 🍴
🅿️👥♿️

Valley Inheritance Museum

Park Buildings
Pontypool, Gwent. NP4 6JH
☎ 0495 752036

Nr Pontypool town centre, by park gates
≥ 🚌 Pontypool

A converted Georgian stable block containing audio visuals, displays and exhibitions which tell the story of the Eastern Valley of Gwent.

Feb–Dec: Mon–Sat 10am–5pm
Sun 2pm–5pm

£©📷🚌✕ 🅿️♿️➤🗑️♿️wc 🍴🅿️
👥🧺♿️

GWENT

Tredegar House

Newport, Gwent. NP1 9YW
☎ 0633 815880

Newport, junction 28 off M4
🚌 to gate

One of the most magnificent C17th houses in Britain. The House and gardens are set within a 90 acre landscaped park. Carriage rides, self–guided trails, craft workshops, boating, and an exciting adventure playfarm.

Easter–Sept 31: Wed–Sun & BH 11.30am–4pm
July–Aug: Tue–Sun 11.30am–4pm
Oct: Sat–Sun 11.30am–4pm

£ © 🚌 🐾 P♿ P ⛴ 👆 🏛 ➜ ⊣ ♿WC
WC 🍴 🛋 🎎 👋 🎦 ♿

Big Pit Mining Museum

Blaenafon
Gwent. NP4 9XP
☎ 0495 790311

About 1m from Blaenafon on B4248 and is well signposted

🚆 Newport or Cardiff 🚌 to Pontypool then to Blaenafon or Forgeside.

Buildings include the winding engine–house, the blacksmiths' shop and the pithead baths. Exhibitions illustrating the history of the South Wales coal industry and the way of life of the mining communities.

Mar–Nov: Mon–Sun 9.30am–5pm
Dec–Feb: ring for details

£ © 🚌 🐾 🥏 P ♿ 👆 🏛 ⊣ ♿WC
WC 🍴 🛋 🎎 ♿ 🎣 🎦 ⚒

Garden Festival of Wales

P O Box 14
Ebbw Vale, Gwent, NP3 6XZ
☎ 0495 305545

S of Ebbw Vale on the A4046
🚆 🚌 Newport/Abergavenny

The dramatic valley setting of Ebbw Vale will form a backcloth for this major event. 1½ million trees, shrubs & plants have been planted to bring this 'garden' alive. Something to suit everyone's taste; street theatre, opera, sporting events & spectacular horticultural shows.

Jun,Jul,Aug: Mon–Sun 10am–8pm
May,Sep,Oct: Mon–Sun 10am–7pm

£ © 🚌 🐾 P♿ P 👆 👆 ⊣ ⇒ 👁 🗄
♿WC 🏠 🍴 🛋 🎎 👋 🎦 ♿

GWYNEDD

Maes Artro Village

Llanbedr
Barmouth, Gwynedd, LL45 2PZ
☎ 0341 23 467

On the coast road between Barmouth & Harlech

🚆 Llanbedr halt

Old Welsh Street, RAF Musuem, aquarium. Woodland walks, playground, garden centre, craft workshops and old farm implements.

Easter–30 Sep: Mon–Sun 10am–5.30pm

£ 🚌 🐾 P♿ P ♿ ➜ ⊣ ⇒ ⊣ ♿WC WC
🍴 🛋 🎎 ♿

Anglesey Sea Zoo

Brynsiencyn
Anglesey, Gwynedd, LL61 6TR
☎ 0248 430411

Britannia Bridge A5 – then A4080
🚌 Bangor

Largest aquarium in Wales showing wide diversity of sealife from around Anglesey. Zoo all under cover.

Mar–Sep: Mon–Sun 10am–5pm
Oct–Feb: Mon–Sun 11am–3pm
Closed 23–26 Dec & 1 Jan

£ © 🚌 🐾 P♿ P ♿ ➜ ⊣ ♿WC WC 🏠
🍴 🛋 🎎 🎦 ♿

Talyllyn Railway

Wharf Station
Tywyn, Gwynedd, LL36 9EY
☎ 0654 710472

Tywyn, A487/B4405. A493
🚆 Tywyn 🚌 Gwynedd

Historic narrow gauge steam railway running into Snowdonia National Park. Opened 1866. The first railway to be taken over by a voluntary organisation.

Apr–Oct: Mon–Sun
Also Xmas Hols

£ © 🚌 🐾 P♿ P P ♿ 👆 👆 🚂 WC
WC 🍴 🛋 🎎 ♿ 🎦

Mawddach Valley Nature Reserve RSPB

Nr Dolgellau
Gwynedd, LL38 2RJ

Reached off A493 from Dolgellau to
Fairbourne.

The Arthog Bog part of the reserve has a
firm path. It is entered via the disused
railway walk from Morfa Mawddach station.
Penmaenpool Wildlife Centre, one mile west
of Dolgellau on A493.

Whitsun–Sep: Mon–Sun
Apr/May/Oct: Sat–Sun

South Stack Cliffs RSPB

Nr Holyhead
Gwynedd.
☎ 0407 3043

Signposted from Holyhead.

550yd track to cliff-top observatory of
Ellin's Tower where TV screen monitors
breeding seabirds in summer.

Ynni Cymru/Power of Wales

Llanberis
Caernarfon, Gwynedd. LL55 4UR
☎ 0286 870636

Caernarfon, A4086

⇌ Bangor 🚌 Llanberis

Main out-station of the National Musuem of
Wales in North Wales, operated jointly with
National Grid Company.

Feb: 10.30am–4pm Pre-booked only
Mar–May: Mon–Sun 10am–5pm
Jun–mid Sep: Mon–Sun 9.30am–6pm
late Sep–Oct: Mon–Sun 10am–5pm

Bangor Cathedral

c/o The Deanery
Cathedral Close
Bangor, Gwynedd
☎ 0248 370 693

Bangor

⇌ 🚌 Bangor

Possibly the oldest Cathedral foundation in
the UK – 525 AD.

Jan–Dec: Mon–Fri 8am–5.30pm
Sat 9.30am–12.30pm
Sun 8am–5.30pm

Snowdon Mountain Aviation Museum

Caernarfon Airport
Llandwrog
Caernarfon, Gwynedd, LL54 5TP
☎ 0286 830800

Caernarfon A499

🚌 Caernarfon to airport

Opened in 1989, the Air Museum is a great
indoor 'hands on' attraction. Planes and
helicopters in realistic landscaped settings.

1 Mar–30 Nov: Mon–Sun 9.30am–5.30pm
Other times by arrangement

The Joys of Life

Coed–y–Parc
Bethesda, Gwynedd, LL57 4YW
☎ 0248 602122

Bangor A5

⇌ 🚌 Bangor

Founded 1983, the former home farm to
Penrhyn Quarry Manager. 12 acres of
cottage garden, wildlife nature reserve,
steam miniature railway, museum and
model village.

Easter–30 Sep: Tue–Sun & BH 11am–5pm

Cochwillan Historic House

Taly–bont
Bangor, Gwynedd, LL57 3AZ
☎ 0248 364608

Bangor off A5/A55

C15th hall house restored to original
appearance. Modern living accommodation
at ends.

Any time upon request.

Snowdon Mountain Railway

Llanberis
Gwynedd, LL55 4TY
☎ 0286 870223

On A4086, 7½m from Caernarfon towards
Capel Curig

⇌ 🚌 Bangor

Railway to summit of Snowdon. 2 carriages
suitable for disabled people– telephone to
check availability.

Train services

£©🚐✕ 🅿 P ♿ 👆 🚌 ♿ WC ‖
🏔 ♿ 🐾 ©

Haulfre Stables & Gardens

Llangoed
Anglesey, Gwynedd
☎ 024 878 709
Beaumaris
⇌ 🚌 Bangor

C19th stable and tackroom with their original fittings and contents. Representing the landed Gentry's way of life in the last century.

Jan–Dec: Mon–Fri: 9am–4.30pm
Sat–Sun: by appointment

F 🚐 ✕ 🅿 P ♿ → ♿ WC 🏔

Highgate Museum

Llanystumowy
Criccieth, Gwynedd
☎ 0766 522071/0286 679098
Criccieth
⇌ 🚌 Bangor or Porthmadog

Highgate Cottage is furnished as it was when Lloyd George lived there as a boy, until 1880. His Uncle Lloyd's shoemaking workshop is also recreated.

Easter–Sep: Mon–Sun 10am–5pm
Sep–Easter: by appointment

£©🚐✕ 🅿 P ♿ 🔨 🏛 → ╴│ ╶│╴
♿ WC 🏔 👥 🐾

Lloyd George Museum

Llanystumowy
Criccieth, Gwynedd
☎ 0766 522071/0286 679098
Criccieth
⇌ 🚌 Bangor or Porthmadog

The newly extended museum includes improved exhibitions, a 'talking head', new audio–visual theatre & Victorian schoolroom.

Easter–Sep: Mon–Sun 10am–5pm
Oct–Easter: by appointment

£©🚐✕ ♿ 🅿 P ♿ │╴ ♿ WC 🏔
👥 🐾

Beaumaris Court Museum

Beaumaris, Gwynedd
☎ 0248 750262 x 269
Beaumaris–Menai Bridge
⇌ 🚌 Bangor

The Court with its C17th origins, renovated in the C19th, is a unique survival of a Victorian Court Room.

Easter, end May–Sep: Mon–Sun
11.30am–5.30pm

£©🚐✕ P 🏔 👆 🏛 ♿ WC ♿ 🎧

Beaumaris Gaol Museum

Beaumaris, Gwynedd
☎ 0248 750262 x 269
Beaumaris–Menai Bridge
⇌ 🚌 Bangor

Built in 1829, Beaumaris Gaol is a grim reminder of the harshness of justice in Victorian Britain.

Easter, end May–Sep: Mon–Sun 11am–6pm

£©🚐✕ P ♿ ♿ 🔨 🏛 → WC 🏔
🎧 🐾

Aberglaslyn Pass & Beddgelert NT

Gwynedd

Path to Gelert's Grave, and part of the footpath through the pass are accessible to wheelchair users. Access to the Trust shop and Information Centre at Llewelyn Cottage, Beddgelert.

Glan Faenol NT

Menai Strait
Gwynedd

On Menai Strait. Car park has accessible path to picnic area.

Llyn Peninsula NT

Nr Aberdaron
Gwynedd

Many accessible viewpoints with car parking. Adapted toilet at Plas–yn–Rhiw, Aberdaron, but limited access to house and garden. Access possible to Porthor beach, nr Aberdaron, known locally as Whistling Sands.

Coed Cae Vali NT

Maentwrog
Gwynedd

The trust has provided a picnic site with access for disabled people; further south at Ganllwyd on the Dolmelynllyn Estate, a car park has ramped access to a riverside picnic site. Wheelchair access round the lake.

MID GLAMORGAN

Rhondda Heritage Park

Lewis Merthyr
Coed Cae Rd
Trehafod, Mid Glam. CF37 7NP
☎ 0443 682036

Pontypridd A4058

≋ 🚌 Trehafod

Set in the colliery buildings of Lewis Merthyr, now huge industrial theatres that house 'The Black Gold'. The story of coal exhibition.

Jan–Dec: Mon–Sun 10am–6pm

Swansea Maritime & Industrial Museum

Museum Sq
Maritime Quarter
Swansea, Mid Glam. SA1 1SN
☎ 0792 650351/470371

City centre

Swansea waterfront development. Historic vessel collection, City museum library. Education, conservation and restoration buildings.

Jan–Dec: Mon–Sun 10.30am–5.30pm

F🚌⚡🕷 P ⚿ ➤ ⊣ ⊣⊢ ♿WC 🐕 🌲

Cyfarthfa Castle Museum & Art Gallery

Brecon Rd
Merthyr Tydfil
Mid Glam. CF47 8RE
☎ 0685 723112

Merthyr

≋ 🚌 Merthyr

1825 period Castle with 160 acres of parkland. Fine & applied art, industrial & social history, costume displays. 3000 years of history.

Jan–Dec: Mon–Thu 10am–6pm
Fri 10am–5pm
Sat 10am–6pm
Sun 2pm–5pm

£©🚌🕷 P ⚿💺🏠 ⊣ ⊣⊢WC 🍴 🌲🚶♿🐕🛈⚿

POWYS

Pontypridd Historical & Cultural Ctr

Bridge St
Pontypridd, Mid Glam. CF37 4PE
☎ 0443 402077

Cardiff A470

≋ 🚌 Pontypridd

Working models, historic objects, recorded voices, archive film, panoramic painting, computer map and exhibitions.

Jan–Dec: Tue–Sat 9am–5pm

£🚌🕷 P ⚿🏠♿WC 🍴 🌲🚶🎧 🐕🛈

Parc Cwm Darran – Country Park

Deri
Bargoed, Mid Glam. CF37 4HE
☎ 0443 875557

Bargoed

≋ 🚌 Bargoed

Site of Ogilvie and Groesfaen Collieries. Caravan and campsite, adventure playground, coarse fishing and walks.

Jan–Dec: Mon–Sun

F🚌🕷 P ⚿💺➤ ⊣ ⇒♿WC 🍴 🚶💧🐕🛈

POWYS

Bird & Butterfly World

Domgay
Llanfyllin, Powys, SY22 5NE
☎ 069 184 751

Welshpool, A490

Tropical butterfly house, avaires housing exotic birds, parrots and birds of prey.

Easter–end Sept 10am–6pm

£©🚌🕷 P 💺➤ ⊣ ♿WC 🍴 🌲🚶♿🐕🛈⚿

Glynderi Pottery

Sennybridge
Brecon, Powys, LD3 8TS
☎ 0874 636564

Sennybridge, A40

Working pottery situated in converted C17th farmhouse and stables in Brecon Beacons National Park.

Oct–Mar: Mon–Fri & most weekends 9am–6pm
Apr–Sep: Mon–Sun 9am–6pm

F 🚌 ⛰ 🐕 ⛬ P ♿ & 🚻 WC ⛪ 🍴
🎒 🏕 🚣 🖼 © ♿

Elan Valley Visitor Ctr

Nr Rhayader, Powys, LD6 5HP
☎ 0597 810880/810898
Rhayader
⮺ 🚌 Llandrindod Wells 11m

70sq miles of moorland, hill and resevoirs.
Spectacular scenery with Red Kite and
other rare birds and plants.

Easter–31 Oct

F 🚌 ⛰ P & ➤ ⊣ 🚻 WC ⛪ 🍴 🎒
🏕 & ©

Centre for Alternative Technology

Machynlleth, Powys, SY20 9AZ
☎ 0654 702400
A487 to Machynlleth

Visitor centre in old slate quarry. Educative,
interactive displays on alternative
technology and lifestyle to improve the
environment.

Mar–Dec: Mon–Sun 10am–5pm

£ © 🚌 ⛰ P & P & ➤ ⊣ 🚻 WC ⛪
🍴 🎒 🏕 ©

The Cambrian Factory

Llanwrtyd Wells
Powys, LD5 4SD
☎ 05913 211
A483
⮺ Llanwrtyd 1m

Spinners and manufacturers of Welsh
tweed run jointly by Powys County Council
and the Royal British Legion as a sheltered
workshop.

Factory: Jan–Dec Mon–Fri 8.15am–4.30
closed holidays
Tea Room: Apr–Oct Mon–Fri 9am–5pm

F 🚌 ⛰ P & 🎫 ➤ 🚻 WC 🍴 🎒
🏕 ♿

Lake Vyrnwy Nature Reserve RSPB

Nr Llanwddyn, Powys
☎ 069 173 278
B4393 to Llanwddyn from Llanfyllin and
proceed to reservoir.

Hide at edge of car park provides views for
wheelchair users at woodland canopy
height. Good views are obtainable of the
lake, woods and moorland from perimeter
roads. New nature trail and hide at north
end of lake now open and accessible to
wheelchair users.

WC

Felin Crewi Working Watermill

Penegoes
Machynlleth, Powys, SY20 8NH
☎ 0654 703113
2m E of Machynlleth, just off A489
⮺ 🚌 Machynlleth

C16th watermill, especially restored to be
accessible to disabled people. Nature trail,
bird hide, water birds and farm animals.

Easter–30 Sept

£ 🚌 ⛰ P & P & & 🦮 🏚 ➤ ⇒ ⊣
🚻 WC ⛪ 🍴 & 🖼 © ♿

Powysland Museum & Montgomery Canal Ctr

The Canal Wharf
Welshpool, Powys, SY21 7AQ
☎ 0938 554656
Welshpool
⮺ 🚌 Welshpool

Historical exhibition of agricultural
equipment, photographs & collections
depicting the development of canal &
railway systems.

Summer: Mon,Tue,Thu,Fri 11am–1pm &
2pm–5pm
Sat–Sun 10am–1pm & 2pm–5pm
Winter: Mon,Tue,Thu,Fri 11am–1pm &
2pm–5pm
Sat 2pm–5pm

F 🚌 ⛰ P & P & 🎫 🚻 WC 🦯 🖼 ©

Llandrindod Museum

Temple St
Llandrindod, Powys, LD1 5DL
☎ 0597 824513
Llandrindod Wells
⮺ 🚌 Llandrindod Wells

Local history museum with emphasis on
town as a Victorian Spa. Excellent sampler
collection, Roman archaeology displays and
programme of changing temporary
exhibitions.

Easter–Sept: Mon–Sun 10am–12.30pm &
2pm–5pm

Oct–Easter: Mon–Fri 10am–12.30pm &
2pm–5pm
Sat 10am–12.30

F🚐🕊️P🅿️⚿🏚️➤🚻♿WC
👥🦮

SOUTH GLAMORGAN

Welsh Folk Museum
St Fagans
Cardiff, S.Glam. CF5 6XB
☎ 0222 555105
Cardiff
🚋 🚐 Cardiff

Open–air museum located within 100 acres
of parkland, consisting of an Elizabethan
castle and over 30 re–erected buildings
reflecting the past in rural and industrial
Wales.

Easter–Oct: Mon–Sun 10am–5pm
Nov–Easter: Mon–Sat 10am–5pm

£©🚐🕊️🍴🅿️♿⇒👁️🍴♿
WC👶🍴👥♿🦮🦯♿

National Museum of Wales
Main Building
Cathays Park
Cardiff, S.Glam. CF1 3NP
☎ 0222 397951
Cardiff
🚋 🚐 Cardiff Central

In the centre of Cardiff's Civic Centre
displaying paintings, silver & ceramics,
coins & medals, fossils and archaeological
artefacts.

Jan–Dec: Tue–Sat & BH Mon 10am–5pm
Sun 2.30pm–5pm

F🚐🕊️🍴P🅿️♿🍵🍴♿WC🍴
👥♿🦮♿

Llanerch Vineyard
Hensol
Pendoylan, S.Glam. CF7 8JU
☎ 0443 225877
Cardiff, M4

Vineyard planted in 1986. 6 acres of vines &
the largest in Wales. Only vineyard in Wales
producing estate bottled wines.
Grass & gravel paths.
Easter–Nov: Mon–Sun 10am–4pm

£🚐🕊️🅿️♿➤🚻♿WC🍴👥
♿🦮©

Cefn Coed Colliery Museum
Blaenant Colliery
Crynant
Neath, W.Glam. SA10 8SN
☎ 0639 750556
Neath
🚋 🚐 Neath

Site of former Cefn Coed Colliery. Surface
buildings now a museum housing
machinery, equipment, photographs and a
recreated coal face.

Apr–Sep: Mon–Sun 10.30am–6pm
Oct–Mar: Mon–Sun 10.30am–4pm

£©🚐🕊️P♿🅿️♿🚻♿WC🍴👥
👥♿

Margam Country Park
Port Talbot
W.Glam. SA13 2TJ
☎ 0639 881635

A48 4m from Port Talbot. Junction 38, M4
🚋 Port Talbot 🚐 Cardiff & Swansea

800 acres of parkland with historic
buildings, ornamental gardens, fallow deer
herd, farm trail, maze, fairytale land and
much more.

Apr–Sep: Mon–Sun 10am–6pm Last entry
4pm
Oct–Mar: Wed–Sun 10am–5pm Last entry
3pm
Limited facilities in winter.

£©🚐🕊️P♿🅿️♿🍴➤🚻♿🍴
♿WC🍴👥👥⬅️🦮©♿

Afan Argoed Country Park
Cynonville
Nr Port Talbot, W.Glam.
☎ 0639 850564

A4107
🚋 Port Talbot

1000 acre beautiful forest park. Welsh
Miners Museum showing industrial history.
Countryside Centre, cycle hire and much
more. Some forest walks have steps.

Apr–Oct: Mon–Sun 10.30am–6pm
Nov–Mar: Sat–Sun 10.30am–5pm

WEST GLAMORGAN

£ © ⟪ ✳ ⬙ P ♿ ⊣ ⊹ ♿ᵂᶜ WC ¶

♿ ⚶ ♿ ⊙ ♿

Rhossili Visitor Centre NT

Coastguard Cottages
Rhossili
Gower, W.Glam. SA3 1PR
☎ 0792 390707
Swansea
🚌 Swansea

Conserves the coastline, beach and hills
around Rhossili.

Ring for dates and times

F ⟪ ✳ ⬙ P ♿ 🏠 ➤ ⊣ ⊹ WC

♿ ⚶

Aberdulais Falls NT

Aberdulais
Nr Neath, W.Glamorgan
☎ 0639 636674

One of the most famous waterfalls in South
Wales. Ramp available to main exhibition on
ground floor. Southern area of site suitable
for wheelchairs, where waterfall and historic
remains can be viewed. Access to upper
part of site with views of waterfall will be
possible in the near future. Adapted WC.

P♿ ⥿ ♿ᵂᶜ WC ⛟ ♿

NORTHERN IRELAND

SYMBOL DESCRIPTIONS

£   Admission charge

F   No admission charge but donation in some places

©   Special concession charge for disabled people, elderly people, carers and children

🚌   Groups must book in advance – special rates may apply

🐕   Guide dogs accepted except in certain areas

𝒯   Sympathetic Hearing Scheme participated in or Loop System

📖   Special information available for disabled people

PARKING

P♿   Designated disabled parking space

🅿   Own car park with a dropping off point within 50 yards

P   Public car park nearby and/or street parking within 200 yards

𝘗   Dropping off point or disabled parking place by telephone appointment

MAIN ENTRANCE

♿   Entrance level or ramped and over 30″ wide

🚶   Steps into building 1–5 or bumpy

▟   Steps into building 6 or more

☞   More suitable entrance freely available, telephone for details or help. Temporary ramps to be made available.

▟   Steps within the buildings that cannot be overcome by ramps

🏢   More than one floor level and no lift

🛗   More than one floor level and suitable lift/stairclimber/stairlift for wheelchair users

OUTSIDE

➤   Routes around the site are free of steps or steps can be avoided

ⅎ   Seats available around the site

⇒   Routes indicated for wheelchair users

👁   Routes indicated for visually handicapped people

🚃   Transport around the site suitable for disabled people and wheelchair users – telephone in advance

🚂   Transport around the site not suitable for disabled people or elderly people

-|-   There are limited areas that cannot be reached due to steps or doorways less than 30″

TOILETS

&wc Unisex toilets designed or adapted for disabled people or public toilets within 50 yards. Radar key required in some

WC Ordinary toilets with level access

WC No toilets on site but public ones nearby

⚭ Baby changing/parents room available

GENERAL

✗ Restaurant/tea room/cafe/ not accessible due to steps/narrow doorway/first floor with no lift

❙❚ Restaurant/tea room/cafe/vending accessible by ramp or level or lift with 30" doors

✗ Shop not accessible due to stairs but may be accessible with help

✓ Shop/sales area accessible by ramp or level and 30" doorway

⚭ Picnic area only, or nearby

♿ Wheelchair users are advised to come accompanied

🎧 Taped guides available/or person

◆ Facilities for visually handicapped/braille or by request

✍ People available to help (telephone beforehand if you require help)

ⓒ Telephone accessible for wheelchair users

ᚴ This site is suitable for elderly people but unsuitable for wheelchair users

♿ Wheelchairs/batricars for loan or hire – telephone for advance booking

NT The National Trust

EH English Heritage

NTS National Trust for Scotland

RSPB Royal Society For the Protection of Birds

FC Forestry Commission

≥ British Rail

🚌 Bus

☎ Telephone

⊖ Underground

215

NOTES

NORTHERN IRELAND

CO. ANTRIM

Ulster Museum

Botanic Gardens
Belfast, N.I., BT9 5AB
☎ 0232 381251

Belfast

≋ Botanic 🚌 Belfast

Displays covering art antiquities, local history, geology, botany and zoology. Set in botanic gardens.

Jan–Dec: Mon–Fri 10am–5pm
Sat 1pm–5pm
Sun 2pm–5pm

Belfast Zoo

Antrim Rd
Belfast, N.I., BT36 7PN
☎ 0232 776277

Belfast A6

🚌 Belfast

One of the most beautiful and modern zoo's in Europe. Train unsuitable for wheelchairs.

Apr–Sep: Mon–Sun 10am–5pm
Oct–Mar: Mon–Sun 10am–3.30pm

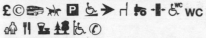

Giant's Causeway Visitor Centre

44 Causeway Rd
Bushmills
Co Antrim, N.I., BT57 8SU
☎ 0265 7 31855

2m from Bushmills town, on A2/B146

≋ Portrush Ulsterbus service 172 & Openstop 🚌 Summer Season

Designated World Heritage Site. An audio–visual show tells the story of this unique hexagonal rock formation which happened over 50,000,000 years ago when deep pools of molten lava cooled slowly, resulting in the famous hexagonal slopes.

Jul–Aug: Mon–Sun 10am–7pm
Nov–Feb: Mon–Sun 10am–4pm
Mar–May: Mon–Sun 10am–5pm
Jun,Sep & Oct: Mon–Sun 10am–6pm
Closed Xmas week

Portrush Countryside Ctr

Bath Rd
Portrush, Co Antrim, N.I.,
☎ 0265 83600

Portrush

≋ 🚌 Portrush

Originally the old bath house, built in C19th. Converted to Countryside Centre in 1978 & now contains information on wildlife and conservation.

Jun–Sep: Mon/Wed–Sun 1pm–9pm

Talnotry Cottage Bird Garden

2 Crumlin Rd
Crumlin, Co.Antrim, BT29 4AD
☎ 084 94 22900

Crumlin, A52 to Belfast

≷ Crumlin

A 200 year old walled garden which houses rare ornamental pheasants, quail and other birds, including birds of prey.

Easter–31 Aug: Sun & BH 2pm–6pm
Other times throughout the year by appointment

£🚐🚈P🅿🚻➤🚽❄wc🍴🪚
🌳🐟🦆ⓕ

CO. ARMAGH

Pinebank Community Centre

Tullygally Rd
Brownlow, Craigavon,
Co Armagh, N.I., BT65 5BV
☎ 0762 341033

2m W of Lurgan on A3

≷ Lurgan 🚌 from Lurgan, Portadown and Craigavon

Originally a farm converted to community centre in 1972. The art gallery holds exhibitions of well known artists. Well appointed pottery.

Jan–Dec: Mon–Fri 8.30am–5pm & 7.30pm–10.30pm
Sat–Sun by appointment

F🚐🚈P🅿🗻🏛➤🚽⟹❄👟wc🍴🦽ⓕ

Ardress House NT

64 Ardress Rd
Portadown, Co.Armagh, BT62 1SQ
☎ 0762 851236

Portadown, exit 13, M1

≷ 🚌 Portadown

C17th farmhouse with good furniture and pictures. Farmyard with display of livestock and implements, garden and woodland walks. Twenty acres with gravel paths.

Apr: Sat–Sun,Gd Fri,Easter
May–Jun: Sat–Sun & BH
Jul–Aug: Wed–Mon
Sep: Sat–Sun

£ⓒ🚐🚈🏇🏝P🅿🅿🗻🐟🏛
🚽❄👟wc🦽👟

The Argory NT

Derycaw Rd
Moy, Dungannon
Co.Armagh, BT71 6NA
☎ 08687 84753

Moy, exit 14 from M1

Magnificent mansion set in 300 acres of wooded countryside. Facinating furniture, imposing stable yard, sundial garden and playground. Gravel paths, some unsuitable for wheelchair users.

Apr: Sat–Sun,Gd Fri,Easter
May–Jun: Sat–Sun & BH
Jul–Aug: Fri–Wed
Sep: Sat–Sun

£🚐🚈🏇🐟P🅿🗻🐟🏛🚽❄👟wc🍴🪚🌳🦽

CO. DOWN

Wildfowl & Wetlands Trust

Ballydrain Rd
Comber, Co Down, N.I., BT23 6EA
☎ 0247 874146

Comber

A centre for Wetlands conservation. A series of lakes with the best collection of waterfowl in Ireland. Magnificent views over Strangford Lough. No dogs due to birds.

Jan–Dec: Mon–Sat 10.30am–5pm
Sun 2pm–5pm

£ⓒ🚐🅿P🗻🏛🚽❄wc🍴🪚🌳🦽ⓕ

Newry Arts Centre

1a Bank Parade
Newry
Co Down, N.I., BT35 6HP
☎ 0693 66232

Newry

≷ 🚌 Newry

1000 sq.metres of workspace, with a very high degree of flexibility, making it suitable for arts, commercial and industrial events.

Jan–Dec: Mon–Sun
11am–4.30pm/7pm–10.30pm

Fⓒ🚐🚈P🅿🗻🏛➤🚽❄wc🍴👟ⓕ

CO. DOWN

Rowallane Gardens NT

Crossgar Rd
Saintfield
Ballynahinch
Co.Down, BT24 7LH
☎ 0238 510721

Saintfield, A7

⇌ 🚐 Belfast

52 acres of natural garden containing plants
from many parts of the world.

Apr–Oct: Mon–Fri 10.30am–6pm
Sat–Sun 2pm–6pm
Nov–Mar: Mon–Fri 9am–5pm

£🚐🎋🐾✏️👜🅿️ 🅿️ 👨‍🦽➜ ⊣ 🚻 WC
🍴 🖼️ 🏕️ 👨‍🦽 ⚘

Castle Ward NT

Strangford
Downpatrick, Co.Down, BT30 7LJ
☎ 039686 204

Strangford, A25

🚐 Downpatrick

700 acre country estate with woodland, lake
and seashore. Unique C18th house, formal
and landscape gardens.

Apr: Sat–Sun,Gd Fri,Easter
May–Aug: Fri–Wed & BH
Sep–Oct: Sat–Sun

£©🚐🎋🐾✏️👜🅿️ ✏️ ⛰️ 🏚️➜
⊣ 🚻 WC 🍴 🖼️ 🏕️ 👨‍🦽 🎧 🤝 ⚘

Murlough Nature Reserve NT

Dundrum
Newcastle, Co.Down
☎ 039675 467

Dundrum

🚐 Newcastle

Sand dune system with heathland and
woodland surrounded by estuary and sea
interpretation centre. 700 acres with slated
wooden walkways, dunes quite difficult.

Reserve:
Jan–Feb: Mon–Sun 10am–5pm

Centre:
Jun–Sep: Mon–Sun 10am–5pm

£©🚐🎋🐾✏️👜🅿️ 🅿️ 👨‍🦽➜ ⊣ 🚻
WC 🖼️ 🏕️ 👨‍🦽 ⚘

The Dundrum Coastal Path NT

Dundrum, Co. Down

At the north end of the village, traverses
1½m of disused railway line which is

suitable for wheelchair users and visually
impaired walkers.

Strangford Lough NT

Co.Down

The Trust's Wildlife Scheme here embraces
the entire foreshore of Lough Strangford
and several islands, totalling 5,400 acres. At
various points on the shore, car parks with
access to viewpoints, ideal for watching the
varied bird life on the lough. A birdwatching
hide on Island Reagh has been adapted for
wheelchair access. Wheelchair users please
park in car park; gate to hide is short
distance back up the road; smooth path,
and ramp.

CO. FERMANAGH

Belleek Pottery

Belleek
Co Fermanagh, N.I., BT93 3FY
☎ 036 565 501

Enniskillen

🚐 Enniskillen

Established in 1857; Ireland's oldest
pottery. Daily tours through factory.

Mar–Oct: Mon–Fri 9am–6pm
Sat 10am–6pm
Sun 2pm–8pm
Nov–Feb: Mon–Fri 9am–5.30pm

£🚐🎋🐾👜🅿️ 🅿️ 👨‍🦽➜ ⊣ 🚶 🚻 WC 🍴
🖼️ 🏕️

Castle Coole NT

Enniskillen, Co.Fermanagh
☎ 0365 322690

Enniskillen, A4

🚐 Enniskillen

Superb C18th neo–classical house with fine
interior furnishings and landscaped
parkland.

Apr: Sat–Sun,Gd Fri,Easter
May–Jun: Sat–Sun & BH
Jul–Aug: Fri–Wed
Sep: Sat–Sun

£🚐🎋🐾✏️👜 🅿️ 👨‍🦽🦽🛶🏚️➜
🚶 🚻 WC 👨‍🦽 🤝

The Crom Estate NT

Upper Lough Erne
Co.Fermanagh

On the shores of Upper Lough Erne.

🏊 ♿ WC

Florence Court House NT

Florence Court
Enniskillen, N.I., BT92 1DB
☎ 036582 249

8m SW of Enniskillen via A4 Sligo Rd & A32
Swanlibar Rd

The finest example of mid–C18th mansion.
Rococo plasterwork, C18th Irish furniture.
House of the Cole family, the Earls of
Enniskillen. Walled gardens, ice–house,
pleasure grounds and water–wheel
operated sawmill.

Apr/May/Sep: Sat/Sun/BH 1pm–6pm
Easter: 1pm–6pm
Jun/Jul/Aug: Mon/Wed–Sun 1pm–6pm

CO. LONDONDERRY

Springhill NT

20 Springhill Rd
Moneymore
Magherafelt, Co.Londonderry, BT45 7NQ
☎ 06487 48210

Moneymore, B18

🚌 Magherafelt

C17th whitewashed house with mid C18th

and early C19th additions. Extensive
outbuildings with costume collection.

Apr: Sat–Sun,Gd Fri,Easter
May–Jun: Sat–Sun & BH
Jul–Aug: Fri–Wed
Sep: Sat–Sun

£🚌☀🏊🌊 P ♿ 🚂 🏛 ⌐ ⊣ ♿
WC ♟ 🎣 🏕 ♿ 🎧 🏊

The Bar Mouth NT

Co.Londonderry
5m W of Coleraine

This wildlife sanctuary has a bird hide
adapted for wheelchair users.

CO. TYRONE

US Grants Ancestral Homestead

Dergenagh Road
Dungannon
Co.Tyrone, BT70 1TW
☎ 08687 25311

Ballygawley, A4 (M1 extension)

Homestead of Ulysses S Grant, 18th
President of the USA.Fully–furnished two–
roomed thatched cottage restored to its
original C19th appearance. Visitor centre
with audio visual and display areas.

May–Sep: Mon–Sat 10am–6pm
Sun 2pm–6pm

£©🚌☀ P ♿➤⊣ ♿ WC ♟ 🎣
🏕♿

READERS' COMMENTS

Please use this page to recommend venues which you think might be considered for the next edition of the book.

Comments – advers or otherwise, are welcome about any of the current *Guide's* entries

Full name and address of establishment:

_____

_____

_____

_____

_____

Phone number:

_____

Comments

_____

_____

_____

_____

_____

_____

_____

Name and address of sender:

_____

_____

_____

_____

_____

We regret that we cannot acknowledge these forms, but they will be properly considered.

Return to:
     Places That Care, 72 High St, Poole, Dorset.

READERS' COMMENTS

Please use this page to recommend venues which you think might be considered for the next edition of the book.

Comments – advers or otherwise, are welcome about any of the current *Guide's* entries

Full name and address of establishment:

_____

_____

_____

_____

Phone number:

_____

Comments

_____

_____

_____

_____

_____

_____

Name and address of sender:

_____

_____

_____

_____

_____

We regret that we cannot acknowledge these forms, but they will be properly considered.

Return to:
Places That Care, 72 High St, Poole, Dorset.

READERS' COMMENTS

Please use this page to recommend venues which you think might be considered for the next edition of the book.

Comments – advers or otherwise, are welcome about any of the current *Guide's* entries

Full name and address of establishment:

_____

_____

_____

_____

Phone number:

_____

Comments

_____

_____

_____

_____

_____

_____

Name and address of sender:

_____

_____

_____

_____

_____

We regret that we cannot acknowledge these forms, but they will be properly considered.

Return to:

Places That Care, 72 High St, Poole, Dorset.

READERS' COMMENTS

Please use this page to recommend venues which you think might be considered for the next edition of the book.

Comments – advers or otherwise, are welcome about any of the current *Guide's* entries

Full name and address of establishment:

_____

_____

_____

_____

_____

Phone number:

_____

Comments

_____

_____

_____

_____

_____

_____

Name and address of sender:

_____

_____

_____

_____

_____

We regret that we cannot acknowledge these forms, but they will be properly considered.

Return to:

Places That Care, 72 High St, Poole, Dorset.

READERS' COMMENTS

Please use this page to recommend venues which you think might be considered for the next edition of the book.

Comments – advers or otherwise, are welcome about any of the current *Guide's* entries

Full name and address of establishment:

_____

_____

_____

_____

Phone number:

_____

Comments

_____

_____

_____

_____

_____

_____

_____

Name and address of sender:

_____

_____

_____

_____

_____

We regret that we cannot acknowledge these forms, but they will be properly considered.

Return to:

Places That Care, 72 High St, Poole, Dorset.

INDEX

ENGLAND

INDEX

DERBYSHIRE

DEVON

DORSET

DURHAM

INDEX

ESSEX

EAST SUSSEX

GLOUCESTERSHIRE

INDEX

HERTFORDSHIRE

HUMBERSIDE

ISLE OF WIGHT

KENT

LANCASHIRE

LEICESTERSHIRE

LINCOLNSHIRE

INDEX

LONDON

MERSEYSIDE

NORFOLK

NORTHAMPTONSHIRE

NORTHUMBERLAND

INDEX

INDEX

INDEX

SCOTLAND

BORDERS

CENTRAL

DUMFRIES & GALLOWAY

FIFE

GRAMPIAN

HIGHLANDS

LOTHIAN

STRATHCLYDE

INDEX

MID GLAMORGAN

POWYS

SOUTH GLAMORGAN

WEST GLAMORGAN

NORTHERN IRELAND

CO. ANTRIM

CO. ARMAGH

INDEX

DESCRIPTION SYMBOLIQUE/SYMBOL ERKLÄRUNG

£   Prix d'entrée
Eintrittsgebühr

F   Aucun prix d'entrée mais quelque fois une donation
Keine eintrittsgebühr, jedoch spende in einige bereiche

©   Prix spécial pour les handicapés, retraités enfants et compagnons
Besondere sondergebühr für behinderte, ältere menschen, pfleger und kinder

🚌   Les groupes sont obligés de faire une réservation en avance – prix spéciaux peuvent s'appliquer
Gruppen müssen im voraus buchen – besondere preise können gelten

🐕   Chiens d'aveugles sont admis sauf dans certain régions
Führhunde werden geduldet ausser in einigen bereichen

⌇   Participation au projet sympathique d'audition ou le système 'Loop'
Vibrations hör – anlage beteilgt oder schleifen – system

📖   Information spécial pour les handicapés est disponible
Spezielle informationen für behinderte sind bereitgestellt

PARCAGE/PARKEN

P♿   Parcage désigné pour les handicapés
Gekennzeichenter behindertenparkplatz

🅿   Propre parking avec endroit pour déposer les personnes au près de 50 m
Eigener parkplatz mit aussteigepunkt innerhalb eines bereiches von 50 yards

P   Parking publique très près et/ou un endroit de stationnement au près de 200 m
Öffentlicher parkplatz in der nähe und/oder parkplatz an der strasse innerhalb eines bereiches von 200 yards

🅿   Endroit pour déposer les personne ou parcage pour les handicapés si ont téléphone pour un rendez-vous en avance
Aussteigpunkt oder behindertenparkplatz nach telefonischer vereinbarung

ENTRÈE PRINCIPAL/HAUPTEINGANG

♿   Entrée équilibré ou avec une rampe et portes plus de 30″ de largeur
Eingangshöhe und mit einer rampe versehen oder 30″ breit

🚶   1–5 marches entrant dans le bâtiment
1–5 stufen in das gebäude oder uneben

▟   6 ou plusieurs marches entrant dans le bâtiment
6 oder mehr stufen in das gebäude

☛   Entrée plus convenable facilement disponible – téléphoner pour détails et aide, rampes temporaraires sont disponible
Bessergeeigneter eingang ungehindert zu nutzen, bitte anrufen bezüglich hilfe oder details, zeitweise sind rampen verfügbar zu machen

◢   Marches dans le bâtiment qui ne peuvent pas être vaincu avec des rampes
Stufen innerhalb des gebäudes die nicht mit rampen überwunden werden können

🏢   Plusieurs étages sans ascenseur
Mehr als ein stockwerk ohne fahrstuhl

🛗   Plusieurs étages avec équipement convenable pour les usagers de chaises roulantes
Mehr als ein stockwerk und geeigneter lift/treppen lift/treppen hebebühnen für rollstühlfahrer

DEHORS/AUSSEN

➔   Routes au tour du terrain libre de marches ou les marches peuvent être évité
Wege um das gebäude herum ohne stufen oder stufen können vermieden werden

⌐   Sièges sont disponible au tour du terrain
Sitzmöglichkeiten stehen rund um das gebäude herum zur verfügung

⇒   Routes indiqués pour les usagers de chaises roulantes
Wege für rollstuhlfahrer gekennzeichnet

👁   Routes indiqués pour les handicapés visuel
Wege für sehbehinderte personen gekennzeichnet

🚃   Transport au tour du terrain convenable pour les handicapés et pour les usagers de chaises roulantes – téléphoner en avance
Transport rund um das gebäude für behinderte und rollstuhlfähler möglich – bitte vorher anfufen

🚫   Transport au tour du terrain impropre pour les handicapés et les retraités
Transport rund um das gebäude für behinderte und ältere menschen nich möglich